# Foreword

25 years ago, when Open House was launched, London was a different city to the one we live in today. Many of the landmarks that we pass by daily were not there, and our business environment looked and felt very different. The term 'start-up' was not one you were likely to hear.

Since then, London has been transformed in many ways, not least in terms of the rise and consolidation of our start-up and scale-up ecosystem. We can say today without hesitation that London is a unique and world-class environment for enterprise, and the best place in the world to start and grow a business.

Meanwhile we have also seen the growth of the Open House initiative, created to give Londoners and visitors a chance to learn about, better understand and argue for quality in our built environments.

Open House provides a much-needed open forum for everyone living and working in the city to discuss the importance of quality in architecture and urban design. Crucially, there are no barriers to access – promoting openness by offering the chance to explore behind the scenes of the city, completely for free.

This year, there are over 800 buildings on show, across every single London borough. What is unique about Open House is th_____ ___ ____ es – government buildings, pri___ _____ _____ __ ____ old.

T__ ____ __ _ ___ ___ __ __ on workspaces, ___ ___ ___ __ __ __ e of work – not ___ __ ___ __ ___ ___ aces in which ___ __ ____ __ __ ___ e; but also, f_____ ___ __ __ ___ ___ ___ uring that so often a___ __ ___ __

___ __y election as Mayor, and following the __ referendum, I launched the #LondonIsOpen campaign to show to the world the best of our city. In partnership with Open House, I want to use this opportunity to help demonstrate and spread that message both among Londoners and through the world. To show that London remains open for business, for creativity, innovation and investment – and Open House is a perfect way to showcase the diverse and dynamic nature of London's economy.

I encourage everyone to spend some time during Open House weekend visiting at least one of the many buildings that are opening their doors. This is a unique opportunity to explore London's architecture, its economy and its people.

As a Mayor of London, I'm delighted to support Open House and proud to see it celebrate its 25th anniversary year.

**Sadiq Kahn,**
*Mayor of London*

# Choose Your Own London

We are so lucky. We have London – Europe's biggest city – and all its wonders, on our doorstep.

## Director's Picks

### 4-8 Hafer Road

→ p. 148

Peter Barber's cool, controlled housing nods and winks – quite deliberately – to the LCC heyday in the 60s and 70s. That's a good thing.

### Blackhorse Workshop

→ p. 146

What's the future of regen? Maybe it's this wood and metal workshop. Maybe it's not. Well worth your time though, especially if you're an aspiring 'maker'.

### Lullaby Factory

→ p. 60

Like a strange little sister to the Lloyds, this secret 'building' is the oddest and most beautiful of all the projects listed this year. 'Nuff said.

This city of houses, in all kinds of styles. This skyscraper city, peppered with 'icons'. This city of ancient guilds. This city of hi-tech hubs. This city with a million side extensions. This city with a shortage of ordinary homes that are cheap enough to rent if you're earning the minimum wage (OK – that's not so lucky).

There are grand government buildings and stylish state schools. Monumental office blocks, and big things underground (Crossrail's tunnels run for 26 miles). This city, a sprawling, rising townscape, north and south of the Thames. This city, home to millions of people, from all over the world. This city. Our city – especially this Open House weekend.

Open House allows us to make our own London, one that is unique, personalised, tempered and cut to fit. Maybe your London space is a residential place, of great social housing like the Silchester Estate.

Or maybe your London is all about concrete (you're going through your 'Brutalist' phase), with perennials like Trellick Tower high on your hit-list, as well as hidden gems like The Embassy of Slovakia. The public realm – and the role landscapes play in shaping our favourite neighbourhoods is another line of inquiry.

Or are you more interested in how the city works? You can find out, for example, how heat and power is provided at Pimlico District Heating Undertaking; Southwark Integrated Waste Management, with its wavy roofline is also well worth a trip. Whatever kind of London you want to see, you can find it in our guide to this year's Open House.

Elsewhere among these pages, to celebrate our 25th birthday, we showcase your favourite buildings and look back over the past quarter century. It is a timeframe in which London has been utterly transformed. A timeframe in which a new skyline has emerged – the Gherkin, the Shard and the London Eye are all younger than Open House! And a timeframe that has seen whole new districts arise. The new London forming in the shadow of Stratford's Queen Elizabeth Olympic Park is one of the most vibrant districts anywhere in the world – more than 100 languages are spoken in its borough, Newham.

Wherever you choose to go, whichever buildings you visit and explore, just remember: London – weird, wonderful, wicked London – is ours! How lucky are we?

**Rory Olcayto,** *Open City Director*

# 25

Years of Open House

Let's go back,
way back,
to 1992 and
the first
Open House...

● John Major wins the election to seal a fourth consecutive Tory government but months later crashes Britain out of the ERM.

● Windsor Castle catches fire, the YBAs star at the Saatchi Gallery for the first time and Paternoster Square is greenlit by planners. Smartphones don't exist. The South Bank wasn't a place to hang out.

● For the lucky 100 who booked, Open House kicks off for the first time. "In France, there is an Architecture Week," reads the press release penned by founder Victoria Thornton. "In Glasgow there is an Open Door Day. In Brussels there is a Heritage Day. But there was nothing in London. Until now."

Open City

Word gets out. There's a buzz. In 1993, four boroughs take part: Greenwich, Camden, Lambeth and Hackney. London is changing. The Mappin & Webb building at Bank is demolished to make way for James Stirling's No.1 Poultry. Further east in Bow, Rachel Whiteread's iconic 'House' – a concrete cast of the interior of a typical East End dwelling – goes on to win the Turner Prize. Weeks later it is demolished too.

The 50p 1993 Open House guide is two A4 sheets, but the programme is familiar. There are debuts by perennials like Camden's Alexandra Road estate, the Hackney Empire, the Queen's House, Greenwich and Lambeth's Stockwell Bus garage.

The 1994 guide lists over 200 buildings in 13 boroughs (and for the first time, features the skyline key, designed by Newell and Sorrell). London gains three significant buildings: the Channel 4 HQ by the Richard Rogers Partnership, Terry Farrell's M16 HQ and Grimshaw's Waterloo Eurostar Terminal, built to serve the just-completed Channel Tunnel. But The Sunday Trading Act (1994) permitting Sunday shopping, will go on to play a far bigger rule in shaping the future of London's townscape.

In 1995 the Hindu temple of Neasden opens, Zaha Hadid wins the Cardiff Bay Opera House competition (only to see it junked a few months later) and Open House expands to be a full weekend event. In 1996 – the year of the Docklands bombing and the first ever Stirling Prize – the weekend festival logs over 38,000 visits to 19 buildings in the City of London alone.

In 1997, the sweeping form of Frank Gehry's Guggenheim Museum in Bilbao is dubbed iconic and critics heralds a new style. In London, the British Library (by Colin St John Wilson) finally completes and Shakespeare's Globe opens. Open House grows – it now has three staff and five volunteers – and for the first time runs a programme exclusively for kids. And the Labour Party wins a landslide election with Tony Blair Prime Minister.

Over 450 buildings and 24 boroughs take part in 1998 but the big stories break elsewhere: Enric Miralles and Benedetta Tagliabue (with RMJM) win the Scottish Parliament competition and English Heritage list Park Hill in Sheffield, reviving interest in British Brutalism. Back in London, Richard Rogers is appointed chair of the Urban Task Force by Deputy PM John Prescott.

**1992** 7th November, the first ever Open House London with 20 buildings and 100 people

**1994** 200 buildings in Open House London

**1996** BBC London becomes media partner

**1998** Education programmes launch with Adopt a School

In 1999, London dominates: the Jubilee Line extension, the British Museum's Great Court (Norman Foster), the Lord's Media Centre (Future Systems) and the Millennium Dome (Richard Rogers) open in time for millennium celebrations. Lottery-funded public building abounds. Nick Raynsford MP, briefly a mayoral candidate, launches Open House at Lancaster House.

London goes into overdrive in 2000: independent candidate Ken Livingstone is elected as Mayor (his HQ, City Hall, designed by Foster and Partners, completes in 2002). Tate Modern opens, transforming a defunct power station into a free-to-enter gallery. Zaha Hadid designs the first Serpentine Pavilion in Hyde Park. Will Alsop's Peckham Library opens and bags the Stirling Prize. The White Cube gallery comes to Shoreditch. And RIBA gives Frank Gehry its seal of approval, the Royal Gold Medal. Open House breaks records: Westminster alone logs 131,000 visits to 91 buildings.

In 2001, Tony Blair wins another election. Months later the World Trade Centre in New York is destroyed in a terror attack. Security is tightened on London's streets. The first in a generation of great London schools completes: BDP's Hampden Gurney in Marylebone but Britain's best building is a Wilkinson Eyre bridge, linking Gateshead with Newcastle. Open House commissions poetry celebrating six London landmarks and Mayor Ken Livingstone launches the 10th Open House at Australia House. In 2002, twenty-nine boroughs and more than 500 buildings take part with Camden creating its own guide to cover Kings Cross's bumper crop.

It's 2003: London introduces the congestion charge. Paternoster Square opens alongside St Paul's Cathedral. Frank Gehry's Maggie's Centre in Dundee completes. And Future Systems' blobby icon for Selfridges plops into place in Birmingham. Open House initiates Open Site, which draws visitors to Wembley Stadium and St Pancras construction projects, and Architecture on the Move providing onboard commentary of buildings seen from DLR trains. And more than one million people take to London's streets to protest against plans to invade Iraq.

| | |
|---|---|
| **2000** | Over 150,000 people attend Open House London |
| **2002** | First Open House Worldwide event in New York |
| **2004** | Inaugural 'Open Site' project |
| **2004** | London Exemplar for planning councillors founded |

In 2004, Open House's new website draws 15 million hits, the Scottish Parliament finally opens and the first London Festival of Architecture takes place. But this is the year of the Gherkin, or 30 St Mary Axe. Not only does it participate in Open House for the first time just months after completion, with mile long queues, it hosts the launch in its top floor restaurant too. Weeks later it wins the Stirling Prize.

In 2005, Tony Blair wins another general election for the Labour Party, London wins the bid to host the 2012 Olympics and the city suffers terror attacks targeting the transport network. The first ever Maggie's and Open House Night Hike takes place, and Open House Junior launches.

By 2006 Open House hosts more than 700 free-to-enter buildings and attracts more than a quarter of a million souls. London's architectural upgrade continues (half of the Stirling Prize's shortlisted projects are based in the capital). The Mayor announces Design for London, a public realm agency built upon the principles of Richard Rogers' Urban Task Force. And the Government introduces the Code for Sustainable Homes to foster low energy design. In Kirkcaldy, Zaha Hadid's Maggie's Centre opens, her first British building, while in the US, influential urban activist and writer Jane Jacobs dies.

Olympic Minister Tessa Jowell launches Open House 2007 at East London's new rail hub, Stratford International. Five future sites, partially developed, also participate in the programme, setting a trend for future events. St Pancras reopens as the Eurostar terminal and Allies and Morrison completes the refurbishment of Royal Festival Hall. Ian Simpson's Beetham Tower, Britain's tallest residential skyscraper, opens in Manchester. Bold Tendencies, a sculpture gallery in a Peckham multi-storey car park opens for the first time. 2008 is all about THE CRASH while London flirts with star brand names: Rogers' Heathrow Terminal 5 opens and Gehry fashions a pavilion for the Serpentine Gallery. Social media starts to predominate.

| 2005 | Open House Junior launches |
| --- | --- |
| 2006 | 'My City Too!' mayoral election campaign launched |
| 2007 | Art in the Open founded |
| 2008 | Green Sky Studios begins, the precursor to Green Sky Thinking |

● 2009 is an Open House refresh: a third of all buildings are new to the programme. Sustainability is emphasised. Trips to the emerging Olympic Park book up. Rogers Stirk Harbour + Partners win the Stirling Prize for the Maggie's Centre in Charing Cross Hospital.

● David Cameron is the new prime minister after the Tories form a coalition government with the Liberals in 2010. London's bike hire scheme launches, Crossrail construction begins and Strata, the first of many hundred residential towers planned for London, completes. Open House – the organisation - is transformed. Open City is formed to 'shelter' both Open House and the educational programmes designed for schools. For the weekend, BT Tower opens its doors for the first time. In Dubai, the world's tallest building, Burj Khalifa, opens.

● In 2011, Open City launches Green Sky Thinking, a weeklong programme of events for professional city-makers, emphasising sustainability. Open House enters the mobile age with the launch of an app - the guide on your phone, with added functionality via GPS technology. Two key Olympic projects, the main stadium and the Velodrome finish ahead of schedule. And a state school, Evelyn Grace Academy, wins the Stirling prize. But London-wide riots cause untold damage and highlight the city's divisions.

The brick façades and shared space streets of Anne Mews – a terrace of homes in Barking by AHMM and Macreannor Lavington and the first new council housing in the borough for a quarter of a century – are the flip side of London's rampant development. Completed in 2012, this is somewhat overshadowed by Olympic 'parkitecture', Renzo Piano's Shard and Granary Square in King's Cross, a hugely popular privately run public space, stealing all the glory.

● In 2013, Battersea Power station, set to close for at least four years, opens for the last time, attracting 40,000 people over two days, setting an Open House record in the process. The programme too, features 853 buildings – the most ever. None of them however, is Raphael Viñoly's Walkie Talkie, which makes headlines around the world for melting cars with its huge concave glass façade.

● Rogers Stirk Harbour + Partners' 'Cheesegrater' building is the Open House smash of 2014 but the public mood is not overly generous to this controversial building type: some see them as symbols of endless greed, others simply demand they be easier on the eye. Much the same arguments are levelled at the Garden Bridge, a semi-private, publically-funded park strung across the Thames, which nevertheless receives planning permission.

| 2009 | 3000 volunteers support Open House with over 16,000 hours of labour |
|---|---|
| 2010 | Open House, the organisation, becomes Open-City |
| 2011 | Open House showcases over 70 landscape and engineering exemplars |
| 2011 | Green Sky Thinking takes place with over 50 events |

In 2015, David Cameron is once again Prime Minister as the Conservative Party wins the general election. The Stirling Prize this year feels politically charged. London's housing 'problem' is thrown into stark relief by two quite different projects: Neo Bankside, dubbed homes for millionaires or 'Oligarchitecture' and Darbishire Place, family homes in the East End by social housing experts Peabody. Neither win, with Burntwood, a state school in Wandsworth, landing the gong. Open House launches in The Foreign & Commonwealth Office with founder Victoria Thornton announcing her retirement as director.

In 2016, the Open House guide is given a make-over but the initiative stays true to its founding mission. Sadly, the year is coloured by the untimely death of Zaha Hadid and the divisive Brexit vote. Yet the event itself is as big as ever and earns the support of the Mayor's Office asking Open House to partner on its post-Brexit campaign #LondonIsOpen. Milan and Lagos join Open House Worldwide. There are now 33 participating cities across 5 continents.

# Open House founder Victoria Thornton

The idea of Open House came via two different routes - the only public debate at the time was around heritage, despite the great contemporary architecture in the capital; I realised that for a public discussion about the city, everyone needed to experience it first hand.

I knew I was onto something when there was an immediate massive response by the public, buildings were over-subscribed. The Independent came to us asking to produce the first ever full Open House London programme.

My 'eek' moment was 9/11 in 2001 – 10 days before Open House and the phones rang with 30 buildings withdrawing in 10 minutes flat. Our media partner the Evening Standard announced 'Open House is closed' (which of course wasn't true). There was huge concern about security, but London's spirit of openness continued.

Receiving the OBE was my proudest moment. It recognised all the work and commitment of all the thousands of people that make Open House happen.

The success of Open House is due to the volunteers and building owners - without their generosity, Open House wouldn't happen. Also the core team of volunteers and staff. These three elements create the huge success that it is.

| | |
|---|---|
| **2011** | Accelerate into University mentoring programme begins |
| **2012** | Open House takes place in 25 cities worldwide/London hosts an international conference |
| **2013** | Battersea Power Station opens for the first and last time before redevelopment. 40,000 people visit. |
| **2016** | New director Rory Olcayto takes over from founding director Victoria Thornton |

# The Top 25

To celebrate our 25th birthday we wondered: what would a 'perfect' London actually look like? After all, in the years that have passed since the first Open House, London's skyline, its streets and its suburbs have changed beyond all recognition, and not always, you might argue, for the best. So we asked you to vote for your favourite Open House building and tell us why.

When your votes came in we drew up a list – just for fun, the top 25. Then we asked designers Graphical House to create icons of each building (in a unified style) and with them fashion what we call the Open House 'capriccio'. Translation? A drawing of an imaginary London townscape formed of the 25 most popular Open House buildings. Whether you think the capriccio presents a perfect skyline or not, the image is compelling: familiar, in that it jumbles old and new as the real London does, but uncanny in that the size and location of each building has clearly been messed with.

**You can buy your own capriccio from our online shop, and there's a colouring-in print too (it's for kids, but we won't ask who it's for when you buy one ;-) See our website for details of where to get your copy.**

You can see the top 25 buildings over the following pages, alongside the best reasons given by you for their greatness. What you have to say about your favourite London buildings is fascinating. It shows the depth of regard we all share for London's great townscape, its incredibly variety – in style, scale, age, colour, function – and the range of emotions it can inspire within us.

Consider the evocative power of this simple reflection on the charms of Battersea Power station: 'It reminds me of an older time and a different type of workforce'. Or this cheeky riff on Trellick Tower: 'Brutal but classy, just like London'. Or this happy thought by a proud employee in Senate House: 'I work here and it's beautiful'.

If you participated in our poll to find the most loved Open House building, thank you. If you voted for the Gherkin, well done, it's come top; Norman Foster's voluptuous skyscraper really has usurped St Paul's as the symbol of London's skyline. The one-word quote we selected from all the supporting reasons says it all: "Iconic".

**1**

## 30 St Mary Axe

**❝ *Iconic***

**Architect**
— Foster + Partners
**Function**
— Offices
**Year of completion**
— 2003

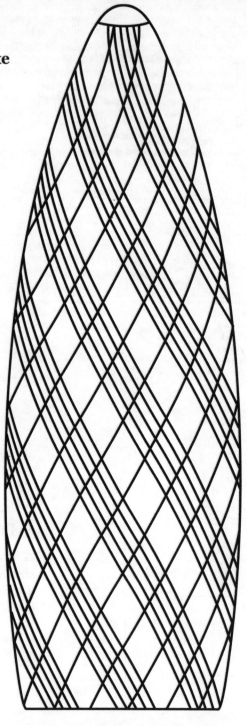

# 2

## St Paul's Cathedral

**66** *The jewel in London's crown (But I have to admit to knowing nothing about architecture)*

Architect
__ Sir Christopher Wren
Function
__ Worship
Year of completion
__ 1710

# 3

## St Pancras

**66** *It's a railway station and hotel – it didn't have to be this good!*

Architect
__ George Gilbert Scott
Function
__ Station
Year of completion
__ 1868

# 4

## The Shard

> 66 *A marker to orientate yourself. Beautiful in all weathers – and lit up at night*

Architect
__ Renzo Piano Building
    Workshop
Function
__ Offices
Year of completion
__ 2012

# 5

## The Barbican

> 66 *Beautiful monster, never gets boring*

Architect
__ Chamberlin,
    Powell & Bon
Function
__ Residential
Year of completion
__ 1969

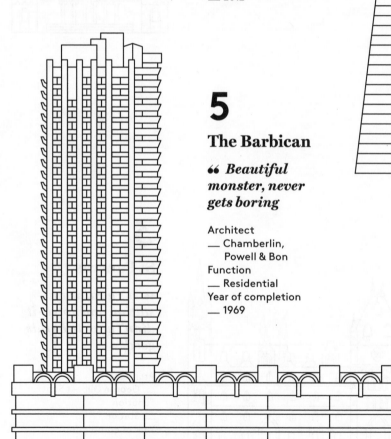

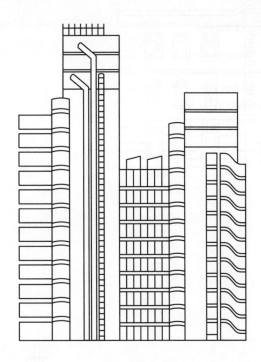

# 6

## Lloyd's of London

*❝ Reminds me of the pipe screen saver we used to have on our computers*

Architect
— Rogers Stirk Harbour + Partners
Function
— Offices
Year of completion
— 1986

# 7

## Houses of Parliament

*❝ For everyone*

Architect
— Sir Charles Barry & Augustus Pugin
Function
— Government
Year of completion
— 1847

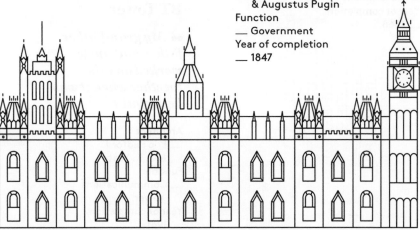

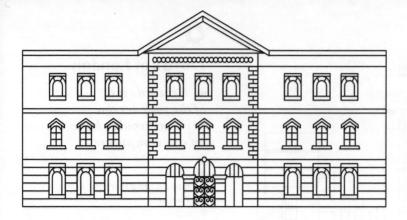

# 8

## Foreign & Commonwealth Office

*❝ Knowing it was so nearly demolished gives me tingles down my spine*

Architect
— George Gilbert Scott
Function
— Government
Year of completion
— 1868

# 9

## BT Tower

*❝ My grandfather, father and uncle worked on this together when it was being built*

Architect
— Eric Bedford
  & G. R. Yeats
Function
— Communications
  tower
Year of completion
— 1961

# 10

## Royal Festival Hall

### 66 *Truly London's living room*

Architect
— Sir Robert Matthew
    & Dr Leslie Martin
Function
— Concert hall
Year of completion
— 1951

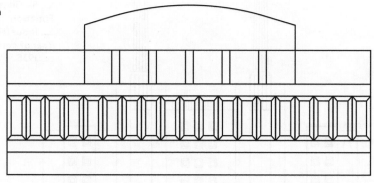

# 11

## Tower of London

### 66 *Still going strong after nearly one thousand years!*

Architect
— William & Robert Vertue
Function
— Fortress
Year of completion
— 1066

# 12

## Battersea Power Station

**❝ It reminds me of an older time and a different type of workforce**

Architect
— Sir Giles Gilbert Scott
Function
— Industrial
Year of completion
— 1935

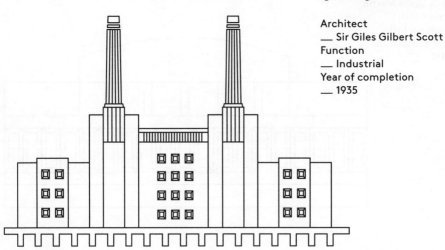

# 13

## Two Temple Place

**❝ I volunteer here and have not quite decided if it is a folly or not**

Architect
— John Loughborough
  Pearson
Function
— Residential
Year of completion
— 1895

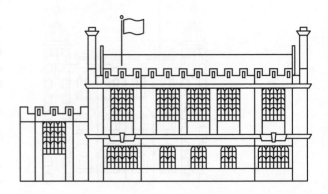

# 14

## King's Cross Station

**❝ *So simple and strong with yellow London bricks***

Architect
— George Turnbull & Lewis Cubitt, John McAslan, Arup (engineers)
Function
— Station
Year of completion
— 1852

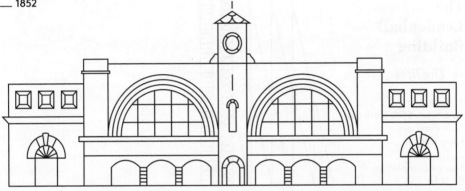

# 15

## Sir John Soane Museum

**❝ *Like walking through a dream***

Architect
— Sir John Soane
Function
— Museum
Year of completion
— 1812

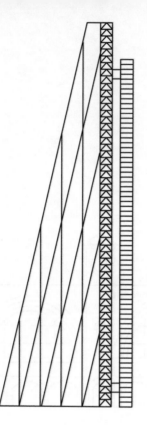

# 16

## The Leadenhall Building

### 66 *The lifts*

Architect
— Rogers Stirk Harbour
  + Partners
Function
— Offices
Year of completion
— 2014

# 17

## City Hall

### 66 *For its 500 metre helical walkway*

Architect
— Foster + Partners
Function
— Offices
Government
— 2002

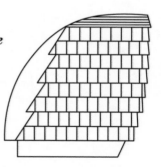

# 18

## Royal Albert Hall

**❝ *It's magnificent. I can't stop staring at the ceiling when I go there***

Architect
— Henry Y.D. Scott & Francis Fowke
Function
— Concert hall
Year of completion
— 1871

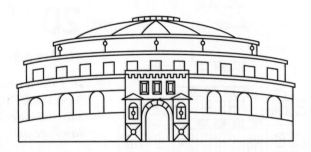

# 19

## National Theatre

**❝ *Because it is properly open***

Architect
— Denys Lasdun and Partners
Function
— Theatre
Year of completion
— 1976

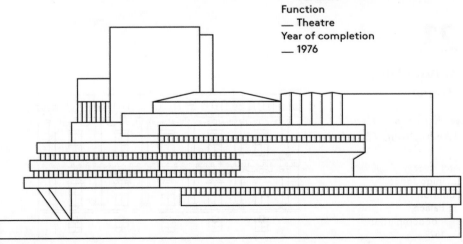

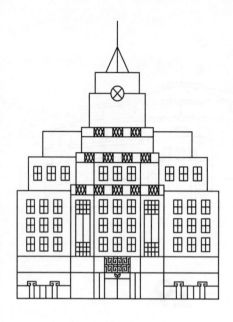

# 20

## 55 Broadway

*❝ Like a piece of New York City in the St James's Park landscape*

Architect
— Charles Holden
Function
— Offices
Year of completion
— 1929

# 21

## Banqueting House

*❝ Rubens' ceiling. The history. The view*

Architect
— Inigo Jones
Function
— Palace
Year of completion
— 1622

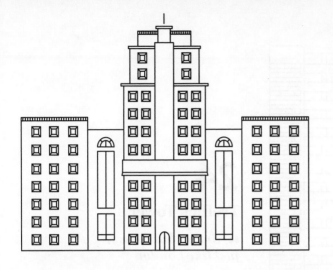

# 22

## Senate House

❝ *I work here and it's beautiful*

Architect
__ Charles Holden
Function
__ Education
Year of completion
__ 1936

# 23

## Guildhall

❝ *Historically, it links us with the past (and I like the stained glass portraits)*

Architect
__ George Dance the Younger,
    John Foxton
Function
__ Government
Year of completion
__ 1440/1789

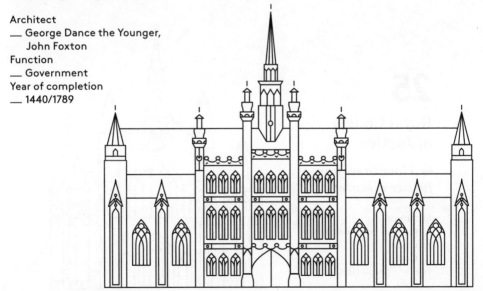

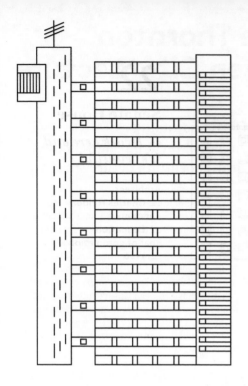

# 24

## Trellick Tower

*66 Brutal but classy, just like London*

Architect
— Ernö Goldfinger
Function
— Residential
Year of completion
— 1972

# 25

## Royal Courts of Justice

*66 I love to see how justice is served...*

Architect
— George Edmund Street
Function
— Court
Year of completion
— 1882

# The Thornton 'Open City' Lecture

Rory Olcayto announces Tate's new Director Maria Balshaw as the inaugural Thornton Lecture speaker.

The lecture is named in honour of Open House and Open City founder Victoria Thornton. Victoria's contribution to London, and the public's appreciation and understanding of architecture and urban design, is immense. Open House – unpretentious, egalitarian and free – is the biggest success story to emerge from British architectural culture in living memory. Literally millions of Britons have enjoyed this friendly September weekend event for the past quarter century. The lecture, to be held annually, has a simple premise: a guest speaker of international repute, addressing the topic of 'the open city'.

Our inaugural speaker is Maria Balshaw, the new Tate director. Maria's ambition is to make the Tate "the most culturally inclusive institution in the world". And while Maria is known for her ability to engage new audiences – she doubled the numbers at the Whitworth Gallery in Manchester during her tenure – she's also passionate about great architecture. Indeed Maria saw her own project, a refurbished and extended Whitworth, vie for the Stirling Prize in 2015, only for it to be pipped at the post by Burntwood school.

Maria believes that people make cities what they are, and that we should celebrate public life at every opportunity. Her first act as Tate Director was to show an artwork in Tate Britain of Khadija Saye, a young artist who died in the Grenfell fire. So while we have no idea how Maria will interpret 'the open city' for her lecture, we know we're in for a treat. Given her passion for architecture, and the arts – and people – and crucially, the public nature of her work, and of course the small fact that she heads up one of London's great cultural institutions, we cannot think of a better speaker for the first Thornton Open City Lecture.

A limited number of tickets will be available through our public ballot for the lecture on November 30th. Details of the ballot will be announced in October.

# Open Londinium

Beneath the City of London's
soaring steel towers
lies Rome, writes historian
*Tom Holland*

Long before England existed, London was a Roman capital. Deep beneath the tarmac and steel of the City of London, fragments of Londinium, like the bones of some titanic beast, can still be found. Sometimes, indeed, the dead are literally underfoot. Anyone visiting the Gherkin for Open House London should be sure to look on Bury Street, to the side of its entrance, for the grave of a Roman girl. Discovered in 1995 as the foundations were being dug, the skeleton was re-interred in 2007. The Lady Mayoress of the City attended, to pay her respects to the 1,600 year old Londoner. The Romans are often closer to us than we might think.

This year, to mark its 25th anniversary, Open House is celebrating London's earliest architecture. The origins of the capital reach all the way back to the reign of the Emperor Claudius, who in AD 43 ordered the conquest of Britain, and whose engineers, seven years later, embarked on the construction of the very first London Bridge. Its annihilation a decade on at the hands of Boudicca's vengeful hordes proved only a temporary setback. By the time that Hadrian arrived in Londinium in 122, the city was securely established as the political, financial and commercial capital of Britain. When walls were built around it at the end of the 2nd century AD, they enclosed an urban space that ranked as the fourth largest north of the Alps.

Portions of these fortifications can still be seen, with a particularly impressive stretch at Tower Bridge. Under the appropriately named London Wall, there is even a chunk of the eponymous masonry stranded in the car park. Equally subterranean is the only fragment of a Roman domestic structure available to view anywhere in the City: the so-called 'Billingsgate House'. Discovered in 1848, its most notable feature is a complex of baths, complete with underfloor heating. Rarely open to the public, the opportunity to visit is a precious one indeed.

A much more recent and spectacular discovery is the amphitheatre, which was located in 1988 directly next to the Guildhall. This is where the inhabitants of Roman London would have assembled to watch gladiators fight: a practice which is the theme of a small exhibition named – appropriately enough – 'Trauma'. If, in many ways, the Romans can seem just like us, then in other ways a large part of their fascination is just how alien they were. To visit the Roman city is to enter a world that is mysterious as well as familiar. Nowhere will better serve to convey this than the London Mithraeum: an underground temple to a bull-slaying Persian god that has led a thoroughly peripatetic existence since its discovery in 1954. Rebuilt soon afterwards on Queen Victoria Street, it has now been moved back to its original site as part of the Bloomberg development, seven metres below the modern street level. Although not ready for Open House, it will be in time for the autumn. The experience promises to be unmissable. The worship of Mithras took place underground, in eerie, shadow-haunted chambers: much like the experience of visiting London's Roman remains.

Joseph Conrad, imagining the wilderness surveyed by the first centurion to navigate the Thames, famously declared that it too, like the upper reaches of the Congo or the Amazon, had once been "one of the dark places of the earth." The chance to explore the first urban settlement to have been founded on the river's banks is one that no Londoner will want to miss. OH

Roman Amphitheatre in Guildhall Art Gallery © Clive Totman ↗

##  Open House Roman buildings/sites to visit

### London's Roman Amphitheatre
→ p. 67
Hidden beneath the City of London's art gallery at Guildhall (image right). Come face-to-face with a Roman skull in the 'Trauma' exhibition – the closest archaeologists have come to identifying a potential gladiator in Londinium.

### Billingsgate Roman House & Baths
→ p. 66
Some of London's best Roman remains and the only accessible Roman house, comprising late 2C house with 3C bath house within its courtyard. First discovered 1848.
→ *cityoflondon.gov.uk/romanbathhouse*

### Leadenhall Market
→ p. 68
Join a guided tour to hear about the history of the market, including its Roman foundations. Sat/Sun 10am, 12pm and 2pm (meet at Central Avenue off Gracechurch Street).

## Outside of Open House weekend

### Londinium: the City's Roman story
(until 29 October 2017)
This Autumn programme will unearth some of the City's long lost stories and its deepest buried secrets, featuring new arts commissions from Boy Blue Entertainment and wiretapper, a new play on the warrior queen Boudicca at Shakespeare's Globe, as well as Gladiator Games on the site of London's amphitheatre, and a wide variety of events, including exhibitions, walks, talks, tours and lectures.
→ *visitlondon.com/romans*

### London Wall and Cripplegate Fort
→ *museumoflondon.org.uk/fort-gate-tours*

### London Mithraeum Bloomberg SPACE
Opening this Autumn, the London Mithraeum will offer visitors an immersive experience of the Roman temple of Mithras in its original location seven metres below ground, as well as a chance to see a collection of the remarkable Roman artefacts found during excavation.
→ *londonmithraeum.com*

In partnership with

# ROCKET
PROPERTIES

# Can I come in?

*Tom Appleton* wonders what London would be like if its commercial buildings had more open ground floors

As a child and a frustrated (early) architect, I would work my pencil across the paper producing buildings and roadways. The only thing these creations had in common was that none of the structures actually touched the ground. Even as an impressionable 8 year old I was aware of the shrinking ground space in our cities and how something was going to have to change.

Fast forward a number of years and being lucky enough to travel to different world cities, it became evident I wasn't the only one wishing things could float above us. Many of the buildings in New York, Chicago, Hong Kong (notable and possibly the best example being the HSBC building by Foster + Partners) and other custodians of the traditional 'skyscraper' seemed to be letting us mere mortals walk around – not the bottom – but the underneath of them, and through into the next one.

I am pleased that this way of thinking has now moved over to London, and where once our traditional Victorian and late 20th century buildings hit the ground with a certain 'here I am', there now seems to be a movement towards inclusivity. This is evident not just at the bottom of buildings such as the 'Cheesegrater' but also in terms of the breaking up of buildings such as the Barts estate where the ground floor user has a much more interactive experience.

We at Rocket Properties are currently working with architects to see how we can make the most of the ground floor experience out of fairly tight City fringe sites. This inevitably leads to a loss of floor space which, being a developer, runs in the exact opposite direction the accountants would have us go in. However, taking a more holistic view of the development, there is likely to be much more justification for a building of a certain scale if the first three or four floors are given back to the community.

These ground floor spaces then develop into courtyards, piazzas and civic squares, all of which we have now, however the difference being the hotel/office/residential accommodation that sits above. A vertical city above an urban park. This works especially well in really hot climates, or as in our case quite wet climates.

Looking at our own City of London, this giving back to the city is mainly about the free-flow of pedestrians. But in a few years from now as space become more of a premium I may be dusting off those old drawings of buildings floating above the whole city and transport routes. Skyscrapers should take up the sky, not the ground. OH

*Tom Appleton is Chairman and co-founder of Rocket Investments*

We are finding that the boundary between inside and outside is blurring, as is the distinction between public and private space. The desire for a clear separation between the two is giving way to a much more fluid situation where the spaces of work, recreation and dwelling are overlapping.

Walking along Whitechapel High Street you can't fail to see the giant, illuminated lettering that announces 'The White Chapel Building'. Once an unloved 1980s bank, we transformed it into a public living room, surrounded by offices that were let in record time by Derwent London to creative, media and technology companies. The artist Lawrence Lek recently chose this as the location for a virtual reality installation Playstation, speculating on a future where work and play are interchangeable. In a mirror of the artwork itself, 3000 people visited the building's vast reception in one night to 'play' in the office.

Fifteen minutes' walk away, in the Bank of England Conservation Area, you'll come to a very different scale of building: Angel Court. You would never imagine that this sleek new glass tower contains the core of a 1970s building. Our aim was to use the spine of the original building to create a contemporary workplace. We transformed the experience at ground level, turning a dark alley into a sunny pedestrian street lined with restaurants and specially commissioned artwork by Sara Barker that echo the history of the area.

The White Chapel Building and Angel Court are private offices that open to the public at ground level and connect to the city. Both retain the memory of the past, while embracing the future of technology and work. These paradoxes express the fluidity and excitement of cities, and are what makes the practice of architecture so fascinating. OH

*Jonathan Kendall is a partner at Fletcher Priest Architects, where he is responsible for leading the urban design and masterplanning work of the practice.*

# Blurring Boundaries

Buildings might look like fixed assets, but *Jonathan Kendall* uses two central London projects to show how they can be adapted to new times

During a recent 'open studio' weekend, we hung a giant inflatable shark in our reception as a whimsical reminder of the endangered Greenland shark that can live for 500 years. Buildings are too often demolished after just a few decades, while the most resilient structures embody the character of a place and can be endlessly reinvented.

Cities are remarkably adaptable. Somehow, their buildings and open spaces change over time to meet the needs of society and cope with rapid developments in technology. Two of our recently completed projects, The White Chapel Building and Angel Court, show how we're grappling with ways of reinventing old buildings and making them resilient to change.

In partnership with

Landscape
Institute
Inspiring great places

# The landscape is the city

Landscape Institute's CEO *Dan Cook* writes
on the infrastructural role that landscape
can play in creating an open city

The landscape Institute consists of more than 5000 members spanning the
fields of landscape architecture/design, planning, management, science
& urban design. If you want to help or if you are wanting a career in this exciting
sector linking natural systems, built environment and human interactions with
places, email contact@landscapeinstitute.org

Open City                                  ↖ Alexandra Road Park © Sarah Blee / J&L Gibbons

Most of our landscapes pre-date modern day development and as a result have normally been the basis for human settlement and land use choices over thousands of years. Rivers, hills, forests and coastlines have shaped, aided and even at times hindered our ability to traverse cities. London is no different.

The definition of landscape in the European Landscape Convention (ELC) covers outside spaces everywhere, at every scale and both built and natural environments. This means landscapes include countryside, green infrastructure and open spaces, plus urban spaces, civic squares, public realm and more.

The Landscape Institute not only backs the view that landscape is the primary infrastructure upon which our cities are built, but that it is vital that all cities plan, design and manage landscape just as they do other types of infrastructure.

It's important to understand that landscape's interaction between nature, built and human environments means that its benefits extend well beyond beauty and aesthetics.

With Brexit putting pressure on the perception of the United Kingdom, cities like London will need to do even more to remain 'open'. Other European Cities such as Berlin, Barcelona, Antwerp, and Bilbao are all rethinking their approach to landscapes, especially their public places, in their effort to attract talent and inward economic investment. Accessibility, well-being, resource security, quality of life, smart use of technology and inclusion are all essential ingredients.

Landscape considered as infrastructure that is well designed, funded and managed will be essential to London staying an open and successful city. OH

**If we are going to develop a more open, succesful city, this is where we need to focus:**

### Inclusion
→ connecting communities with food growing, creating a sense of pride and ownership in local green spaces

### Technology
→ augmented and virtual reality provides a basis for many to use the outdoors – we should reflect on the craze of games like Pokemon Go that has connected millions to outdoor spaces
→ with the Ordnance Survey creating an accessible online map of the UK's greenspaces, we can also expect to see many more interactive applications that help communities use outdoor space

### Resources
→ London has long had its allotments, but new commercial ventures are looking to roofs and underground spaces to grow food more sustainably

### Funding
→ new private rented sector housebuilding funded by Real Estate Investment Trusts, creating larger scale and longer term interests in managing public realm
→ garden cities created around the edges of London

**The Low Line**
→ p. 137
Emerging pedestrian walkway along a Victorian viaduct linking Southwark tube with London Bridge

**Clapham Old Town and Venn Street**→ p. 117
Radically redesigned public realm which re-balanced the street in favour of the pedestrian and cyclist

**Sayes Court** → p. 120
A site of horticultural innovation, birthplace of the National Trust – now being transformed into a new public garden

Landscape & public realm highlights this year

# Motown no more

Can cities ever feel 'human' if we design them around the car, asks architect and town planner *Riccardo Marini*

What makes us happy, feel good, feel human? Jan Gehl, the Danish architect and pioneer of people-centred town planning, has a simple answer: 'maður er manns gaman', or 'man is man's joy'. It's an old Norse saying and one I swear by. So why is it that we find it so hard to create places where people want to linger, perambulate and simply see and be seen?

It's all about the car. Most of our cities developed long before the advent of the internal combustion engine, so their urban fabric developed primarily in response to the human scale. You can see where I'm going here: forget the many benefits this private mode of transport has evidently brought – because its impact upon our cities is nothing short of catastrophic.

Humanity is hooked. We're still selling the car as an aspirational dream. But you'll never see an advert that shows the reality of urban driving – travelling in traffic at walking pace.

Here's a thought. When you're stuck in traffic remind yourself: 'YOU ARE THE TRAFFIC'. This is serious. It's not just the fact that cars are clogging up our streets, metaphorically squeezing the life out of them; cars and their emissions are literally killing us.

That's a bleak reality that too many people who should know better are ignoring. Some, like ex-Mayor of New York Michael Bloomberg are taking a stand, addressing the urban spatial balance, returning roads to streets and making New York a city for people once again. Ann Hidalgo is doing the same for Paris.

What saddens me is that London was way ahead of both Paris and New York not so long ago. Considerable progress was made in developing a more people-centred public realm in the capital under Mayor Ken Livingstone (full disclosure: TFL commissioned Gehl, my employer, resulting in a 122-page report, 'London: towards a fine city for people', in 2004). When Livingstone failed to be re-elected in 2008, so did the commitment to redefining London's streets.

Of course, there has been some good work carried out in London. But what's missing is a coherent city vision, with political champions and the will and resources to deliver it. Without these, London will bump along, always reacting in a piecemeal fashion, not learning and thus wasting money, time and resources.

Everyone I talk to – and I talk with a lot of professionals in this sector – seems to know what the issues are and what the solutions could be.

So why is progress not happening? We're still living in an age of 'trophy projects'. You'll know them when you see them. These projects are usually lavished with the finest materials and have overly finessed details (the windows, the doors, rooflines, railings, 'bling' in other words).

Yet the kind of places people like to dwell and linger need not be so thoroughly 'presented': a simple buggy test is sometimes all that is needed to make a place more people-centred, more walkable, more human. That means testing a neighbourhood to see what is broken, missing or needed – streetlamps, benches, and wider pavements for example – and then in a pragmatic fashion tackling these 'bugs' one by one. But in such a way that the result is a public realm fit to walk and cycle in first.

And then maybe – and it's a really big maybe – we can invite a few cars to join us. OH

*Riccardo Marini is a masterplanning and urban strategy expert at Gehl in Copenhagen*

# Housing is a human right

Leading experts give their view on why a society that provides good homes for everyone is doing something right

Silchester Estate © Philip Vile ↗

## The Housing Association's View

*Former Peabody CEO **Steve Howlett** on why housebuilders must work closely with the communities they serve*

With its amazing history, historic buildings, open spaces and cultural attractions, it's clear to see what brings so many people to London. Many people from all over the globe live and work here, helping to sustain our tolerant, diverse and open culture.

The capital is a city of wealth and opportunity, but many of its communities have not benefitted from London's increasing prosperity. There is an urgent need for more affordable homes across London to accommodate its growing population and to reduce homelessness. These need to be built to a high standard, to create thriving communities that we can be proud of. We must also ensure that the workers that are key to London's success can afford to live and work here.

Housing associations are building more homes than ever before and we have also seen the return of local authority house-building for the first time in a generation. There are other organisations innovating with the design of homes and providing bespoke products for first time buyers.

There's a lot that can be achieved through good design and planning, but a sense of community often grows from active involvement in the neighbourhood, and the spirit of togetherness and friendliness that goes along with that. By working with local residents to provide the things they want, such as green spaces, shops, cafés, and good public transport links, we can make a real difference to the very fabric of London.

## The Architect's View

*Dawson's Heights architect **Kate Macintosh** on housing on housing, bikes and human rights*

During Les Trente Glorieuses – the post-WW2 consensus across Europe when it was generally accepted that decent shelter, education and health provision were the legitimate responsibility of governments – housing was not seen as an investment, or a repository for wealth, but as a right, which any civilized society should confer on its citizens as is recognised under the Geneva Convention.

Once housing is viewed as a commodity for speculation and trade, exploitation of the vulnerable follows naturally in its wake. That in our wealthy country, there are 28% children growing up in poverty – without the protection of a secure home – shows an abrogation by government of its first responsibility: to protect its citizens from harm.

Utopian cities must offer a balance between the universal need for belonging and identity, and the urge for freedom, choice and connectivity. For many decades it is the latter of these which has dominated.

The great destroyer of urban space is that supposed liberator, the private car. I regard the cities which have realised the need to restrain the car and prioritised walking and cycling as offering the utopian vision for the future.

In Copenhagen, 50% of all citizens commute by bike every day and there are more bikes than inhabitants. Many of our major cities that today are packed with cars actually have a past as cities of bicycles.

# The Charity's View

*Shelter suggests a new approach to housebuilding, one that will enable us to build high quality popular and affordable homes with a 'civic' approach.*

In England we are not building enough homes – and haven't for at least a generation. It's at the heart of most housing problems we see, from rocketing house prices and falling home ownership, to increases in homelessness.

Not only that, but we are building too slowly and often ending up with unattractive and unpopular developments. A majority of people think the quality of new housing supply is 'poor' or 'very poor'. Members of the public are worried about the lack of facilities such as healthcare, education places and transport.

Shelter counters despair and disappointment with a new vision for housebuilding. 'New Civic Housebuilding' argues that our current system cannot solve England's shortage on its own, and instead offers a long-term, sustainable solution: increase housebuilding outside the speculative model through land market reform – combined with targeted public investment.

English housebuilding is dominated by one business model: 'speculative' housebuilding. These developers take big risks in the hope of achieving big rewards, the biggest of which is their land purchases. They base their price on their estimate of sale prices they will get for the homes they build. Whichever firm is able to squeeze its costs the most wins.

The reason new housing is prohibitively expensive is because developers' profits are dependent on maintaining high market values, so they build out slowly to not flood the local market and minimise affordable housing. Ultimately, sticking with the status quo would just see housing choices worsen.

We advocate using targeted land market intervention to build homes. 'Civic' housebuilding starts by bringing in land at a fairer cost and channels competition into raising the quality of homes, planning in active consultation with the community. We have seen this model in our history, but never at sufficient scale to rival speculative building.

We should be ambitious about what we can build. We are rightly proud in Britain of our heritage: historic market towns, universities, pioneering Victorian engineering. We know we can build beautiful, genuinely affordable homes. We can connect them to places of work and build them along with good new schools, medical facilities, public spaces and high streets. We've just got to get back into the habit. ᴏᴴ

CLARION
HOUSING GROUP

# People come first

Clarion Group's Director of
Regeneration *Bob Beaumont*
writes on commitment to
creating lasting neighbourhoods

**Influence and capacity to transform lives**
In 2016 Circle Housing and Affinity Sutton
merged to form Clarion Housing Group, the
largest housing group in the country with plans
to build 50,000 new homes over 10 years.
In April of this year they submitted proposals to
transform three existing estates in the London
Borough of Merton. These proposals will see
£1 billion invested in the borough, delivery of
2,800 new homes and rehousing of all existing
tenants and homeowners who wish to remain.

**Local people are the experts**
People come first. Working with existing
communities defines an approach to creating
better, happier, safe places to live and work.
By creating a shared vision for regeneration we
can collectively realise the long-term benefits.
In turn we're enhancing places where people
will want to spend time, work and put down
roots for generations to come.

**Homes that will last 100 years**
We have over 100 years' heritage of place-
making and remain committed to supporting
our communities for the long term. We squeeze
every possible benefit for the community
out of our investment. Last year alone we
invested £264.6m into building new homes
and improving existing ones. Successful
regeneration is where the benefits continue
long after new homes have been built. Clarion's
new homes and public spaces set the scene for
change and – working alongside local businesses
and community organisations – we create
job opportunities and improve community
facilities, green spaces and transport links. OH

OH **Innovative
approaches to
housing in this year's
programme**

**4–8 Hafer Road** → p. 148
A co-housing project, the brainchild
of a group of residents living in a
1950s council block on a post-war
bombsite infill.

**Dawson's Heights** → p. 133
Designed by Kate Macintosh when
she was only 26.

**Darbishire Place** → p. 140
Stirling-prize shortlisted housing on an
existing Peabody estate from 1870.

**New Ground, Pollard Thomas
Edwards Architects** → p. 48
Cohousing for a group of 20 older
women, pioneering a radically different
approach to growing old.

# Ho Ho Ho – it's off to work we go

## Novelist and critic *Will Wiles* on how we work today

The office – and the workplace in general – is a paradoxical place. It is second only to our home in terms of the hours we spend there. Deduct the hours spent asleep from the home's total and the gap narrows. But we have precious little control over that second home. Even being there entails only questionable free will. In theory we can work wherever we please in a glorious, fluid free market; in daily reality, it's more complicated, and we can be pinned in place by a web of obligations and practicalities, at the centre of which is the overriding economic imperative to keep working.

And, other than a few knick-knacks and photos, most often we can't do much to shape our working environment. In Mike Judge's underrated 1999 film *Office Space*, a dehumanised drone working for a faceless American corporation that makes software for banks has a minor breakdown and loses all his terror of being fired. This being the only force that holds him in place, he begins to act without fear of consequences. He brings a power tool into the office and with it dismantles the grey acoustic walls of his cubicle, unblocking a view of the window and the trees beyond. It is an almost inconceivable rebellion against the existing order: he takes personal control over his environment.

Two of London's grandest Victorian buildings, the Foreign Office and the Midland Hotel at St Pancras Station, had dreary midlife periods in the post-war years as maltreated offices, before undergoing major renovation. The city's fabric is improved as a result, but one can't help but feel that they might have been more interesting places to explore before, when they were buried treasure; and perhaps they were freer places to work. Where are the buried treasures now? Still out there.

Perhaps in the future, preferred locations will be the citadels the tech firms are building for themselves in the city, such as Google's landscraper in the new world behind St Pancras. Though outwardly paragons of pastoral care and play-hard beanbag ping-pong fun, the new aristocracy may find they have built themselves a Versailles, part prison and part fishbowl, windows fogged from the *citoyens* keen to catch a glimpse. And who wants to have their slacking rebadged as creativity and presented as shareholder value? Talk about taking the fun out of it.

About five years ago I emancipated myself from the office environment. Working two rooms away from where you sleep has its advantages, not least the congenial commute. But I quickly found that I missed certain aspects. The presence of other people, the daily chitchat and gossip, was important, of course. But there was also the civil ritual of going to a second place, where different rules apply, in order to do work (that's what 'office' means, by the way, from the Latin 'to perform a task'). In the 21st century, there is a new breed of facilities to meet this need among the growing army of freelance creative workers – the co-working hub, where the self-employed can enjoy a workplace that hums with a bit more than central heating, and can nibble at the edges of the Google life.

But when I started to fantasise about renting a bolt-hole somewhere, and my dream office formed in my mind, it was quite different: a small room off an institutional corridor of tile or lino, with shelves and metal filing cabinets and perhaps a door with a frosted glass section, where a signwriter could paint my name. It's revealing that this fantasy definitely emanates from a date before the invention of the integrated circuit: it's out of Chandler or Le Carré. Places like this still exist, in the buried treasure category, and my suggestion is that you start with London's amazingly fine selection of older municipal buildings and town halls. OH

# Made right here

## Making things is still big business in the city by the Thames

Open City

Despite often being hidden from the streetscape, London is home to thousands of industrial sites, from large-scale factories like the Ford plant in Dagenham - which employs 2000 people - to tiny spaces producing anything from bread to bicycles.

As part of this year's programme we have partnered with the Greater London Authority to celebrate manufacturing in the capital, with the aim of encouraging and promoting local industry by drawing attention to the range of products made here in London.

## Manufacturing in numbers

# 2000+

Manufacturers in London

# 1m+

Small-Medium Enterprises (SMEs) in London

| They make up | And provide |
|---|---|
| **99%** | **50%** |
| of London's businesses | of London's employment |

## (OH) Manufacturing highlights in the programme

**Kaymet Factory** → p. 133
A hidden 1960s building, originally a printing works and now the operational factory of Kaymet, maker of trays and trolleys since 1947

**National Theatre** → p. 116
The biggest 'factory' in Central London, where 150 people are employed, making sets, props and costumes

**639 Tottenham High Road** → p. 91
Former gas showroom fully refurbished by the GLA and now providing local people with employment skills and helping them get started in business

**Sweetdram – SODA** → p. 86
Industrial print works transformed into headquarters of a new drinks manufacturer

**Blackhorse Workshop** → p. 146
Supported by funding from the Mayor of London, a new public space dedicated to making and mending

**Fuller's Griffin Brewery** → p. 102
The brewery has existed in its present form for almost 200 years and employs about 400 people

**Goldfinger Factory** → p. 109
Award-winning design, build and teaching platform housed on the ground floor of the Grade II listed Trellick Tower

# Happy Birthday Foster + Partners

*Norman Foster's* pioneering studio – fifty this year – is hosting
a special exhibition showcasing its amazing portfolio

Open City

This year marks significant milestones for both Open House and Foster + Partners, as they celebrate their 25th and 50th anniversaries respectively. For the past 20 years, Foster + Partners have opened their London studios to visitors for Open House weekend, giving them a glimpse into the creative process behind some of the projects at the practice.

This year, they are opening more of their studio space than ever before. You will have the opportunity to see the way they work, with interactive displays to give an insight into the work of specialist teams, alongside a special exhibition focusing on upcoming projects.

Foster + Partners is a global studio for architecture, urbanism and design, rooted in sustainability. Founded in 1967 by Lord Foster, it has a worldwide reputation for integrating architecture with engineering and other allied disciplines to establish an innovative approach to the design of buildings, spaces and cities. OH

## OH Foster + Partners suggested building trail

Over the course of Open House weekend, use this itinerary to take in as many Foster + Partners projects as possible

### Saturday 16

**7am    30 St Mary Axe**
Start at the Gherkin. Bring a book and a thermos of coffee - the building doesn't open its doors until 9am but those in the know start queuing early.

**10.30am  City Hall**
Walk across the river via London Bridge and approach City Hall, focal point of the More London development that marked a radical change for London in reorienting the city's government towards the East.

**12pm    Crossrail Place**
Heading further east, explore the roof garden of Crossrail Place, with its lattice roof providing a counterpoint from the towers of Canary Wharf.

**3pm    Capital City Academy**
Take the Jubilee line up to Brent and catch the first tour of Foster + Partners first school project, built to accommodate modern teaching methods.

### Sunday 17

**10am    One Bishops Square**
Have breakfast in Bishops Square, bridging the City and the East End and Spitalfields Market, before having a tour of number One, occupied by Allen & Overy.

**10.30am  The Walbrook**
Pass by the almost complete Bloomberg Headquarters, opening next year, and pop into The Walbrook, with its distinctive exterior solar shading, but also a hidden garden at the rear paved with slate.

**12pm    Millennium Bridge**
Journey across the river by walking across the famous Millennium Bridge. Developed with sculptor Anthony Caro and Arup engineers, it was the first new crossing on this part of the Thames in more than a century, and now a key element in London's pedestrian infrastructure.

**3pm    Foster + Partners Studio**
Finish your weekend at the home of Foster + Partners, in their custom-built double-height studio space, where they will be showing a special exhibition to celebrate their anniversary.

**Paddington Central**

# Open House Junior

Young minds are fascinated
by buildings and places and how
they fit together

Open House has a long history of running programmes for children. They just get it, in a way that adults don't (they don't get hung up on style, for starters).

It's also why Open City, the charity behind Open House, runs architectural and urban study programmes for schools across London, year-round. Open City's mission is to positively affect how Londoners think about the buildings and places they inhabit and give them the means to help shape them too. Starting with young Londoners is crucial.

Dinah Bornat, a partner at ZCD Architects, which has long researched the way children play on streets, says her firm's findings shows children are the generators of community life.

"In our practice we advocate for safe places to play that all age groups can use, ones that are easy to reach and spread throughout developments. We start by taking time to understand what children want: using techniques that put children at the heart of the process. This is the best way to get neighbourhood design right for everyone." Open City agrees, and our Open House Junior programme gives children the chance to learn about design through play. OH

## OH Family activities

**Junior Activity Hub
@ Paddington Central**

**On your marks, Get Set, Lego!**
Kingdom Square (outside 4 Kingdom
Street) Sat & Sun 11am–4pm
Join this quick-paced race to build the
biggest and best LEGO™ structure.
Enter the competition and be in for a
chance to win exciting prizes.

**City of Bridges**
Paddington Central Canalside,
by the Westway, Sat & Sun 11am–4pm
Be inspired by Paddington's many
bridges, using an engineering toolkit,
come along and add to the gigantic city
of bridges.

**Playmake**
Sheldon Square, Sat & Sun 11am–4pm
Play. Make. Create! Paper forests,
tinsel towers, luminous lava fields…
if you can imagine it, you can make it!
The Archivate Collective crew – a team
of architects and designers – will be
helping children make their city.

**City of a Thousand Architects**
City Hall, Sat 11am–3pm
Become an architect for the day! Plan,
design and build a future skyline.

**Build a View Shaper**
The Leadenhall Building,
Sat 11am–4pm
As part of the City of London's
Sculpture in the City programme,
children can create a framed view of
the city, inspired by the sculptures
around The Leadenhall Building.

# The Open House App.

## Our new free guide to London's best buildings & places.

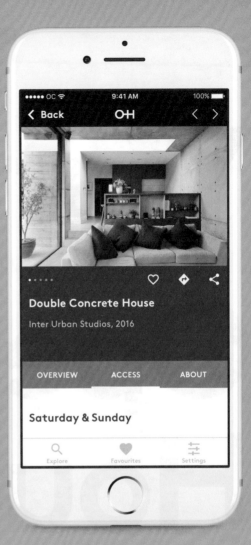

This year Open House has launched a free app for the first time, including opening details of every building and event in the programme, as well as extensive factual information.

- Images for every building and event
- Save favourites to plan your weekend
- View buildings near you
- Explore Open House curated collections and highlights
- Filter results by day, architectural type and period

Available on the App Store and Google Play from 17 August.

# This Year in Open House

For the first time we have all 33 of the London boroughs participating in our 25th programme and we hope to continue to be able to showcase the whole of the capital. Keep lobbying your local councillors to ensure their inclusion for next year!

# Boroughs Index

# How to use the guide

The programme listings on the following pages are ordered by borough area. Open House is part funded by individual local authorities.

The Index (p.164) lists buildings by type. You can also use our online search facility at *openhouselondon. open-city.org.uk* and our app to find the buildings you want to visit. All access to buildings is on the first come basis unless otherwise specified.

**Key to listings**
B   Bookshop
d   Some disabled access
D   Full wheelchair access
P   Parking
R   Refreshments
T   Toilets

🚶 Address/meeting point
🕐 Opening times
⊘ Booking required
🚇 Nearest tube/rail station

**Accessible by ballot only**
10 Downing Street → p. 152
BT Tower → p. 57
The View from The Shard → p. 136

Ballots will be open from 17–31 August. See each building's entry online to enter.

**VocalEyes Audio Described Tours**

Blind and partially sighted people are able to enjoy audio-described tours of four of London's iconic buildings during Open House Weekend: Salters' Hall, Lloyd's Register Group, Freemasons' Hall and Canada House. The tours are led by VocalEyes describers with building representatives or designers. To find out more and book visit *vocaleyes.co.uk*

# Barking & Dagenham

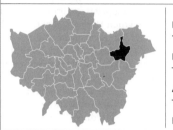

| | |
|---|---|
| Borough area (km²) | 36.1 |
| Population | 209,000 |
| Average age | 33 |
| First Open House | 2000 |

### Barking Abbey with St Margaret's Church
🏃 The Broadway, North Street, Barking, IG11 8AS
🕐 Sat 10am–3pm (bell tower may not be open).
T·R·P·D
🚇 Barking
Grade I listed church with monuments, art, stained glass. Arts & Crafts work by George Jack, Walker Organ (1914). Captain Cook married here. Abbey dates from 666AD, includes ruins, Curfew Tower, Chapel of Holy Rood with 12C Rood Stone. Ronald Wylde Associates (restoration), 2005

### Barking Riverside
🏃 Barking Riverside Project Office, Renwick Road, Barking, IG11 0DS
🕐 Sat 10am–5pm. T·R·P·d
🚇 Estuary Close
A new sustainable neighbourhood being created alongside 2km of south-facing Thames river frontage. A partnership with The GLA and L&Q, with masterplan developed by Lifschutz Davidson Sandilands, 10,800 homes will house up to 29,000 people. Lifschutz Davidson Sandilands, 2014
*www.barkingriverside.co.uk*

### CU London Campus (ex Dagenham Town Hall)
🏃 Rainham Road North, Dagenham, RM10 7BN
🕐 Sat guided tour of the new university campus, ½ hourly (10am-12.30pm, max 50). T·R·P·D
❗ Pre-book only: cul@coventry.ac.uk
🚇 Dagenham East, Romford
Grade II listed Art Deco style building in mulberry stock brick with imposing Portland stone portico, considered to be one of the finest examples of 1930s civil architecture. The building features a 3-level marble foyer. E Berry Webber, 1936

### Dagenham Library
🏃 1 Church Elm Lane, Dagenham, RM10 9QS
🕐 Sat 10am–5pm. T·D
🚇 Dagenham Heathway
A contemporary flagship building, the library is a shared 2-storey public building with a Council 'One Stop Shop'. A striking glazed façade with 82 residential units above the library features coloured balcony panels. Architecture PLB, 2010

### Eastbury Manor House
🏃 Eastbury Square, Barking, IG11 9SN
🕐 Sun 12pm–5pm. T·R·P·D
🚇 Upney, Barking
Architecturally distinguished and well-preserved, brick-built, Elizabethan Grade I listed manor house. Contains 17C wall-paintings, wood panelling, a charming walled garden and a fine Tudor turret. Many original features have been restored. Richard Griffiths Architects, 2003

### Nursery Building - 'Children's House'
🏃 Kingsley Hall, Parsloes Avenue, Dagenham, RM9 5NB
🕐 Sun 12.30pm–2.30pm (some refurbishment work ongoing but most of building will be open) + Exhibition about the school and Kingsley Hall. T·R·P·D
🚇 Becontree, Chadwell Heath
Designed in 1925/6, the 'Children's House' has been in continuous use for children's work since it was opened by Ishbel MacDonald in 1932. The first recognised nursery school on any new housing estate, as well as the first in Essex. Charles Cowles Voysey, 1931

### Studio 3 Arts
🏃 The Galleon Centre, Boundary Road, Barking, IG11 7JR
🕐 Sat 11am–5pm (max 40, not offices) + 'Kids on the block' children's activity. T·R·D
🚇 Barking
Gascoigne Estates' 4000 homes are being rebuilt as part of a 10 year regeneration programme. Studio 3 Arts provides local people with a safe, creative and welcoming space on the estate, particularly through a complex time of transition. Barking and Dagenham Borough architects, 1970

### The Ice House Quarter (featuring the Granary, Malthouse & Boathouse)
🏃 80 Abbey Road, Barking, IG11 7BT
🕐 Sat 10am–1pm (max 20, granary 3rd floor, Malthouse Studios & Boathouse Terrace). T·R·D
🚇 Barking
Home to the Granary and Malthouse, originally ↱

built for Randalls Malt Roasters c1860. The restored buildings include a Victorian Granary and adjacent Malthouse located on the River Roding/Barking Creek. *www.rooff.co.uk*

## Valence House

🚶 Becontree Avenue, Dagenham, RM8 3HT
🕐 Sat 11am–5pm + architectural tour at 12pm (max 20)·Local studies tour at 2pm·Behind the scenes tour at 4pm. R·T·P·B·d
🚇 Dagenham Heathway, Chadwell Heath

Grade II* listed 15C manor house with medieval moat. Recently discovered late 16C wall painting and impressive oak panelling. Evocative museum galleries that bring Barking & Dagenham's past alive.

## White House, Becontree Estate

🚶 884 Green Lane, Becontree, RM8 1BX
🕐 Sat 10am–4pm (max 20, no entry to artists' bedrooms unless by permission) + ½ hourly overview and Hardy Amies tour + 'White House - a retrospective' (max 20). T·R·d
🚇 Becontree, Chadwell Heath

A new public space for artistic and social activity. Artists are invited to live at the house, 4-6 months at a time, to make new art and to connect local people so that they can develop a community asset to benefit all. Apparata, 2016

# Walks + Tours

## Barking Town Centre Tour

🚶 Meet: Outside Barking Town Hall, 1 Town Square, Barking, IG11 7LU
🕐 Sat 10am, 2pm (max 25). T
❗ Pre-book only: david.harley@lbbd.gov.uk
🚇 Barking

Barking (a Housing Zone and Artist Enterprise Zone) has seen significant development over recent years with substantial growth plans for the future. These guided tours will set these out and visit existing award winning schemes.

## Becontree Estate Bus Tour, Dagenham

🚶 Meet: bus departure outside Civic Centre, Dagenham, RM10 7BN
🕐 Sun 10am (max 50, includes visits to Valence House, Kingsley Hall and three vacant council properties plus numerous stops at strategic places of interest) T·P·d·R
🚇 Dagenham East, Romford

Guided bus tour led by ex-Becontree Housing Manager Bill Jennings. Built by the LCC during the 1920s and early 1930s, the estate was once the largest of its kind in Europe, with over 25,000 houses. Later building programmes extended the estate to house an estimated hpopulation of 90,000.

The Ice House Quarter © Tim Crocker ↘

# Barnet

| | |
|---|---|
| Borough area (km²) | 86.7 |
| Population | 389,600 |
| Average age | 37 |
| First Open House | 1995 |

## Belarusian Memorial Chapel
🚶 Marian House, Holden Avenue, N12 8HY
🕐 Sat 1pm–5pm (max 35). D
🚇 Woodside Park
Built for the Belarusian Diaspora Community in London to commemorate the 30th anniversary of the 1986 Chernobyl nuclear disaster. It is the only all wooden church in London. Spheron Architects, 2016

## Friends Meeting House
🚶 North Square, NW11 7AD
🕐 Sun 1pm–5pm. T·R·B
🚇 Golders Green
Delightful brick and tile building inspired by the famous 1688 Meeting House at Jordans in Buckinghamshire. A simple building in a tranquil setting. Frederick Rowntree, 1913

## Hampstead Garden Suburb Free Church
🚶 Central Square, NW11 7AG
🕐 Sat 10am–7pm/Sun 1pm–7pm. T·R·P·D
🚇 Golders Green
Grade I listed Non-conformist church, set in the suburb's integrally planned Central Square to balance St Jude's Church nearby, but with a low concrete dome. Distinctive interior with large Tuscan columns on high brick plinths. Sir Edwin Lutyens, 1911

## New Ground
🚶 5b Union Street, Chipping Barnet, EN5 4DF
🕐 Sat 10am–1pm/Sun 2pm–5pm (max 30, common room, garden, some flats) + hourly architect-led tours. T·R·D
🚇 High Barnet, New Barnet
25 homes designed with the Older Women's Co-Housing group using PTE's 'fabric first' approach which maximises the benefits of orientation, air-tightness and insulation and following the co-housing model. Pollard Thomas Edwards, 2016

## Phoenix Cinema
🚶 52 High Road, N2 9PJ
🕐 Sun tour of cinema led by an expert volunteer, every 45 mins (10.30am-1.30pm, max 10). T·R·D
⚠ Pre-book only: 020 8444 6789
🚇 East Finchley
One of the oldest cinemas in the country with 1910 barrel-vaulted ceiling and Art Deco wall reliefs by Mollo and Egan. Grade II listed. S Birdwood, 1910

## St Jude on the Hill
🚶 Central Square, NW11 7AH
🕐 Sat/Sun 11am–6pm. T·R·P·B·d
🚇 Golders Green
Eccentric Edwardian church, Grade I listed. Described by Simon Jenkins as 'one of Lutyens' most distinctive creations'. Extensive 20C wall-paintings by Walter Starmer, memorial to horses of WWI. Local archives display. Sir Edwin Lutyens, 1911

## Waterlow Court
🚶 Heath Close, NW11 7DT
🕐 Sun 1pm–5pm (max 12, access to part of the grounds and a ground floor flat). T·R
🚇 Golders Green
Communal low cost housing built for single professional working women as part of Henrietta Barnett's vision for Hampstead Garden Suburb; now private homes. Mackay Hugh Baillie Scott, 1909

## Wrotham Park
🚶 Wrotham Park, Barnet, EN5 4SB
🕐 Sun hourly tours (10am-3pm, max 20, no tour at 1pm). P
⚠ Pre-book only: 020 8275 1425
🚇 High Barnet
A privately-owned Grade II listed Palladian mansion with grand interiors restored in 1883, set in 300 acres of parkland in the midst of 2,500 acres. Built for Admiral The Hon. John Byng. Isaac Ware, 1754

Supported by

Pollard Thomas Edwards

Hampstead Garden Suburb Residents Association

WROTHAM PARK

HAMPSTEAD · GARDEN · SUBURB · TRUST

Golders Green Unitarians

Phoenix Cinema 1910-2010

Belarusian Memorial Chapel © Hélène Binet ↗

## Walks + Tours

**Hampstead Garden Suburb Artisans'
Quarter Walk**
🚶 Meet: register inside St Jude on the Hill,
   Central Square, NW11 7AH
🕐 Sun 2pm, 4.30pm (max 25).
🚇 Golders Green
Guided walks of 'the most nearly perfect example
of the 20C Garden Suburb' (Pevsner), designed by
Unwin & Parker, Lutyens, Bunney, Baillie Scott and
others. Informally laid out terraces and picturesque
Arts and Crafts vernacular cottages.

# Bexley

| | |
|---|---|
| Borough area (km²) | 60.6 |
| Population | 244,300 |
| Average age | 39 |
| First Open House | 1997 |

LONDON BOROUGH OF
**BEXLEY**

### Crossness Beam Engine House
🚶 The Old Works, Thames Water Sewage Treatment Works, Bazalgette Way, SE2 9AQ
🕐 Sun self-guided tour at 10am, 2pm (max 50). T·R·P·B·d
ⓘ Pre-book only: bit.ly/2eDUog0
🚉 New Cross, Abbey Wood
The southern outfall of the Victorian sewerage system designed by Joseph Bazalgette. A complex of Grade I and Grade II listed buildings. Contains four of the largest beam engines in the world and amazing Victorian decorative ironwork. Charles H Driver, 1832

### Danson House
🚶 Danson Park, Danson Road, Welling, DA6 8HL
🕐 Sun 10am–4pm (max 20, no access to offices on top level). T·D
🚉 Welling, Bexleyheath
A stunning Grade I listed Georgian villa designed by the architect of the Bank of England. Set in more than 200 acres of magnificent parkland overlooking the sparkling Danson Lake. Sir Robert Taylor, 1763

### Erith Lighthouse
🚶 Erith Pier, 6 Wharfside Close, DA8 1QR
🕐 Sat/Sun 9am–5pm (max 10) + architect-led tour at 2pm (max 20). T·R·D
🚉 Erith, Slade Green, Woolwich Arsenal
An extraordinary Thames-side structure hosting special dinners and events this summer. Devised and programmed by DK-CM and The Decorators, the project is commissioned by Bexley Council and funded by the Mayor of London. DK-CM, 2017

### Erith Playhouse
🚶 38-40 High Street, Erith, DA8 1QY
🕐 Sun 12pm–4pm + backstage tours, ½ hourly (max 8). T·R·d
🚉 Erith
195 seat repertory theatre, rebuilt in 1973 retaining the heart of the theatre - the original 'Oxford Cinema' auditorium dating from 1913. Still operating carbon arc follow spots c1956.

### Erith Yacht Club
🚶 Anchor Bay, Manor Road, Erith, DA8 2AD
🕐 Sun 12pm–5.30pm (access to club house, informal tours) + exhibition on club history. T·R·P·d
🚉 Slade Green, Erith
Uniquely positioned clubhouse on Thames floodplain adjacent to a petrified forest. Built on pilings next to the last remaining salt marsh in London. The building design facilitates sailing, training, youth sailing and social activities. Pellings, 2011

### Hall Place & Gardens
🚶 Bourne Road, Bexley, DA5 1PQ
🕐 Sat/Sun tours at 10am, 3pm (max 60). T·R·P·D
ⓘ Pre-book only: 01322 621238
🚉 Bexleyheath, Bexley
Once the country residence of Sir John Champneys, a former Lord Mayor of London. Fine Great Hall with minstrel's gallery and Tudor kitchen. Set in formal gardens on the River Cray with splendid 18C gates.

### Red House
🚶 Red House Lane, Bexleyheath, DA6 8JF
🕐 Sat/Sun 11am–5pm (max 50). T·R·B·d
🚉 Bexleyheath
The only house commissioned, created and lived in by William Morris, founder of the Arts and Crafts movement, with much original detail and of extraordinary architectural and social significance. Philip Webb & William Morris, 1860

## Thamesmead

### Lakeside Centre
🚶 Southmere Lake Complex, 2 Bazalgette Way (formally Belvedere Road), Thamesmead, SE2 9AN
🕐 Sat/Sun 2pm guided renovation tour, including refreshments (max 30, duration 30 mins). R
ⓘ Pre-book only: bit.ly/2tKNeIN
🚉 Abbey Wood
Iconic Lakeside Centre undergoing renovation led by Bow Arts in partnership with Peabody, supported by the Mayor's London Regeneration Fund (LEAP). The centre will fully reopen in 2018 as a cultural hub for Thamesmead. GLC, 1971/Architecture 00, 2017

### Sporting Club Thamesmead
🚶 Bayliss Avenue, Thamesmead, SE28 8NJ

🕐 Sat 8am–6.30pm /Sun 8.30am–5.30pm. T·R·P·D
🚇 North Greenwich, Abbey Wood
Set in a tranquil green area of Thamesmead, designed to reinforce the nature around it. 3G pitches, outdoor multi-use games area and café-bar with panoramic views over parkland and pitches - home teams include Charlton Athletic Women's FC. Saville Jones Architects, 2012

### The Link Thamesmead
🚶 Bazalgette Way (formerly Belvedere Road), Off Harrow Manorway, Thamesmead, SE2 9BS
🕐 Sat/Sun 12pm–6pm. T·R·d
🚇 North Greenwich, Abbey Wood
An innovative, state-of-the-art community hub aimed at young people but offering something for everyone, while utilising under-valued space in arches below a highway. Home to local organisations like Theatre Street and the Archway Project. Saville Jones Architects, 2011

### Thames Innovation Centre
🚶 2 Veridion Way, Erith, DA18 4AL
🕐 Sat 10am–1pm (downstairs only). T·P·D
🚇 Belvedere
A 50,000 sq ft award-winning business and innovation centre at the heart of Veridion Park, a 68-acre mixed use development with plans for 680,000 sq ft office and warehouse space. Balfour Beatty Ltd, 2006

### The Sandford Dental Implant Clinic
🚶 306 Broadway, Bexleyheath, DA6 8AA
🕐 Sat 10am–5pm (max 30). T·d
🚇 Bexleyheath
Light-filled and loftily spacious this is independent of yet contiguous with the more conventional NHS dental clinic. Showing state of the art dental design in the UK, designed from a cross infection control and ergonomic standpoint. Mitzman Architects, 2012
www.mitzmanarchitects.com

Sandford Dental Implant Clinic © Nick Kane ↘

↗ Building of a New Town: Architecture Tour of Thamesmead

### Townley Grammar School
🚶 Townley Road, Bexleyheath, DA6 7AB
🕐 Sat 10am–12pm. T·P·d
🚇 Bexley, Bexleyheath
Modern buildings for arts, science and indoor sports provide quirkiness and colour. Sustainable features include underground labyrinth for summer cooling. New computer suite named for pioneer Ada Lovelace. Studio E Architects, 2007

## Walks + Tours

### Lesnes and Thamesmead: Architectural Visions from the 12th and 21st centuries
🚶 Meet: Lesnes Abbey Woods, New Road, Abbey Wood, DA17 5RE
🕐 Sun 11am (max 30). T·R
❗ Pre-book only: 0203 045 3692 (Box office only open 9am-5pm Mon-Fri)
🚇 Abbey Wood
Discover the origins of Lesnes Abbey, founded by Richard de Luci in 1178, and the architectural history of Thamesmead, described in the 1960s as the 'Town of the 21st Century.'

### The Building of a New Town: An Architecture Tour of Thamesmead
🚶 Meet: in front of The Barge Pole Pub, Harrow Manor Way, Thamesmead, SE2 9SU
🕐 Sat 11am (max 30, duration 2 hours).
❗ Pre-book only: archives@bexley.gov.uk
🚇 Abbey Wood
Discover Thamesmead's iconic architecture with Bexley archivist, Simon McKeon, on this guided walking tour. Learn about the origins of Thamesmead, how and why this 'New Town for London' was built fifty years ago. Greater London Council, 1967

# Brent

| | |
|---|---|
| Borough area (km²) | 43.2 |
| Population | 332,100 |
| Average age | 36 |
| First Open House | 1995 |

## 85 The Avenue
⚐ 85 The Avenue, NW6 7NS
🕐 Sat 10am–5pm/Sun 10am–4pm (max 12, ground and first floors).
🚇 Queen's Park, Kensal Rise
Refurbishment and extension of a Queen's Park semi. Crittall-style glazing & black larch cladding. Large open-plan kitchen with oak floor, exposed brick and open-joisted ceiling. Imaginative touches and inspiring use of colour and finishes. The Vawdrey House, 2016
*www.thevawdreyhouse.com*

## BAPS Shri Swaminarayan Mandir
⚐ 105-119 Brentfield Road, Neasden, NW10 8LD
🕐 Sat/Sun 11am–6pm + ½ hourly tours (all areas except monks' quarters, admin block, kitchen, gym) T·R·P·B·D
🚇 Wembley Park, Harlesden
Europe's first traditional Hindu temple is a masterpiece of exquisite Indian craftsmanship. Using 5,000 tonnes of Italian and Indian marble and the finest Bulgarian limestone, it was hand-carved in India before being assembled in London. C B Sompura, 1995

## Brent Civic Centre
⚐ Engineers Way, Wembley, HA9 0FJ
🕐 Sun 2pm–6pm (max 30). T·D
🚇 Wembley Central, Wembley Stadium
The Civic Centre streamlines all aspects of Brent Council's activities. Spaces arranged around a soaring atrium. A circular drum houses event and community space. BREEAM Outstanding. Multiple awards, including RIBA National Award 2014. Hopkins Architects, 2013

## Capital City Academy
⚐ Doyle Gardens, NW10 3ST
🕐 Sat hourly tours (1pm-4pm, max 8). T·P·D
🚇 Willesden Green, Kensal Green
Foster and Partners' first school; first new build City Academy; glass/stainless steel, slightly curved following slope of the grounds surrounded by sports fields and park. Unique with its clean, curved lines reflecting sky and surrounds. Foster + Partners, 2003

## Modern Side Extension
⚐ 6 Creighton Road, NW6 6ED
🕐 Sat 1pm–5pm.
❗ Pre-book only: margaret@coffeyarchitects.com
🚇 Queen's Park, Kensal Rise
Conservation area-friendly brick, glass and bi-fold doors unite in a complex three-dimensional composition. Respectful to neighbours, it shows that the smallest architectural projects can be transformational. Coffey Architects, 2015

## Simon Court
⚐ 22 Simon Court, 16 Saltram Crescent, W9 3JA
🕐 Sat 11am–6pm (max 8, access to flat 22 only).
🚇 Westbourne Park, Queen's Park
The transformation of an unusual flat positioned in the apse of a Victorian church. New timber mezzanine and staircase and the careful retention and restoration of the original church create an unusual pied-à-terre. Sam Tisdall Architects, 2016

## The Library at Willesden Green
⚐ 95 High Road, NW10 2SF
🕐 Sat/Sun 10am–5pm (access to performance space Sat afternoon only) T·R·D
🚇 Willesden Green, Brondesbury Park
A modern 4-storey building incorporating the much-loved Victorian library. The distinctive patterned brickwork samples colours from surrounding buildings, and a dramatic central atrium provides natural ventilation and daylight throughout. Allford Hall Monaghan Morris, 2015

## The Pearl of Metroland (Mondriaan House)
⚐ 20 Forty Avenue, Wembley Park, HA9 8JP
🕐 Sat/Sun 10am–5pm (max 4). T
🚇 Sudbury Town, Preston Road
A standard semi of 1924, converted 1960s, deconverted 2014, with colour scheme designed to highlight original architect's intentions, based on complementary colour contrasts. The kitchen is a 'Mondriaan' in 3 dimensions, in primary colours.

## The Tin Tabernacle / Cambridge Hall
⚐ 12-16 Cambridge Avenue, NW6 5BA
🕐 Sat/Sun 1pm–5pm. T·R·d

↱

🚇 Kilburn Park, Kilburn High Road
1860s corrugated iron chapel. Inside transformed after the last war into a ship by local people, complete with decks, portholes, bridge and even a Bofors gun.

### Underground Bunker, Neasden
🚶 109 Brook Road, NW2 7DZ
🕐 Sat 8.30am–5.30pm (max 25) + ½ hourly tours (max 25) T·d
ℹ️ Pre-book only: katy.bajina@networkhomes.org.uk
🚇 Dollis Hill, Willesden Junction
Used during WW2 by Winston Churchill's War Cabinet. Purpose-built reinforced concrete, bomb-proof subterranean war citadel, 40ft below ground, with Map/Cabinet Rooms, housed within a sub-basement protected by 5ft thick concrete roof.

## Walks + Tours

### Roe Green Village
🚶 Meet: Village Green, opposite entrance to Roe End, Roe Lane, NW9 9BJ
🕐 Sun 11am, 2.30pm. d
🚇 Colindale, Kenton
Built to provide workers' housing for employees of AirCo (the Aircraft Manufacturing Company based in nearby Colindale), Roe Green was designed in the garden village idiom by Sir Frank Baines, principal architect at HM Office of Works. Sir Frank Baines, 1918

### The Willesden United Synagogue Cemetery
🚶 Meet: Beaconsfield Road, NW10 2JE
🕐 Sun 10.30am lecture by architect followed by tour at 11am (max 50) T·P·d
ℹ️ Pre-book only: www.theus.org.uk/ willesdenopenhouse
🚇 Willesden Green, Willesden Junction
Complex of funerary buildings which survive remarkably intact are noted by Historic England as being the finest example of British Jewish funerary non-conformist adapted religious architecture. Lewis Solomon & Son, Nathan Solomon Joseph, Harry Ford, 1873

### Wembley Park Masterplan
🚶 Meet: Quintain Wembley Park Office, 5 Exhibition Way, Wembley Park, HA9 0FA
🕐 Sat/Sun hourly tours 10.30am-1.30pm (max 15). T·D
🚇 Wembley Park, Wembley Stadium
Drawing on an iconic heritage and setting, Wembley Park's 85-acre mixed-use, residential, retail, leisure and commercial district is at a fascinating stage. Tour is with the team from Quintain and the Designers working at Wembley Park.
*www.wembleypark.com*

Wembley Park ↘

# Bromley

| | |
|---|---|
| Borough area (km²) | **150.13** |
| Population | **327,900** |
| Average age | **40** |
| First Open House | **1999** |

THE LONDON BOROUGH

### Bethlem Royal Hospital
🚶 Monks Orchard Road, Beckenham, BR3 3BX
🕐 Sat tour of boardroom and hospital grounds at 11am, 1pm (max 20) · Tour of hospital chapel at 12pm (max 20). T·P·D
⚠ Pre-book only: bit.ly/1K1HnDh
🚉 East Croydon, Eden Park
Hospital's Board Room in its former Administration Building, repurposed as Bethlem Museum of the Mind, with Dutch-style interior of the Hospital Chapel. Cheston and Elcock, 1930

### Bromley Parish Church
🚶 Church Road, Bromley, BR2 0EG
🕐 Sat 10am–5pm/Sun 12pm–6pm + hourly tours of church and tower (10am-3.30pm) + talks, exhibition and recitals. T·R·D
🚉 Bromley South, Bromley North
J.Harold Gibbons designed the new church in 1948 to blend with the 14C tower which was heavily damaged during the war. New community rooms were added in 1982 and solar panels for energy efficiency have also been installed. J. Harold Gibbons, 1957

### Bromley and Sheppard's College
🚶 London Road (entrance via Wren Gates, no vehicle entry), Bromley, BR1 1PE
🕐 Sat 10am–3pm + tour at 10am, 12pm, 2pm (max 25). T·B·d
⚠ Pre-book only: 02084604712
🚉 Bromley North
Founded to house the widows of clergymen, the original building consisted of 20 houses built around a classically-styled quadrangle. Captain Richard Ryder - one of Sir Christopher Wren's surveyors - was in charge of design and construction. Captain Richard Ryder, 1666

### Bromley's Environmental Education Centre at High Elms (BEECHE)
🚶 High Elms Country Park, Shire Lane, BR6 7JH
🕐 Sat 11am–4pm (no access to Darwin Room) / Sun 11am–4pm. T·P·D
⚠ Pre-book only: beeche@idverde.co.uk
🚉 Orpington
Sustainable building set within Victorian estate.

A single-storey timber frame with lime rendered straw bale walls, sedum roof, woodchip boiler and other green features. Platform to view sedum roof. Borras Construction, 2008

### Crystal Palace Subway
🚶 Crystal Palace Parade, SE19 1LG
🕐 Sat/Sun 11am–4pm (max 80, expect queues).
🚉 Crystal Palace
Magnificent subway under Crystal Palace Parade resembling a vaulted crypt. The subway connected the High Level Station (Charles Barry Junior 1865; demolished 1961) to the Crystal Palace (Joseph Paxton 1854; burnt down 1936). New gate(2016). Charles Barry Junior, 1865

### Orpington Priory
🚶 Church Hill, Orpington, BR6 0HH
🕐 Sun 10am–5pm (max 10). T·R
🚉 Orpington
Grade II listed building dating back to 1270. Following the dissolution of Christ Church Priory in Orpington in the 1530s, the house became a rectory. Additions were built in 1959 to put in a library.

### Self-guided Architecture of Chislehurst Walk
🚶 Organised by the Chislehurst Society, BR7 5AP
🕐 Sat/Sun self guided architectural tour, www.chislehurst-society.org.uk/CATTWALK.pdf
🚉 Chislehurst
A look at some of the large houses built in the late nineteenth and early twentieth century by Ernest Newton, C H B Quenell and other noted architects. Ernest Newton, E.J.May, 1890

### St Nicholas Church, Chislehurst
🚶 Church Lane, Chislehurst, BR7 5PE
🕐 Sat 10am–5pm/Sun 12pm-5pm + (Sat) Churchyard tour at 10am, 12pm, 3pm (max 15, duration 45 mins) · Tower/Clock tour at 11am, 2pm (max 6, suitable shoes, fitness & required to sign an indemnity) + (Sun) Churchyard tour at 12pm, 3pm (max 15, duration 45 mins) · Tower/Clock tour at 2pm. T·R·P·d
🚉 Chislehurst
Medieval Parish Church, 15C, enlarged & rebuilt in ↱

Crystal Palace Subway © James Balston ↗

19C. Shingle spire 1857, by Wollaston. Chancel by
Ferrey, lengthened with East wall by Bodley & Garner.
Scadbury Chapel, where buried the Walsinghams,
with rood screen. Clock by Dent, 1858.

### The Odeon, Beckenham
🚶 High Street, Beckenham, BR3 1DY
🕐 Sun 10am–1pm (max 4). d
🚇 Beckenham Junction
Art Deco cinema with proscenium arch, stained
glass windows and typically Deco mouldings. Robert
Cromie, 1930

### The Old Palace, Bromley Civic Centre
🚶 Stockwell Close, Bromley, BR1 3UH
🕐 Sun 10am–3pm (max 20, main entry hall and
   function rooms only) + ½ hourly tour (11am–
   4pm). T·d
🚇 Bromley North, Bromley South
Old Palace was the official residence of the Bishops of
Rochester. Present building dates from 1775, although
there have been manor houses on the site since 10C.
Richard Norman Shaw, Ernest Newton, 1775

## Walks + Tours

### HG Wells walk
🚶 Meet: in front of the main entrance to Primark,
   Market Square, Bromley, BR1 1HE
🕐 10.30am tour (max 40). D
🚇 Bromley South, Bromley North

A walk around the streetscapes that the young
Herbert George Wells knew when he was growing
up, experiencing the built environment that would
later shape his novels. Ernest Newton, Berney and
Son, 1898

### In Ziggy's Footsteps - The walking tour of David Bowie's Beckenham
🚶 Meet: outside main entrance, Beckenham
   Junction Train Station, Station Approach,
   Beckenham, Greater London, BR3 1HY
🕐 Sat 10am, 2pm tours (max 8).
❗ Pre-book only:
❗ bowiewalkingtour@inziggysfootsteps.com
🚇 Beckenham Junction
Bowie moved to Beckenham in 1969 and lived there
for over 4 years, leaving as an international star.
This guided walk visits the main architectural
locations where Bowie and the Spiders lived,
performed and spent their day to day lives.

### Jubilee Country Park history walk
🚶 Meet: Tent Peg Lane car park, Off Crest View Drive,
   Petts Wood, BR5 1BY
🕐 Sun 10.30am tour (max 40, duration 90 minutes.
   Wear footwear suitable for rough or muddy
   terrain. Assistance dogs only.) P
🚇 Petts Wood
Beautiful local nature reserve, Jubilee Country Park,
with Bishop's hunting ground, farmland, golf course
and WWII Heavy Anti-Aircraft Gun Site.

# Camden

| | |
|---|---|
| Borough area (km²) | 21.8 |
| Population | 242,500 |
| Average age | 36 |
| First Open House | 1993 |

Camden

### 2 Willow Road
🏃 2 Willow Road, Hampstead, NW3 1TH
🕐 Sat/Sun 11am–5pm (max 15, no access to the garden or the basement level)
🚇 Hampstead, Hampstead Heath
Goldfinger's unique Modernist home, largely in original condition. Designed for flexibility, efficient use of space and good day-lighting. Complete with fittings and furniture designed by Goldfinger and an impressive modern art collection. Ernö Goldfinger, 1939

### 8 Stoneleigh Terrace (Highgate New Town, Stage 1)
🏃 8 Stoneleigh Terrace, N19 5TY
🕐 Sat/Sun hourly tour (2pm-4pm, max 25). T
🚇 Archway
Built during the golden era of Camden public housing by an architect who studied with Ernö Goldfinger and worked with Denys Lasdun. Peter Tábori, Camden Architect's Department, 1972

### 8a Belsize Court Garages
🏃 8a Belsize Court Garages, NW3 5AJ
🕐 Sat/Sun ½ hourly tour 10.30am-12.30pm (max 15).
🚇 Swiss Cottage, Belsize Park
Originally a late 19C coachman's living quarters and stable, this mews house combines an award-winning architect's studio and spacious light-filled maisonette after a 2-phase carbon-reducing retrofit. Sanya Polescuk Architects, 2012

### 10 Brock Street
🏃 10 Brock Street, Regent's Place, NW1 3FG
🕐 Sat/Sun 10am–5pm (lobby and reception areas only). D
🚇 Euston, Euston Square
This 14-storey office building uses modern technology to operate in an environmentally sustainable way, looking on to the Regent's Place Plaza. Wilkinson Eyre Architects, 2013

### 20 Triton Street, Regent's Place Estate
🏃 20 Triton Street, Regent's Place, NW1 3BF
🕐 Sat/Sun 10am–5pm (lobby and reception areas only). D
🚇 Euston, Euston Square
10-storey office complex housing a restaurant and a community theatre. The accessible part of the building is the atrium, where artwork by Gary Webb is displayed. Terry Farrell and Partners, 2009

### 39-47 Gordon Square (Birkbeck School of Arts)
🏃 43 Gordon Square, WC1H 0PD
🕐 Sat/Sun 11am–6pm + hourly tours (11am-5pm, max 20). T
🚇 Russell Square, Euston
Georgian terrace, centre of the Bloomsbury Group activities. Grade II listed. Includes radical interior intervention at basement and ground floor levels. RIBA Award Winner 2008. Thomas Cubitt, 1830

### 44 Willoughby Road
🏃 44 Willoughby Road, NW3 1RU
🕐 Sat 2pm–6pm/Sun 11am–2pm.
🚇 Hampstead, Hampstead Heath
New-build open-plan studio house designed as a floating box with integrated gardens on each level and mesh screens for privacy and sun control. Sustainable features include heat pump, PV panels & water collection. RIBA award shortlist 2012. Guard Tillman Pollock Architects, 2012

### Acland Burghley School
🏃 93 Burghley Road, NW5 1UJ
🕐 Sat 10am–5pm (max 60). T·d
🚇 Tufnell Park, Gospel Oak
An important example of 1960s comprehensive school design in the Brutalist style. Acland Burghley has recently celebrated its 50th anniversary and a Grade II listing. Howell, Killick, Partridge & Amis Architects, 1966

### Adaptable House
🏃 6 Doughty Mews, WC1N 2PG
🕐 Sun 11am–5pm (max 20). T·R·d
🚇 Russell Square, Farringdon
Self-build conversion followed by 35 year occupation, from party house to office to family home for 6, and now home and studio. Ash Sakula Architects, 1983

## Alexandra Centre

🏃 Ainsworth Way, NW8 0SR
🕐 Sat 10am–5pm (max 10). D
🚇 Swiss Cottage, South Hampstead
Centre providing learning and short-stay
accommodation for 16-25 year olds with profound
and multiple learning disabilities and/or autism,
preparing students for semi-independent living.
Haverstock, 2017

## Alexandra Road Park

🏃 Langtry Walk/Rowley Way/Abbey Road, NW8 0SW
🕐 Sat 11am–6pm + tour of the Park, hourly (12pm-
5pm, max 15). T·R·d
🚇 Swiss Cottage, South Hampstead
Unique modernist sculpted linear park, with series of
outdoor 'rooms', defined by topography and concrete
walls. Recently restored. Park is integral to the
iconic Alexandra Road estate. Original Tenants Hall
overlooking park also open. Janet Jack, 1979

BT Tower © C1 Photography ↗

## Alexandra and Ainsworth Estate

🏃 Rowley Way, NW8 0SF
🕐 Sat 10am–5pm + residents-led tour of 5 different
flats, every 15 mins (11am-4pm, max 10). T
🚇 Swiss Cottage, South Hampstead
The estate is among the most ambitious social
housing schemes of its time. Listed Grade II* in 1993.
A rare opportunity to visit 5 different flats within
the estate including 13(b) Rowley Way where many
original features have been retained. Neave Brown,
1968

## Artchive - Philip Hughes Studio

🏃 62 Rochester Place, NW1 9JX
🕐 Sat 10am–5pm. d
🚇 Camden Town, Camden Road
Private gallery and art archive. Mews workshop
converted to artist's studio/summerhouse. A
diaphanous, glass gallery bathed in light, provides a
connection between the original building, garden and
the owner's home. RIBA Award Winner 2005. Sanei
Hopkins Architects, Hughes Meyer Studio, 2004

## BT Tower

🏃 45 Maple Street, W1T 4BG
🕐 Sat/Sun 9.30am–6.30pm (max 100, access to
revolving floor 34). T·R·D
ⓘ By public ballot ONLY: openhouselondon.open-
city.org.uk/listings/2735. Ballot will close
11.59pm 1 September)
🚇 Euston Square, Euston
An enduring, distinctive feature of the London
skyline for the last 52 years, this is a rare opportunity
for members of the public to visit the famous
revolving floor, 158m above the capital. GR Yeats, Eric
Bedford, Min of Public Buildings & Works, 1965

## Burgh House

🏃 New End Square, NW3 1LT
🕐 Sun 11am–6pm. T·R·B·d
🚇 Hampstead, Hampstead Heath

Grade I listed Queen Anne house retaining original
panelling and staircase with a café, modern
gallery and museum, set in a small Gertrude Jekyll
terrace garden.

## Cecil Sharp House

🏃 2 Regent's Park Road, NW1 7AY
🕐 Sun 1pm–5pm + tour at 1pm (max 20). T·R·D
🚇 Camden Town, Camden Road
Purpose built to house the English Folk Dance and
Song Society, this Grade II listed building was
designed by members of the Art Workers Guild of the
time. Stillman and Eastwick-Field, 1930

## Connock & Lockie

🏃 33 Lamb's Conduit Street, WC1N 3NG
🕐 Sun tour every 45 mins (11am-4.30pm, max 15).
T·d
🚇 Holborn, King's Cross
Refurbishment and extension of a Grade II Listed
property for a traditional tailor's shop. Bespoke
design elements enable clientele to experience
every step of tailoring and become familiar with
every member responsible for making it. Benedetti
Architects, 2016

## Conway Hall

🏃 25 Red Lion Square, WC1R 4RL
🕐 Sat/Sun 10am–5pm (library and foyer. Main
Hall and gallery dependent on what events are
running) + hourly tours (11am-4pm). T·d
🚇 Holborn
Headquarters of Conway Hall Ethical Society, a
long-standing organisation renowned as a hub for
free speech and progressive thought. Grade II listed
building with both Arts and Crafts and Art Deco
features adding to it's distinctive style. Frederick
Herbert Mansford, 1929

## Dunboyne Road Estate (formerly Fleet Road Estate)

🚶 36 Dunboyne Road, NW3 2YY
🕐 Sun tours at 2pm, 3pm, 4pm (max 10).
❗ Pre-book only: bit.ly/2tu7SBz
🚇 Hampstead Heath, Belsize Park

Grade II listed low rise/high density housing scheme for LB Camden known as Fleet Road. No.36 is a split level maisonette retaining many of the original features such as sliding partitions and fitted joinery work. Neave Brown & LB Camden Architects Dept, 1969

## Eleventh Church of Christ, Scientist

🚶 11 St Chad's Street, WC1H 8BG
🕐 Sat 10am–5pm/Sun 12pm–5pm (no access to the offices upstairs) + lecture by architect Sun 1pm. T·B·D
🚇 St.Pancras, King's Cross

New home for Eleventh Church of Christ, Scientist, London with 60-seat auditorium, reading room, bookshop, Sunday school, offices and supporting spaces by converting and expanding an existing dilapidated building in a conservation area. Benedetti Architects, 2015
*www.eleventhlondon.com*

## Fenton House

🚶 Hampstead Grove, NW3 6SP
🕐 Sat/Sun 11am–5pm. T·d
🚇 Hampstead, Hampstead Heath

Beautiful town house retaining many original features and housing important decorative arts collections. Surrounded by a walled garden. William Eades, 1686

## Fitzrovia House

🚶 18 Colville Place, W1T 2BN
🕐 Sat 1pm–5pm (max 10, steep stairs. Overshoes provided).
🚇 Tottenham Court Road, Goodge Street

Re-use and connection of a former workshop to new living spaces Inserted in the shell of a bomb damaged Georgian house. West Architecture, 2015

## Freemasons' Hall

🚶 60 Great Queen Street, WC2B 5AZ
🕐 Sun 10am–5pm. B·D
🚇 Covent Garden, Charing Cross

Monumental classical exterior belying elaborate and varied interior decoration: extensive use of mosaic, stained glass, decorated ceilings and lighting. Ashley and Newman, 1927

## Garden Court Chambers

🚶 57-60 Lincoln's Inn Fields, WC2A 3LJ
🕐 Sat 10am-4pm/Sun 10am-1pm hourly tours (max 25) + exhibition illustrating the history and architecture of the buildings T·d
🚇 Holborn, Charing Cross

Inigo Jones' design at No. 59-60 copied by No. 57-58, with portico and elliptical staircase added by Soane. Refurbished by current occupiers, a barristers' chambers. Retains original features, staircases, fireplaces, and mouldings. Inigo Jones 1640s/Sir John Soane, 1700

## German Historical Institute

🚶 17 Bloomsbury Square, WC1A 2NJ
🕐 Sun 10am–2pm + tours every 15 mins (max 20). T·R·D
🚇 Tottenham Court Road, Euston

This Grade II* listed building includes an Adam-style ceiling on the 1st floor and a beautiful staircase with wrought-iron balustrade. Once home to the Pharmaceutical Society of Great Britain, it now houses an historical research institute.

## Gibbs Building, Wellcome Trust

🚶 215 Euston Road, NW1 2BE
🕐 Sat 10am–5pm (ground floor atrium, 5th floor viewing gallery only) + talks on Thomas Heatherwick Sculpture · Art activity for families. T·R·B·D
🚇 Warren Street, Euston

HQ of the Wellcome Trust - a global charitable foundation dedicated to achieving improvements in health by supporting the brightest minds. Open plan design around a light-filled atrium featuring spectacular artwork. RIBA Award Winner 2005. Hopkins Architects, 2004

## Government Art Collection

🚶 Queen's Yard, 179a Tottenham Court Road, W1T 7PA
🕐 Sat/Sun 10am-4pm hourly curator-led tours (max 25). T·d
❗ Pre-book only: bit.ly/2umdPOF
🚇 Euston Square, Euston

Guided tour of premises and behind-the-scenes look at how this major collection of British art operates.

## Gray's Inn

🚶 WC1R 5ET
🕐 Sun 12pm–4pm. T·d
🚇 Holborn, Blackfriars

700 year old legal collegiate institution.  ↦

↘ Eleventh Church of Christ, Scientist © Agnese Sanvito

Hall includes 16C screen. Much of inn redesigned in neo-Georgian style after 1941 bombing. Sir Edward Maufe, 1560

## Hampstead Friends Meeting House
* 120 Heath Street, Hampstead, NW3 1DR
* Sun 1pm–5pm (max 50, no access downstairs). T·R·d
* Hampstead, Hampstead Heath

Listed Arts and Crafts freestyle building with plain interior and many charming original features, sympathetically modernised in 1991. Entrance via listed gateway. Frederick Rowntree, 1907

## Hidden House
* 59 Kingsway Place, Sans Walk, EC1R 0LU
* Sat/Sun 11am–6pm.
* Farringdon, Angel

A series of internal spaces constrained in plan by a listed perimeter garden curtilage and held in section by a series of floating ocular rooflights. This special place is difficult to find, but well worth the effort. Coffey Architects, 2016

## Highgate Literary & Scientific Institution
* 11 South Grove, N6 6BS
* Sun 1pm–5pm (max 15, access to the main building including the Victoria Hall, library and members' room) + ½ hourly tours. T·d
* Archway, Highgate

Fine stuccoed building overlooking Pond Square, and home to Institution since 1840. Formed from 1790 coach house, stables and yard, with final additions c1880.

## Isokon Building (Lawn Road Flats)
* Lawn Road, NW3 2DX
* Sat/Sun tours every 10 mins (11am-3.30pm, max 10, access to individual flats solely at discretion of owners on the day). T·B
* Belsize Park, Hampstead Heath

A Grade I listed residential block of flats in Hampstead, designed by the Canadian modernist architect Wells Coates for Jack and Molly Pritchard. Wells Coates, 1934

## Keats House
* Keats Grove, NW3 2RR
* Sat 11am-5pm/Sun 11am-5pm (interactive screens at entrance give information about areas of the house which are not step-free) + hourly tours (max 20) + family day 1pm-4pm. T·B·d
* Belsize Park, Hampstead Heath

Early 19C Grade I listed building and former home of the poet John Keats. William Woods, 1814

## Kenwood House
* Hampstead Lane, NW3 7JR
* Sat/Sun 10am-5pm (dairy and the stable block also open, 11:00 to 16:00) + Kenwood's Hidden Buildings tour at 11am. T·R·P·B·d
* Hampstead, Hampstead Heath

Outstanding Neo-classical villa, with world-class paintings by Rembrandt, Vermeer, Van Dyck, Reynolds, Turner and Gainsborough, set in beautiful grounds on Hampstead Heath. The exceptionally beautiful library is one of Adam's masterpieces. Robert and James Adam, George Saunders, 1764

## Lauderdale House
* Highgate Hill, Waterlow Park, N6 5HG
* Sun 11am-4pm + tour with Nick Peacey at 11am · tour with Peter Barber OBE at 12.30pm (max 20) + drop-in family craft workshop: 'Tudor ruffs, brooches and chickens' 10.30am-1.30pm (max 40) T·R·D
* Archway, Upper Holloway

Grade II* listed building in Waterlow Park dating to 1582 and recently refurbished. Original Tudor wooden framework adapted by successive owners over the centuries. Today the house runs primarily as an arts, heritage and education centre. Haines Phillips Architects, 2016

## London Mathematical Society
* De Morgan House, 57-58 Russell Square, WC1B 4HS
* Sun 10am-5pm. T·R·d
* Russell Square, Euston

Two Grade II listed buildings, 4-storey yellow stock brick with a rusticated stucco base. No. 57 has an attic level with a garden at the rear. Staircases are intact and each room still retains the high ceilings and ornamental fireplaces. James Burton, 1803

## London School of Hygiene & Tropical Medicine
* Keppel Street, WC1E 7HT
* Sat 10.30am-4pm/Sun 10am-2.30pm + hourly tours. T·D
* Goodge Street, Euston

Beautiful Grade II listed Art Deco building with highly decorated façade, period library, north courtyard extension and new south courtyard building. P Morley Horder & Verner O Rees, 1929

## Lullaby Factory, Great Ormond Street Hospital for Children
* Great Ormond Street, WC1N 3JH
* Sat architect and hospital led tours, (2pm-4pm, max 8). T·R·D
* Pre-book only: bit.ly/2uf6JN1
* Russell Square, Holborn

This award-winning installation creates a magical world deep inside the hospital, not usually accessible by the public. New elements this year include an interactive xylophone bench. Studio Weave, 2012

## Lumen United Reformed Church and Café
* 88 Tavistock Place, WC1H 9RS
* Sat 10am-5pm (max 20, access to the 1824 crypt will be limited) + ½ hourly tours (10am-4.45pm, max 15). T·R·d
* King's Cross St. Pancras

A remodelled shell of a 1960s church building, which itself includes the crypt of an 1820s church hit by a

V2 missile in 1945. Includes a café, two dramatic 8m high windows and a distinctive conical reflective space. RIBA Award Winner 2009. Theis + Khan, 2007

## Mews House
🚶 30 Murray Mews, Camden, NW1 9RJ
🕐 Sat/Sun 10am–5pm (max 20). T
🚇 King's Cross St. Pancras, King's Cross
A mews house that ensures privacy by deriving much of its daylight from roof glazing at the head of a triple height open stairwell. The circulation routes flow out to the rear garden and upstairs to the owners' beehives on the roof terrace. Jeff Kahane + Associates, 1989

## Montpelier Community Nursery
🚶 Montpelier Gardens, 115 Brecknock Road, N19 5AH
🕐 Sun 1pm–5pm (max 20). D
🚇 Tufnell Park, Kentish Town
New-build nursery situated within communal gardens with a unique cross laminated timber structure with passive environmental design principles. RIBA National Award and Stephen Lawrence Prize 2013, Highly Commended Camden Design Awards 2014. AY Architects, 2012

## Mount Pleasant
🚶 Mount Pleasant, 52-54 Mount Pleasant, WC1X 0AL
🕐 Sat/Sun hourly tours led by council staff and Peter Barber Architects (10.30am-3.30pm, max 8). d·T
🚇 Farringdon, King's Cross
A former Victorian workhouse that has been transformed through LB Camden's Community Investment Programme into a state of the art facility for 50 homeless people laid out around a beautiful suntrap courtyard. Peter Barber Architects, 2014

## Nordoff Robbins
🚶 2 Lissenden Gardens, NW5 1PQ

Mews House ⭨

🕐 Sat/Sun 10am–5pm + Lecture by architect at 2pm · Life Changing Music at 1.30pm. D
🚇 Tufnell Park, Gospel Oak
A refurbishment of the world's largest purpose-designed music therapy centre for Nordoff Robbins, housed within a 19C substation. Exemplary therapy rooms and a fun material palette deliver an exciting new identity for the charity.

## Paul McAneary Architects' Office
🚶 6 Flitcroft Street, WC2H 8DJ
🕐 Sat/Sun 11am–6pm (max 15) + ½ hourly tours (11am-4.30pm, max 10). T
🚇 Covent Garden, Leicester Square
Architect's own studio designed and built by themselves over 4 years. Containing numerous innovative experimental and bespoke details designed using their trademark 'warm minimalism'. Mini architectural exhibition. Paul McAneary Architects, 2015

## Phoenix Gardens Community Building
🚶 The Phoenix Garden, 21 Stacey Street, WC2H 8DG
🕐 Sat/Sun 11am–6pm + architect + gardener-led tour of building and garden at 3pm. D
🚇 Tottenham Court Road, Covent Garden
The first purpose-built new-build community centre to be built in central London for generations, located within the renowned Phoenix Gardens. Office Sian Architecture + Design, 2016
*officesian.com*

## Regent High School
🚶 Chalton Street, entrance opposite Cranleigh Street, NW1 1RX
🕐 Sat 10am–3.30pm + architect-led tour with Walters & Cohen at 11am (max 20) + I-spy trail for children. T·D
🚇 Euston, King's Cross
New build and refurbishment. The new building features a triple-storey 'arcade' that links to the existing Victorian building, simplifies movement around the school and provides passive supervision. Walters & Cohen Architects, 2014

## Royal College of General Practitioners
🚶 30 Euston Square, NW1 2FB
🕐 Sat/Sun 10am–5pm. T·R·D
🚇 Euston Square, Euston
Grade II* listed building. Recently restored to showcase magnificent Edwardian faience tile work, mosaic floor and other historic features in transformed modern surroundings that now provide the new headquarters of the RCGP. Arthur Beresford Pite, 1908

## Royal College of Physicians
🚶 11 St Andrew's Place, Regents Park, NW1 4LE
🕐 Sun 10am–5pm + ½ hourly tours (11am-4pm, Duration 90 mins). T·B·D
🚇 Regent's Park, Euston
Dramatic interior spaces and white mosaic exterior ↪

elevated on piloti. Grade I listed and one of London's most important post-war buildings. Sir Denys Lasdun, 1964
www.rcplondon.ac.uk

## Sainsbury Wellcome Centre
🏃 25 Howland Street, W1T 4JG
🕐 Sat 1pm–5pm + Q&A with the architects in the lecture theatre. T·D
🚇 Goodge Street
An exceptionally adaptable neuroscience centre clad with a unique white cast glass and with an art-science public colonnade. Ian Ritchie Architects, 2015

## Senate House
🏃 University of London, Malet Street, WC1E 7HU
🕐 Sat 10am–5pm + access to library on hourly tours only (11am-4pm) + pop-up exhibitions throughout the building. T·R·D
🚇 Euston Square, King's Cross
London's tallest secular building when it opened as the HQ of the University of London, this Grade II* listed landmark features classicism and Art Deco elements. Pop-up exhibitions on display. Charles Holden, 1933
www.senatehouselibrary.ac.uk

## Shaftesbury Theatre
🏃 210 Shaftesbury Avenue, WC2H 8DP
🕐 Sat tours of backstage areas led by theatre/ project team members, ½ hourly (9am-11.30am, max 30, NB tours cover 8 floors with no lift.) T·R
🚇 Covent Garden, Tottenham Court Road
Built in an elaborate Renaissance style with high level Diocletian windows and a prominent grand cupola. The new Fly Tower is a contemporary intervention, that accommodates the theatre's technical requirements within a unified geometry. Bertie Crewe, 1911
www.shaftesburytheatre.com

## Sir John Soane's Museum
🏃 No 12, 13 & 14 Lincoln's Inn Fields, WC2A 3BP
🕐 Sat 10am–4pm (max 40, NB no access to main museum) + family drop in activity (max 12). T·B
🚇 Waterloo, Temple
Special access to no. 14 Lincoln's Inn Fields, built by Sir John Soane in 1824 and let out in his lifetime as a private house. A rare and beautiful example of the architect's late work with a number of fine interiors. Sir John Soane, 1812

## SPPARC Architecture Studio
🏃 10 Bayley Street, Bedford Square, WC1B 3HB
🕐 Sat/Sun 10am–5pm (max 50) + workshop tour at 1pm (max 10) + models and exhibition · Lecture by Trevor Morriss, Principal of SPPARC Architecture Sat 12pm, Sun 3pm (max 30). T·R
🚇 Euston Square, Charing Cross
This award-winning practice has an exciting UK and International portfolio and invites you to take part in live debates, explore its workshops, listen to talks & become part of the design process. SPPARC Architecture, 2014
www.spparcstudio.com

## St George's Bloomsbury
🏃 Bloomsbury Way, WC1A 2SA
🕐 Sat 10am–6pm/Sun 12pm–5pm. T·D
🚇 Russell Square, Euston
St George's Bloomsbury is one of the twelve new churches designed and paid for under the 1711 Act of Parliament for building fifty new Churches, and the sixth and final London Church designed by Hawksmoor. Nicholas Hawksmoor, 1720

## St Pancras Chambers and Clock Tower
🏃 The Forecourt, St Pancras Station, Euston Road, NW1 2AR
🕐 Sat/Sun guided tours of hotel and apartments, every 20 mins (10am-4pm, max 15). T·d
ⓘ Pre-book only: openhousestpancraschambers2017. eventbrite.co.uk
🚇 St.Pancras, King's Cross St. Pancras
Former Midland Grand Hotel, now St Pancras Renaissance Hotel and Chambers apartments. Includes hotel lobby and clock tower. George Gilbert Scott, 1868

## St Pancras International
🏃 Meet at special assistance meeting point (next to Starbucks) Euston Road, N1C 4QP
🕐 Sat/Sun hourly tours (10am-4pm, max 20). T·P·B·D
🚇 Euston, King's Cross St. Pancras
A unique Grade I listed Victorian railway station completed in 1868. After a transformation, St Pancras International has redefined railway stations for the 21st century and is a destination in its own right. Gilbert Scott, 1868/Tooley & Foster Partnership, Lansley 2007

## Swiss Cottage Library
🏃 88 Avenue Road, NW3 3HA
🕐 Sat 11am–5pm (reserve stock of books on display) + hourly tours. T·R·D
🚇 Swiss Cottage, South Hampstead
Grade II listed building by renowned Modernist which has been refurbished and remodelled whilst protecting the building's landmark status. Basil Spence, 1963

## The Bartlett School of Architecture, UCL
🏃 22 Gordon Street, WC1H 0QB
🕐 Sun hourly tours (11am-3pm, max 15). T·D
ⓘ Pre-book only: bartlett.comms@ucl.ac.uk
🚇 Euston Square, King's Cross
Following a 'deep retrofit', 22 Gordon Street has been completely overhauled to create an open, accessible and stimulating learning environment for all staff and students. Hawkins\Brown, 2016

## The Building Centre and NLA
🏃 26 Store Street, WC1E 7BT

○ Sat/Sun 10am–5pm + New London's Tall Buildings Talk with Peter Murray at 1.30pm · NLA Drop-in Family Workshops at 12pm. T·B·D

🚇 Tottenham Court Road, King's Cross

The Building Centre is a not-for-profit organisation which educates the construction industry and those it serves. NLA is an independent forum for discussion, debate and information about architecture, planning and development in London.

## The Coach House

🚶 2a Belsize Park Gardens, NW3 4LA

○ Sun hourly tours (10am-4pm, max 10, no tour at 1pm. No children under 12).

⚠ Pre-book only: www.superhomes.org.uk

🚇 Swiss Cottage, Hampstead Heath

Victorian house retrofitted to save 70% carbon. Features high comfort internal and external insulation, high performance double glazing, heat recovery ventilation, LED low energy lights, remote switching plugs.

## The Francis Crick Institute

🚶 1 Midland Road, NW1 1AT

○ Sat 10am–5pm (general access to 'Open for Discovery' exhibition in the Manby Gallery and café on the ground floor only) + ½ hourly tours (11am-3pm, max 30). T·R·d

⚠ Pre-book only: www.crick.ac.uk/events

🚇 St.Pancras, Euston

This new, world-class, interdisciplinary biomedical research centre occupies a distinctive steel, glass and terracotta-clad building in the heart of London. Its innovative design fosters scientific collaboration and public engagement. HOK/PLP Architecture, 2011

## The Wiener Library

🚶 29 Russell Square, WC1B 5DP

○ Sun 1pm–5pm (max 40) + Tour of the library and archive, ½ hourly (max 15). T·D

🚇 Russell Square, Euston

Sensitive yet bold refurbishment of historic Grade II listed townhouse for The Wiener Library including dramatic first floor reading room, new mezzanine and ground floor exhibition spaces. Barbara Weiss Architects, 2011

## Tottenham Court Road Station

🚶 Oxford St, W1D 2DH

○ Sat/Sun hourly tours (11am-3pm, max 15). T

⚠ Pre-book only: www.cvent.com/d/25qcc4

🚇 Tottenham Court Road

This tour will take participants through the history of the station, covering its earliest days as an early deep tube hub to its 1980s restoration to the recent expansion of the ticket hall and preparation for Crossrail. Gillespies, Stanton Williams, Acanthus, HawkinsBrown, Taylor Woodrow BAM Nuttall, CH2M HILL, 2016

## Valhalla

🚶 89 Swains Lane, Highgate, N6 6PJ ↦

Shaftesbury Theatre © Peter Cook ↘

○ Sat/Sun 10am–2.30pm (external view only) + talk on the design at 10am, 12pm, 2pm.
🚇 Archway, Kentish Town

An outdated façade is transformed by the ancient Japanese art Shou Sugi Ban. The wood is charred, cooled & treated with natural oil. A contemporary home now sits in sympathy with its neighbours Waterlow Park and historic Highgate Cemetery. Denizen Works, 2016

### Victoria Hall King's Cross
🚶 25 Canal Reach, King's Cross, London, N1C 4DD
○ Sat 1pm–5pm + ½ hourly tours (max 12). T·R·D
🚇 King's Cross St. Pancras

Student's residence providing a collegiate environment in an urban setting. The design draws from adobe architecture of the Middle East. Central to the building's character are two courtyard gardens, designed by Vladimir Djurovic. Stanton Williams Architects, 2016

### Victorian Waterpoint
🚶 St Pancras Cruising Club, Camley Street, N1C 4PN
○ Sat/Sun 10am–5pm. T·R
🚇 St.Pancras, King's Cross St. Pancras

At around 9m x 6m and 3-storeys high, the top floor originally contained a vast 70 cubic metre capacity cast iron water tank. This tank now forms an impressive viewing gallery; the exterior has ornate brickwork and elaborate detailing. Sir George Gilbert Scott, 1872

### Wedderburn Road
🚶 3 Wedderburn Road, NW3 5QS
○ Sat 10am–1pm (max 10, entrance from the side door, access to extension and garden only). d
🚇 Swiss Cottage, Hampstead Heath

An exquisitely detailed contemporary extension and alteration to a Grade II listed detached Victorian property. The new extension, which is built almost entirely of glass, is topped with a crisp marble clad canopy which appears to float. Finkernagel Ross, 2016

### White on White
🚶 13 St Mark's Crescent, NW1 7TS
○ Sun 10am–1pm (max 5, access to extension only via the stairs down to the garden)
! Pre-book only: bit.ly/2uEaRXX
🚇 Camden Town

A very, very small glass extension that aims to be all but invisible from the Canal tow path by carefully selecting materials to blend in with the background of the original house, and also by partially sinking it into the ground. Gianni Botsford Architects, 2013

### Wright & Wright Architects Studio
🚶 89-91 Bayham Street, NW1 0AG
○ Sat/Sun 10am–5pm (max 30) + 'Heavy Weight & Thick-Skinned' exhibition. T·R
🚇 Mornington Crescent, Euston

Set within a former piano works in the heart of Camden, Wright & Wright's studio occupies the roof space of the original 1820s building, which was refurbished when the practice moved in over twenty years ago.
*www.wrightandwright.co.uk*

## Walks + Tours

### King's Cross Public Realm
🚶 Meet: King's Cross Visitor Centre, Western Transit Shed, 11 Stable Street, N1C 4AB
○ Sat/Sun ½ hourly tours (10am-3pm, max 20). T·R
! Pre-book only: www.kingscross.co.uk/tours
🚇 King's Cross St. Pancras

King's Cross is a 67 acre development in Central London being transformed into a new city quarter with 20 regenerated heritage buildings, new homes, offices, public spaces, shops, galleries, bars, restaurants, schools and a university. Townshend Landscape Architects, 2012

Francis Crick Institute © Paul Grundy ↘

# City of London

**CITY** OF **LONDON**

| | |
|---|---|
| Borough area (km²) | 2.9 |
| Population | 8,800 |
| Average age | 43 |
| First Open House | 1992 |

### 1 Finsbury Circus
- 1 Finsbury Circus, EC2M 7EB
- Sat/Sun 10am–1pm (max 20). T·D
- Moorgate, Euston

Grade II listed building that has been comprehensively redeveloped to provide a high quality contemporary interior, with a fully glazed spectacular atrium roof to maximise daylight and aspect. Sir Edward Lutyens, 1925

### 4 Bayer House
- Golden Lane Estate, EC1Y 0RN
- Sun ½ hourly tours (11am-4.30pm, max 10, closed 1pm-2pm).
- Liverpool Street, Barbican

Part of Golden Lane Estate which was the first public housing to be listed. A maisonette with much of the original detailing and finishes. Chamberlin Powell & Bon, 1957

### 5 Lambert Jones Mews, Barbican
- 5 Lambert Jones Mews (entrance via Lauderdale Place), Barbican, EC2Y 8DP
- Sat tours every 20 mins (10am-4.45pm, max 10, closed 1pm-2pm. No children under 10 years old.)
- St. Paul's, Moorgate

One of eight mews houses at western edge of the Barbican with direct access to the Barbican garden. Chamberlin Powell & Bon, 1985

### 30 St Mary Axe (The Gherkin)
- 30 St Mary Axe, EC3A 8EP
- Sat/Sun 8am-3pm (max 30). D
- Bank, Liverpool Street

30 St Mary Axe, affectionately known as the 'Gherkin', is a landmark 40-storey office building in the heart of London's financial centre and is unlike any other ever conceived. Foster + Partners, 2003

### 100 Victoria Embankment - Unilever House
- 100 Victoria Embankment, EC4Y 0DY
- Sat 10am-5pm (atrium only). T·D
- Blackfriars

Landmark curved Grade II listed building which has been transformed to give it a new lease of life. RIBA Award Winner 2009. James Lomax Simpson, 1930

### Angel Court
- One Angel Court, EC2R 7EQ
- Sat 10am-5pm (max 50, general access to lobby/ reception area only) + ½ hourly tours of sky floor, garden terrace, and garden floor (max 16) + talk from architect Nick Worley at 2pm (max 50, lecture will be held in the lobby area). T·D
- Moorgate, Liverpool Street

An ethereal tower, entirely translucent at day revealing its internal environment at dusk. This building has been transformed into a sustainable urban workplace benefitting occupants and the public alike. Fletcher Priest Architects, 2017
*www.fletcherpriest.com*

### Apothecaries' Hall
- Black Friars Lane, EC4V 6EJ
- Sun 11am-4pm. D
- Blackfriars

A courtyard building with some of the best-preserved 17C livery hall interiors, on the site of the Blackfriars Priory on which the original hall burnt down in 1666. Courtyard refurbished in 2017. Thomas Locke, 1672

### Barbican Centre
- Silk Street, EC2Y 8DS
- Sun 10am–11pm + hourly tours (1.30pm-4.30pm, max 20). T·R·B·d
- Pre-book only: 020 7382 8891
- St. Paul's, Liverpool Street

A Grade II listed building, the Barbican is Europe's largest multi-arts and conference venue and one of London's best examples of Brutalist architecture. Chamberlin Powell & Bon, 1963

### Bells and Belfries at St Botolph Aldgate
- St Botolph's Church, Aldgate High Street, EC3N 1AB
- Sat 10am-5pm/Sun 11.30am-5pm + talks and demonstrations. T·R·d
- Aldgate East, Liverpool Street

Rare opportunity to see the bells and belfry of this church by the architect of Mansion House, with demonstrations taking place. Inside is London's oldest organ. George Dance the Elder, 1744

30 St Mary Axe (The Gherkin) © Grant Smith/VIEW Pictures ↗

### Bevis Marks Synagogue
🚶 Bevis Marks, EC3A 7LH
🕐 Sun 11am–3pm + ½ hourly tours & talks. T·D
🚇 Aldgate, Liverpool Street
One of the best-preserved houses of worship of its period still in use and oldest synagogue in Britain. Contains one of the finest collections of Cromwellian and Queen Anne furniture in the country. Joseph Avis, 1701

### Billingsgate Roman House and Baths
🚶 101 Lower Thames Street, EC3R 6DL
🕐 Sat/Sun 11am–4pm. T
🚇 Tower Hill, Fenchurch Street
Some of London's best Roman remains and the only accessible Roman house, comprising late 2C house with a 3C bath house built within its courtyard. First discovered in 1848.

### Bishopsgate Institute
🚶 230 Bishopsgate, EC2M 4QH
🕐 Sat 10am–5pm + ½ hourly tours. T·R·d
🚇 Liverpool Street
This beautifully restored historic Grade II* listed building combines elements of Arts and Crafts/Art Nouveau/Victorian architecture. Charles Harrison Townsend, 1894

### Carpenters' Hall
🚶 1 Throgmorton Avenue, EC2N 2JJ
🕐 Sat 10am–4pm. T·D
🚇 Moorgate, Bank
Livery Hall first built in 1429, much altered then demolished and rebuilt in 1880, destroyed in 1941 except for external walls (W W Pocock). Designed as a showpiece for the craft of carpentry, the third Hall on the site. Herbert Austen-Hall, Clifford Wearden, 1956

## City Information Centre
🏃 St Paul's Churchyard, EC4M 8BX
🕐 Sat 9.30am–5.30pm + ½ hourly architect-led tours (10am-12pm, max 20) / Sun 10am–4pm. D
🚇 Blackfriars, City Thameslink
London's main tourist information centre is clad in a specially manufactured system of 220 pre-finished stainless steel panels. This subtly reflective surface provides a striking counterpoint to St Paul's. RIBA Award Winner 2009. Make Architects, 2007

## City of London Police Museum
🏃 5 Aldermanbury, EC2V 7HH
🕐 Sat 10am–4pm + museum staff on hand to talk about the model as trial evidence. T·B·D
🚇 St. Paul's, City Thameslink
Contains the 1911 architectural model of the buildings where the Houndsditch Murders took place. Made out of wood, designed and produced by a City of London Police Officer for the Old Bailey trial of the suspected murderers.

## Custom House
🏃 20 Lower Thames Street, EC3R 6EE
🕐 Sat/Sun 10.30am–5pm + displays, historical talk, children's quiz. T·d
🚇 Monument, Fenchurch Street
Iconic elegant late-Georgian building partly rebuilt by Smirke after subsidence. The 58m neo-classical Long Room was the central reporting point for all London Customs business in the 19C. Sir Robert Smirke, 1813

## Dr Johnson's House
🏃 17 Gough Square, EC4A 3DE
🕐 Sat/Sun 10am–5pm (max 80). T·B
🚇 Blackfriars, Chancery Lane
Fine example of an early 4-storey town house with original panelling, open staircase and famous 'swinging panels' on the open-plan first floor. Johnson compiled his famous 'Dictionary of the English Language' (1755) here. Richard Gough, 1698

## Drapers' Hall
🏃 Throgmorton Street, EC2N 2DQ
🕐 Sun 10am–4pm (No access to Garden). T·d
🚇 Moorgate, Liverpool Street
Livery hall first built in the 1530s, twice destroyed by fire and rebuilt (1666 & 1772). Late 19C façade and opulent Victorian interior. H Williams and Sir T G Jackson, Sir Charles Reilly, 1860

## Explore Broadgate
🏃 Broadgate Welcome Centre, Finsbury Avenue Square, Broadgate, EC2M 2PA
🕐 Sat/Sun 201 Bishopsgate green rooftop tour , ½ hourly (10am-4pm, max 15). T·D
⚠ Pre-book only: bit.ly/2uNvBwP
🚇 Liverpool Street, Moorgate
Broadgate is home to an outstanding series of buildings designed by renowned architects including Skidmore, Owings & Merrill. Model of the campus in the Broadgate Welcome Centre, guides available in receptions of several buildings. Arup Associates and SOM, 1984
*www.broadgateestates.co.uk*

## Fishmongers' Hall
🏃 London Bridge, EC4R 9EL
🕐 Sat/Sun tour at 10.30am, 12pm (max 60). T
⚠ Pre-book only: bit.ly/2eFIKAY
🚇 London Bridge, Cannon Street
Fishmongers' Hall is a rare example of a Greek Revival building. Designed by the architect Henry Roberts, a student of Sir Robert Smirke, the Hall's classical simplicity is contrasted by the magnificence of its interior rooms. Henry Roberts, 1834

## Four Seasons Hotel London at Ten Trinity Square
🏃 10 Trinity Square, EC3N 4AJ
🕐 Sat architect-led tours, every 45 mins (10am-3.15pm, max 15, no access to private member's Club, tower or back of house). T·D
⚠ Pre-book only: sara.gunderson@fourseasons.com
🚇 Aldgate, Fenchurch Street
The Grade II* listed building is the former headquarters of the Port of London Authority and played host to the inaugural reception of the United Nations General Assembly in 1946. Now a Four Seasons Hotel, the building has been restored. Sir Edwin Cooper, 1922

## Gresham College - Barnard's Inn Hall
🏃 Barnard's Inn Hall, Holborn, EC1N 2HH
🕐 Sat 11am–3pm + video loop/talk (max 80). T·D
🚇 Chancery Lane
Barnard's Inn dates back to the mid 13C. The hall contains three wooden bays dating from 15C with later linenfold wood panelling added in the 1600s. It was the Mercers' School and today is home to Gresham College (free lectures for all).

## Guildhall Galleries

### Guildhall
🏃 Gresham Street, EC2V 7HH
🕐 Sat/Sun 10am–5pm + ½ hourly tours. T·D
🚇 Barbican, Cannon Street
The City's seat of municipal government since 12C. Grade I listed, rare example of medieval civic architecture with post-war extensions and rebuilding. John Croxton, 1440

### Guildhall Art Gallery
🏃 Guildhall Yard, EC2V 5AE
🕐 Sat/Sun 10am–5pm + ½ hourly gallery tours, (10.30am-4pm) + 'Nature Morte' exhibition (contemporary art reinvigorates the Still Life tradition). T·B·D
🚇 Mansion House, City Thameslink
Houses the City of London's art collection, built over remains of London's 2C Roman amphitheatre. Façade uses Portland stone and Collyweston stone slates. ↪

Interior uses finishes of marble, American elm, damask and painted wall coverings. Richard Gilbert Scott, 1999

## Guildhall Library
🚶 Aldermanbury, EC2V 7HH
🕐 Sat 9.30am–5pm + library tour at 11am, 3pm + 'The Discovery of Roman London'. T·B·D
🚇 Mansion House, City Thameslink
Purpose built over 5 floors to house printed books and manuscripts. Features include former pneumatic tube ticket delivery system and 56 listed translucent pyramid roof lights. Sir Giles Scott, Son + Partners, 1974

## Guildhall Yard
🚶 Guildhall Yard, EC2V 7HH
🕐 Sat 12noon-5pm/Sun 11am-4pm hourly 'House of Sound' installation. T·D
🚇 St. Paul's, Moorgate
The House of Sound: an immersive composition of London's changing sound, as well as the impact of the built and social environment in this historic Yard. Sonic trail across Cheapside from 11 Sep. Composed & created by Iain Chambers.

## King's College London, The Maughan Library
🚶 Chancery Lane, WC2A 1LR
🕐 Sat/Sun 1.30pm–5pm + short talk about the history of the building (talks will take place in the Weston Room as advertised on the day.) T·d
🚇 Temple, Charing Cross

London's first fireproof building, built to house records of the Court of Chancery. Now renovated to house a fine university library. J Pennethorne and Sir John Taylor, 1851

## Leadenhall Market
🚶 Gracechurch Street, EC3V 1LR
🕐 Sat/Sun 10am–5pm + tours (11am-4pm). D
🚇 Aldgate, Moorgate
Classic cast-iron Victorian covered market by the architect of Tower Bridge and Smithfield Market. Sir Horace Jones, 1881
*cityoflondon.gov.uk/things-to-do/leadenhall-market*

## Leathersellers' Hall
🚶 7 St Helen's Place, Bishopsgate, EC3A 6AB
🕐 Sat 10am-4pm hourly tours by the archivist (max 25, duration 45 mins, no tour at 1pm). T·D
ⓘ Pre-book only: enquiries@leathersellers.co.uk
🚇 Liverpool Street, Bank
New Livery Hall behind a retained early 20th century façade. This is the 7th Hall in the Leathersellers' Company's history since its foundation in the Middle Ages. Eric Parry Architects, 2016

## Lloyd's Register Group
🚶 71 Fenchurch Street, EC3M 4BS
🕐 Sat 10am–5pm (access to Rogers building entrance and reception only; Collcutt building reception hall, library and General Committee room) + ½ hourly architect talk about Rogers ↗

Building (max 50) + Heritage & Education Centre digitisation project. T·D

🚇 Tower Hill, Liverpool Street

Sumptuous building with many original decorative and architectural features. Sympathetically extended by Richard Rogers Partnership whose glass and steel structure soars above as a fine example of high-tech architecture. RIBA Award winner. Thomas Collcutt, 1901
*www.lr.org/en*

## Masonic Temple, Andaz Liverpool Street (former Great Eastern Hotel)

🚶 Entrance on Bishopsgate, EC2M 7QN

🕐 Sun 10am–5pm (max 20, entry to temple only). T·D

🚇 Liverpool Street

Grade II listed grand Victorian railway hotel refurbished with stylish contemporary interiors. Greek Masonic Temple with magnificent Grade I listed interior of marble and mahogany, built 1912 at immense cost. Charles Barry, 1884

## Middle Temple Hall

🚶 Middle Temple Lane, EC4Y 9BT

🕐 Sun 1pm–5pm. T

🚇 Temple, Blackfriars

London's finest surviving Elizabethan Hall (1562), 101ft long and 41ft wide, highly atmospheric, with double hammerbeam roof, screen and notable paintings. 17C and C20 additions.
*www.middletemplehall.org.uk*

## Museum of London

🚶 150 London Wall, EC2Y 5HN

🕐 Sat/Sun 10am–5.45pm + ½ hourly architectural tour (11am-4.30pm, max 30) T·R·B·D

🚇 St. Paul's, City Thameslink

Part of an ambitious redevelopment of the area following WW2 bombing, this building forms part of the Barbican complex. The architects were inspired by post-war modernism to include green design elements and raised walkways. Philip Powell and Hidalgo Moya, 1976

## Rogers Stirk Harbour + Partners at The Leadenhall Building

🚶 122 Leadenhall Street, EC3V 4AB

🕐 Sat architect-led tours of RSHP's studio (10am-4pm, max 40). T·d

⚠ Pre-book only: bit.ly/2ufEPjI

🚇 Monument, Cannon Street

Architects, Rogers Stirk Harbour + Partners are located in award-winning The Leadenhall Building. The tour will include a visit to level 14 which has spectacular views of St Paul's Cathedral, Lloyd's of London and Canary Wharf. Rogers Stirk Harbour + Partners, 2014
*www.rsh-p.com*

## Salters' Hall

🚶 4 London Wall Place, EC2Y 5DE

🕐 Sat 11am–6pm + hourly tours of the hall, exhibition and archive (11.30am-4.30pm, max 26) + children's trail. T·D

🚇 Moorgate, Liverpool Street

A rare example of a Brutalist Livery Hall which underwent extensive refurbishment in 2016. New Pavilion, exhibition and archive space and garden. Sir Basil Spence, 1976

## Skidmore Owings & Merrill Studio - Broadgate Tower

🚶 4th Floor, Broadgate Tower, 20 Primrose Street, EC2A 2EW

🕐 Sat 12pm–4pm (max 40, SOM offices only). T·D

🚇 Liverpool Street, Shoreditch High Street

Tours by the architects offer an opportunity to gain insight into the workings of this globally renowned architecture, engineering and urban planning firm within a building they designed. Skidmore Owings & Merrill, 2008

## St Bartholomew's Hospital, Great Hall and Maggies Centre

🚶 St Bartholomew's Hospital, West Smithfield, EC1A 7BE

🕐 Sun 10am–5pm (accompanied access to the Great Hall, meeting rooms and Maggie's Centre) + hourly tours of Maggie's Barts Cancer Care Centre (10.30am-4.30pm, max 20) T·d

⚠ Pre-book only: barts.archives@bartshealth.nhs.uk

🚇 St. Paul's, Farringdon

Bart's was founded in 1123 and rebuilt by Gibbs. Grade I listed North Wing showcases spectacular canvases by William Hogarth and historic Great Hall; new Maggies Centre by Steve Holl adjoins. Church of St Bartholomew the Less also open. James Gibbs, 1730/Steven Holl, 2017

## St Botolph Building

🚶 138 Houndsditch, EC3A 7DH

🕐 Sat hourly tours (10am-4pm, max 40) + tenant art exhibition. T·R·D

🚇 Aldgate East, Liverpool Street

Grimshaw's design creates a highly adaptable commercial building for landlord DEKA Immoblien and agents CBRE. Grimshaw, 2010

## St Bride Foundation

🚶 Bride Lane, Fleet Street, EC4Y 8EQ

🕐 Sun 11am–5pm (theatre partially accessible) + Adana Letterpress Demonstration · Exhibition of Items from the St Bride Library Collection.B·T·R·d

🚇 St. Paul's, City Thameslink

Built in 1893 as a printers' institute in the Anglo-Dutch style, with sandstone dressings, steeply pitched tiled roof and gables; many original features remain including the swimming pool and library. Robert C Murray, 1894

## St Paul's Cathedral - Triforium Tour
ᛏ St Paul's Cathedral, St Paul's Churchyard, EC4M 8AD
🕐 Sat 11am–6pm (max 15, access via 160 steps. Unsuitable for those with mobility issues or vertigo). T·R·B
ⓘ Pre-book only: www.stpauls.co.uk/openhouse
Blackfriars, City Thameslink, St Paul's The tour includes: Sir Christopher Wren's Great Model and other designs for the new Cathedral; the 18C library and the stunning view down the nave from the West Gallery. Sir Christopher Wren, 1710

## Stationers' Hall
ᛏ Ave Maria Lane, EC4M 7DD
🕐 Sun 10am–5pm + ½ hourly tours (max 30). T·R·B·d
🚇 St. Paul's, City Thameslink
17C livery hall with courtroom and garden. Oak panelling and stained glass windows. Undamaged in WW2. Selected items from the archives on display. Robert Mylne, 1673

## The Banking Hall, 8-10 Moorgate
ᛏ 8-10 Moorgate, EC2R 6DA
🕐 Sat 10am–5pm (max 50, access to 7th Floor, including terraces and meeting rooms displaying ING UK Art Collection) + tour led by TP Bennett at 12pm (max 15) · ING UK Art Collection tour, hourly (11am-4pm, max 10). T·D
🚇 Moorgate, Liverpool Street
ING UK moved to 8-10 Moorgate in 2016. The building blends a historic exterior (including its original Portland stone façade) with a modern 135,220 square feet of office space. City Heritage Award winner 2015. Allies and Morrison, 2016

## The City Centre
ᛏ City Centre, within Guildhall Complex (entrance at 80 Basinghall Street, leading from Gresham Street), EC2V 5AR
🕐 Sat/Sun 10am–4pm + 'A Smarter City' exhibition · 'Modern Architecture in the City of London' talk with Peter Murray, Chairman New London Architecture and The City Centre at 12pm · City of London Model talk and Q&A at 2pm. T·D
🚇 Mansion House, City Thameslink
An overview of the latest developments and architecture in the City of London via the interactive 1:500 scale Pipers model that shows the future skyline with all of the proposed new towers.

## The City Churches

## St Helen Bishopsgate
ᛏ Great St Helen's, EC3A 6AT
🕐 Sat/Sun 10am–5pm. T·R·B
🚇 Bank, Liverpool Street
One of the few City buildings to survive the Great Fire. Contains the best pre-Great Fire collection of monuments in any London parish church. Damaged by terrorist bombs in 1992, then extensively and controversially reordered in 1993.

## St Lawrence Jewry
ᛏ Guildhall Yard, EC2V 5AA
🕐 Sat/Sun 10am–5pm + hourly history talks (10.30am-4.30pm) + mosaics exhibition. T·R·D
🚇 St. Paul's, Liverpool Street
11C site with a stunning Wren building from the 17C. Now the official church of the City of London Corporation. Stunning ceiling and windows by Christopher Webb. Sir Christopher Wren, 1677

## St Mary Aldermary
ᛏ Watling Street, EC4M 9BW
🕐 Sat 10am–5pm. T·R·D
🚇 Mansion House, Cannon Street
Guild Church, first mentioned c1080. Oldest of the City churches dedicated to St Mary. Only Wren church built after the Great Fire, courtesy of a bequest, in late Gothic style. Sir Christopher Wren, 1677

## St Mary-le-Bow
ᛏ Cheapside, EC2V 6AU
🕐 Sat/Sun 10am–5pm (access to crypt only during tours) + guided tours 1pm, 2.30pm. T·d
🚇 St. Paul's, Moorgate
Founded by William the Conqueror's Archbishop Lanfranc in 1080 (the significant crypt survives) St Mary-le-Bow was rebuilt, notably by Wren after the Great Fire and by Laurence King in 1964 after WWII destruction. Home of Bow Bells. Sir Christopher Wren, 1683

## St Stephen Walbrook
ᛏ 39 Walbrook, EC4N 8BN
🕐 Sat 10am–5pm (closed 12pm-3pm)
🚇 Bank, Cannon Street
Wren's own and 'finest City Church'. Fantastic architecture with different shapes, twelve Corinthian columns and covered by huge dome - first of its type. Central stone altar by Henry Moore installed in 1987. Birthplace of the Samaritans. Sir Christopher Wren, Nicholas Hawksmoor, Sir John Vanbrugh, 1672

## The Salvation Army International Headquarters
ᛏ 101 Queen Victoria Street, EC4V 4EH
🕐 Sat 11am–6pm + tours by architect and members of The Salvation Army, every 20 mins. T·R·B·D
🚇 Blackfriars, Mansion House
A transparent and welcoming working environment with full-height glazing and feature steel columns. Brief was to create a space 'modern in design, frugal in operation and evangelical in purpose'. Sheppard Robson, 2004

## The Temple Church
ᛏ off Fleet Street, EC4Y 7BB
🕐 Sun 1pm–4pm. B·D
🚇 Chancery Lane, Charing Cross
Medieval architecture meets Wren's refurbishments in this inspiring building, the Mother Church of the Common Law. The Magna Carta exhibit has William Marshal and King John where they would have debated and agreed clauses of Magna Carta.

The Banking Hall, 8-10 Moorgate © Mitsui Fudosan ↗

### The Walbrook
🚶 25 Walbrook, EC4N 8AF
🕐 Sat 1pm–5pm/Sun 10am–1pm (max 30, reception and one lift lobby to view the two atriums) T·D
🚇 Cannon Street, Bank

An iconic building with a distinctive, uncompromisingly modern design. The exterior is encased with solar shading, keeping the building cool in summer and warm in winter. Foster + Partners, 2010

### Tower 42
🚶 25 Old Broad Street, EC2N 1HQ
🕐 Sat hourly tours 10am–5pm (max 50, Vertigo 42 viewing area only). D
ⓘ Pre-book only: bit.ly/2uNzx0s
🚇 Bank, Liverpool Street

The City's original tallest skyscraper, consisting of 3 hexagonal chevrons, at 601ft Tower 42 was the first to break previous restrictions on tall buildings in London. Glass entrance added during a comprehensive refurbishment in 1995. Richard Seifert & Partners, 1981

### Trades of the Walbrook: A Future for the Past
🚶 Paternoster Square, EC4M 7DX
🕐 Sat 10am–5pm (max 25). D
🚇 St. Paul's

This event offers the opportunity to meet some of the soldiers, traders and craftsmen whose stories were uncovered by the discovery of the Bloomberg writing tablets during excavations at the site of Bloomberg's new European headquarters.

### Trinity House

- 🏃 Trinity Square, Tower Hill, EC3N 4DH
- 🕐 Sat 10am–1pm (max 60). T·D
- 🚇 Tower Hill, Fenchurch Street

Fine late Georgian exterior with interior painstakingly reconstructed after destruction by incendiary bomb in 1940. Good fittings, statues and works of art from original building. Samuel Wyatt, 1796

### Vintners' Hall

- 🏃 Upper Thames Street, EC4V 3BG
- 🕐 Sat 10am–4pm. T·D
- 🚇 Mansion House, Cannon Street

Built immediately after the Great Fire, the Hall is an outstanding example of mid 17C craftsmanship. Richly panelled and with a magnificently carved staircase, it contains paintings, plates, charters and other treasures dating back to 14C. Edward Jarman, 1671

### Watermark Place

- 🏃 1 Angel Lane, EC4R 3AB
- 🕐 Sat 10am–5pm (General access to Level 6 and the roof terrace only). T·R·D
- 🚇 Monument, London Bridge

Landmark office building and European HQ of Nomura International, featuring spectacular riverfront views and rooftop gardens with award-winning kitchen garden maintained by staff volunteers. Fletcher Priest Architects, 2009

The Walbrook ↘

### Watermen's Hall

- 🏃 18 St Mary-at-Hill, EC3R 8EF
- 🕐 Sat tours at 9am, 10.30am, 12pm, 1.15pm (max 35). d
- ⚠ Pre-book only: apply in writing with self-addressed envelope. Max 2 tickets per application
- 🚇 Monument, Fenchurch Street

Only remaining Georgian hall in the City of London, and perfect example of domestic architecture of the period. William Blackburn, 1780

### Whitefriars and Northcliffe

- 🏃 65 Fleet St (HQ Freshfields), EC4Y 1HT
- 🕐 Sun 10am–1pm (max 10, access to ground and 6th floors only). T·R·D
- 🚇 Blackfriars, Waterloo

Developed in 1989 by Kumagai Umi & YRM; Northcliffe House built in 1925 by Ellis & Clarke, form the London offices of international Law Firm Freshfields Bruckhaus Deringer LLP. Features include atria, views, historic interest. YRM, Ellis & Clarke, 1989

### Yeoman Warders Club, Tower of London

- 🏃 Yeoman Warders Club, HM Tower of London, EC3N 4AB
- 🕐 Sat/Sun tours every 90 mins (10.30am-3pm, max 20). T·D
- ⚠ Pre-book only: 02031666275
- 🚇 Tower Hill, Fenchurch Street

Part of original outer wall c1280. Salvins restoration (1870) of the Tower gave the outer appearance it has today. Became accommodation for Yeoman Warders in the Victorian era. In the 1970s it became the Yeoman Warders Club. King's Engineers, King Edward 1st, 1280

## Walks + Tours

### Broadgate Art Tour

- 🏃 Meet: Broadgate Welcome Centre, 3 Finsbury Ave, London, EC2M 2PA
- 🕐 Sat tours with Broadgate's art curator Rosie Glenn, 10am, 2pm, 4pm.
- 🚇 Bank, Moorgate

Broadgate boasts an impressive art collection from acclaimed British and international artists. Stunning outdoor sculptures, impressive models and intricate paintings.
*www.broadgateestates.co.uk*

### City Alleyways East

- 🏃 Meet: outside Guildhall Art Gallery, Guildhall Yard, EC2V 5AE
- 🕐 Sat/Sun 10.30am-3pm, tours every 45 mins (max 30). D
- 🚇 Bank, Cannon Street

Discover lanes, alleys and corners on this walk to London Bridge. See TV's most famous alleyway, where wizards shop and discover some new uses for churches. See where the fire started that destroyed the City.

Whitefriars and Northcliffe ↗

### City Alleyways North
🚶 Meet: outside Guildhall Art Gallery, Guildhall Yard, Guildhall Yard, EC2V 5AE
🕐 Sat/Sun 11am-3.30pm, tours every 45 mins (max 30). D
🚇 Bank, Cannon Street

Discover lanes, alleys and corners of the City, some with a gruesome past. Stand on the site of public executions and meet some of the City's famous inhabitants. Hear of famous trials and of the bodysnatchers.

### City Alleyways South West
🚶 Meet: outside Guildhall Art Gallery, Guildhall Yard, EC2V 5AE
🕐 Sat/Sun 10.45am-3.15pm, tours every 45 mins (max 30). D
🚇 Bank, Cannon Street

Discover lanes, alleys and corners on this to Blackfriars Bridge. Includes Shakespeare, St. Paul's and how the King got dressed.

### Sculpture in the City 2017
🚶 Meet: The Churchyard, St Botolphs without Bishopsgate, Bishopsgate, EC2M 3XF
🕐 Sat tours 12pm, 2.30pm (max 20). The open air exhibition is accessible 24 hours a day.
❗ Pre-book only: bit.ly/2tuKDXZ
🚇 Bank, Liverpool Street

An urban sculpture park of contemporary art installations by leading international artists set within the iconic towers of the City of London.

# Croydon

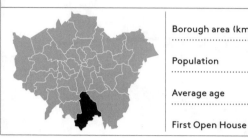

| | |
|---|---|
| Borough area (km²) | 86.5 |
| Population | 386,500 |
| Average age | 37 |
| First Open House | 2006 |

**CROYDON**
www.croydon.gov.uk

## Airport House
🏃 Purley Way, Croydon, CR0 0XZ
🕐 Sat/Sun 11am–4pm (max 48, main reception area and route into the Air Traffic Control Tower) + ½ hourly historical tours (max 18). T·R·P·B·d
🚊 East Croydon, Purley
Unique Grade II* listed 1928 Government building constructed in a restrained neoclassical style. Britain's first airport terminal. Landmark building incorporating the world's oldest Air Traffic Control Tower. Air Ministry- Directorate of Works and buildings, 1926

## Bernard Weatherill House
🏃 8 Mint Walk, Croydon (corporate reception off Fell Road), CR0 1EA
🕐 Sat 9am–12pm (max 50, access to reception, 8th floor common areas and terraces). T·D
🚊 West Croydon, East Croydon
300,000sqft of BREEAM excellent accredited modern commercial accommodation spread over 12 storeys with a public access facility on the ground floor at the heart of the building. EPR Architects, 2013

## Church of St Mary the Blessed Virgin
🏃 Addington Village Road, Addington, CR0 5AS
🕐 Sat 1pm–5pm/Sun 1.30pm–4pm (max 20). T·R·P·d
🚊 Addington Village Tram
Founded in 11C, with Jacobean memorial c1615. Burial site of 5 Archbishops of Canterbury. Edward Blore, 1080

## Croydon Saffron Central
🏃 Former Taberner House next to The Queens Gardens, in between Fell Road & Park Lane, Croydon, CR9 3JS
🕐 Sat 1pm–5pm (max 25) + hourly talk 'Who put the crocus in Croydon?' (1.30pm-4.30pm, max 20). D
🚊 West Croydon, East Croydon
The world's largest urban pop up saffron farm? Life started by re-creating the crocus valley then building a bee haven on the former Taberner House site. Now looking for a new home as the site is developed. Croydon Community, Ally McKinlay, 2015

## Croydon Town Hall and Clocktower Complex
🏃 Katharine Street, Croydon, CR9 1ET
🕐 Sat 10am–1pm (max 20, no physical access to bell tower) + Town Hall guided tour, every 45 mins + Create a Croydon Skyline family workshop at 11am. T·R·D
🚊 West Croydon, East Croydon
Guided tours of the original Town Hall, including council chamber and meeting rooms. Clocktower complex and Museum of Croydon open to the public throughout the day. Charles Henman, 1895

## Good Food Matters
🏃 Mickleham Way, New Addington, CR0 0PN
🕐 Sun 11am–3.30pm. T·R·P·d
🚊 Wimbledon, East Croydon
A learning centre to support and empower those marginalised by society, teaching them the process of growing and cooking their own food. Geraghty Taylor Architects, 2013

## Old Palace, Croydon
🏃 Old Palace Road, Old Town, Croydon, CR0 1AX
🕐 Sat tour at 2pm (max 30). T
❗ Pre-book only: 020 8680 8499 or 020 8256 1594
🚊 West Croydon, East Croydon
Grade I listed manor house, former summer residence of Archbishops of Canterbury from 13-18C. Elizabeth I and other monarchs regularly visited. Contains one of the finest great halls with its original roof from 1440s.

## Saffron Square
🏃 Wellesley Road, Croydon, CR9 2BY
🕐 Sat/Sun 'High Tea at The Tower' tour at 2pm (max 20). T·R·D
❗ Pre-book only: natalie.harris@berkeleygroup.co.uk
🚊 West Croydon, East Croydon
Saffron Tower is an iconic 45 storey tower, clad in muted tones of pinks and mauves to represent an image of a crocus flower. Benefitting from floor to ceiling glazing, it offers stunning views across the Croydon skyline and beyond. Rolfe Judd, 2013

## Shirley Windmill
🏃 Postmill Close, Upper Shirley Road, Croydon, CR0 5DY ↱

Bernard Weatherill House ↗

⏲ Sun 12pm-4pm, tours every 20 mins (max 15). T·R·d
🚆 East Croydon
The present brick tower windmill was built 1854 to replace a post mill destroyed by fire. Now renovated to near-working condition, it is the only surviving windmill in Croydon.

### The Stanley Halls
🚶 12 South Norwood Hill, SE25 6AB
⏲ Sun 10am–5pm (max 40, general access to exhibition only) + tours about William Stanley, architect and philanthropist (10.15am, 12.15pm, 2.15pm, 4.15pm, max 20) + 'The Development of the Stanley Halls' exhibition. T·R·d
🚆 Norwood Junction
A public hall, theatre and gallery in grand Edwardian style. Grade II listed, Stanley made fun of the Victorian style with grand ornamentation. It reflects Stanley's interest in science, the arts and public cultural improvement. William Ford Robinson Stanley, 1903

### Thornton Heath Library
🚶 190 Brigstock Road, Thornton Heath, CR7 7JB
⏲ Sat 12pm–3pm (max 20) + ½ hourly tours. T·d
🚆 Thornton Heath
Carnegie Library with original features, refurbished with dramatic façade making a statement on the high street. White concrete and glass pavilion reading area is complemented by rich oak flooring. Rejuvenated children's library and garden. Eric Edwin Hodder and G F Carter, 1914/FAT, 2010

### Whitgift Almshouses
🚶 North End, Croydon, CR9 1SS
⏲ Sat tours at 10.30am, 11.45am, 2pm, 3.15pm (max 30, access to quadrangle, Chapel and Audience Chamber). T
❗ Pre-book only: 020 8680 8499 or 020 8256 1594
🚆 East Croydon
Tudor almshouses dating from 1596 and founded by the Archbishop of Canterbury John Whitgift. Chapel and Courtyard with original 16C clock.

# Ealing

| | |
|---|---|
| Borough area (km²) | 55.5 |
| Population | 351,600 |
| Average age | 36 |
| First Open House | 1995 |

www.ealing.gov.uk

## Chestnut Grove
🚶 56 Chestnut Grove (access via side gate), W5 4JS
🕐 Sat PassivHaus tours by PH Consultant at 3pm, 4.30pm (max 15). T·R
⚠ Pre-book only: dora.varszegi@gmail.com (max 2)
🚇 South Ealing
A 1925 semi, refurbished to Certified PassivHaus Standard, with a side and rear extension. Robert Juhasz, 2010

## Dormers Wells High School
🚶 Dormers Wells Lane, Southall, UB1 3HZ
🕐 Sat 10am–1pm + ½ hourly tours. T·P·D
🚇 Greenford, Southall
Rebuilt as part of the BSF programme, the school aims to encourage educational aspiration through supporting social inclusion and community cohesion. Very Good status by CABE, BREEAM Excellent. Nicholas Hare Architects, 2012

## Ealing Town Hall, Nelson Room, Council Chamber and Mayor's Office
🚶 New Broadway, W5 2BY
🕐 Sat ½ hourly tours (11am-3.30pm, max 12, tour includes Nelson Room, Council Chamber and Mayor's Office). T·R·D
🚇 Ealing Broadway
Late Victorian ragstone Gothic Town Hall with sumptuous Imperial staircase. Recently restored. Charles Jones (West Wing), 1888

## Gogglebox
🚶 24 Princes Gardens, W5 1SD
🕐 Sun 10am–5pm + ½ hourly architect-led tours (max 15, downstairs and garden only). P
🚇 Ealing Broadway, North Ealing
Striking glass extension that transforms inside outside living. Ever-changing vistas of garden, terrace & sky. Structural frameless glazing, glass beams, Tom Dixon pendants, zinc cladding, cedar deck with integrated bike/bin store. KSKa Architects, 2016
*www.kska.co.uk · Facebook KSKa Architects*

## Heath Lodge
🚶 3 Church Road, W7 0BB
🕐 Sun 10am–5pm.

🚇 Northfields, Hanwell
An example of how site limitations can create opportunity and uniqueness. Building a sense of place, in accordance with the design principles set out in 'Better Places to Live.' Autor Architecture, 2016

## Norwood Hall
🚶 Khalsa Primary School, Norwood Green Road, Southall, UB2 4LA
🕐 Sun 10am–1pm (max 5). T·P·D
🚇 Hounslow Central, Southall
Much modified and extended in late 19C with Arts and Crafts details but recognisably a Soane house with echoes of his own nearby house at Pitzhanger Manor. 19-acre walled garden contemporary with house. W Kent, Sir John Soane, Sir Charles Barry, 1803

Gogglebox ↘

### Pitzhanger Manor
🏃 Walpole Park, Mattock Lane, W5 5EQ
🕐 Sat architect-led hard-hat tour of current restoration work at 11am, 2pm (max 12). T·d
❗ Pre-book only: pitzhanger@ealing.gov.uk (Please specify preferred time, names and shoe sizes)
🚇 Ealing Broadway
Designed by Sir John Soane for his own use and set in Walpole Park. Grade I listed building, illustrating Soane's inventive use of space and light. Currently undergoing extensive restoration, the House will re-open to the public in 2018. Sir John Soane, 1800/ Julian Harrap Architects, 2018

### Rehearsal Rooms
🏃 3 Victoria Road, North Acton, W3 6HU
🕐 Sat hourly tours (11.15am-3.15pm, max 8). T
🚇 North Acton
A mixed-use development aiming to address London's housing shortage by providing quality homes for long-term rent. 173 purpose-designed flats, communal facilities and commercial uses promote a vibrant community. Newground Architects, 2014
www.newgroundarchitects.com

### St Mary the Virgin Perivale
🏃 Perivale Lane, Perivale, UB6 8SS
🕐 Sat/Sun 10am–5pm (max 30) + talk by Professor Alan Gillett OBE FRICS on history of the church and town of Ealing Sat 11.30am, Sun 3pm. P
🚇 Perivale, Ealing Broadway
Grade I listed 12C church with later additions, now an arts centre run by The Friends of St Mary's.

### Swiss Watch
🏃 57 Coningsby Road, W5 4HP
🕐 Sat 10am–5pm (max 15, Downstairs and patio only) + ½ hourly tours.
🚇 South Ealing, Ealing Broadway
Small but perfectly formed terrace home transformation as beautifully detailed as a 'Swiss' watch. Frameless glass extension, large pivot doors, cantilevered frameless glass bay & secret storage pod, artfully create the illusion of space. KSKa Architects, 2016
www.kska.co.uk · Facebook KSKa Architects

Swiss Watch ↘

### The White House
🏃 46 Park View Road, Ealing, W5 2JB
🕐 Sat/Sun 10am–4pm (max 30, private rooms not available) + La Bayadere Ballet performance at 3pm (Approx 7 minutes). T·R·P·d
🚇 Ealing Broadway
Louis XVI Palace set in the private gardens and based on the owner's grandmother's palace in Poland. Marble arch entrance is the first in London for over 200 years. Extremely opulent interiors with marble, gold cornices and chandeliers. John Zylinski, 2009
www.whitehouselondon.com

## Walks + Tours

### A Ruskinian Walk Through Shared Heritage
🏃 Meet: Building 3, Chiswick Business Park, 566 Chiswick High Road, W4 5YA
🕐 Sat 12pm/Sun 2pm. T
🚇 Gunnersbury
RIBA award-winning Chiswick Business Park; William Morris oriented South Acton Estate, birthplace of artist Patrick Caulfield; Woodland Park Ice House; home of William Willett, builder, wall-engineer, Daylight Saving Time originator.
www.sarag.org

### Brentham Garden Suburb
🏃 Meet: The Brentham Club, 38 Meadvale Road, W5 1NP
🕐 Sat/Sun 10.30am (max 30). T·R·P·B·d
🚇 Hanger Lane, Ealing Broadway
Britain's first co-partnership garden suburb, first houses built 1901. Parker and Unwin's plan introduced 1907, mainly Arts and Crafts style; fascinating social history (organised by The Brentham Society.). Parker & Unwin, G L Sutcliffe, G C Pearson & others, 1901

### Ealing Common Walk
🏃 Meet: at Hanger Lane end of Inglis Road, Ealing, W5 3RN
🕐 Sat 2pm–4pm (max 50). d·T·R
🚇 Ealing Broadway, Ealing Common
Walk across Ealing Common taking in the range of architectural styles. Highlights: the home of a Wimbledon champion and the death mask of a prime minister.

### Hanwell Flight of Locks & Three Bridges
🏃 Meet: The Fox public house, Green Lane, W7 2PJ
🕐 Sat/Sun Hanwell Flight guided walk, hourly (1pm-4pm, max 35). T·R·P·D
🚇 Southall, Boston Manor
Restored flight of locks at Hanwell is a Scheduled Ancient Monument. Three Bridges is a unique stacked intersection of road, rail and canal and Brunel's last major railway project. Walks led by knowledgeable enthusiasts. Isambard Kingdom Brunel, James Barnes (Resident Engineer), William Jessop (Chief Engineer), 1794

# Enfield

| | |
|---|---|
| Borough area (km²) | 80.8 |
| Population | 333,000 |
| Average age | 36 |
| First Open House | 1995 |

## Christ Church Southgate and the Minchenden Oak Garden

🚶 Waterfall Road, Southgate, N14 7EG

🕐 Sat/Sun 10am–5pm (stepped access to Lady Chapel and Chancel) + hourly tours (11am-4pm). T·R·P·B·d

🚇 Southgate, Palmers Green

Grade II listed church with fine collection of Pre-Raphaelite stained glass windows by Morris & Co. including Burne Jones and Rossetti. Wall paintings. Mosaic reredos. Minchenden Oak - ancient pollarded oak more than 800 years old. George Gilbert Scott, 1861

## Deephams Sewage Treatment Works

🚶 AMK Site Office, Picketts Lock Lane, N9 0BA

🕐 Sat ½ hourly tours (10am-4pm, max 10, includes site induction and tour in minibus.). T·R·d

❗ Pre-book only: rachelgroves@murphygroup.co.uk

🚇 Tottenham Hale, Ponders End

London's fourth largest sewage works. Thames Water is upgrading the process while continuing to treat the 209,000 tonnes of flow arriving each day. This can increase to over 1.3 million tonnes during heavy rainfall.

## Domino Houses

🚶 Corbett Grove, Bounds Green, N22 8DQ

🕐 Sat 10am–5pm + architect-led tours at 11am, 2pm.

🚇 Bounds Green, Bowes Park

8 new monolithic black brick houses with a curving green roof and domino language of circular porthole windows dotting its façade. Code 4 Sustainable Homes, finalist in 2016 Brick Awards, Special Mention for the 2016 Architizer A+Awards. Studio Verve, 2015

## Forty Hall & Estate

🚶 Forty Hill, Enfield, EN2 9HA

🕐 Sat/Sun 11am–4pm. T·R·P·D

🚇 Turkey Street, Enfield Town

This Grade I listed Carolean Mansion hall is set in a fine estate. Built as a family home by of Sir Nicholas Rainton, Lord Mayor of London 1632-33 and Master of the Haberdasher's Guild.

## King George V Pumping Station

🚶 Swan & Pike Road, Enfield, EN3 6JH

🕐 Sat/Sun 10am–5pm. P

🚇 Enfield Lock

Designed to pump water from the River Lee into the King George V reservoir, the building houses three old disused gas Humphrey pumps, and two electric pumps. William Booth Bryan, 1913

## Lee Valley Athletics Centre

🚶 Lee Valley Leisure Complex, 61 Meridian Way, Picketts Lock, N9 0AR

🕐 Sat/Sun 10am–5pm + Sun architect-led tours, every 90 mins (11am-4pm). T·R·P·D

🚇 Edmonton Green, Tottenham Hale

A world-class indoor training facility, the only one of its kind in the South East, this naturally lit and ventilated building is highly sustainable. David Morley Architects, 2007

## Myddelton House

🚶 Bulls Cross, Enfield, EN2 9HG

🕐 Sat 10am–4pm (max 50, downstairs only). T·R·P·D

🚇 Turkey Street

Neo-classical yellow Suffolk stock brick villa with mid 19C extension to north and west front. Victorian conservatory to side. Adam style ceilings to ground floor. Home of the great horticulturist E.A. Bowles. George Ferry and John Wallen, 1818

## Old Vestry Offices

🚶 22 The Town, Enfield, EN2 6LT

🕐 Sat 10am–1pm (max 10).

🚇 Southgate, Enfield Chase

Tiny polygonal building originally for the beadle. Used as local police station until 1930s and then as offices. Grade II listed.

## Parish Church of St Andrew Enfield

🚶 Market Place, Enfield, EN2 6LL

🕐 Sat 10am–4pm/Sun 12pm–4pm (max 20, ramp to church but not to bell ringing room). T·D

🚇 Enfield Chase, Enfield Town

Listed church, recently refurbished. 1750s organ with fine wooden case, many fine memorials. Eight-bell peal - the oldest bell dates from 1680.

Domino Houses © Luke White ↗

### Priory Hospital North London
🚶 Grovelands House, The Bourne, N14 6RA
🕐 Sat tours tours 10am, 11am, 12pm (max 20) T·R·P
❗ Pre-book only: sabrinacator@priorygroup.com
(Acute psychiatric hospital, please respect
privacy of clients and any restrictions on the
day. )
🚇 Southgate, Winchmore Hill
Grade I listed neo-classical villa designed for Walker
Gray. Grounds laid out by Repton. Elegant trompe
l'oeil breakfast room. John Nash, 1797

### Queen Elizabeth II Stadium
🚶 Donkey Lane, Enfield, EN1 3PL
🕐 Sat/Sun 11am–2pm. T·R·P·D
🚇 Oakwood, Enfield Town
Two-storey concrete sports pavilion in streamlined
1930s style. Building work interrupted by WW2
and completed in 1952. Distinctive 'drum' contains
stylised staircase leading to glass-walled café and
sheltered spectator seating.

### Royal Small Arms Factory
🚶 RSA Island Centre, 12 Island Centre Way, Enfield
(off A1055 Mollison Avenue), EN3 6GS
🕐 Sat 11am–6pm + tour of the clock tower with the
keeper, every 15 mins (12pm-5pm, max 2, access
via ladder and at keeper's discretion). T·P·d
🚇 Enfield Lock
Grade II listed arms factory closed to public for 170
years, buildings on site included a church (the original
font is displayed at the centre), a police station and a
school. Now a mixed-use community and commercial
centre. Clock c1783. Board of Ordnance, 1854

### Salisbury House
🚶 Bury Street West, N9 9LA
🕐 Sat 12pm–3pm. T
🚇 Bush Hill Park
Grade II* listed gabled and brick 1625 Tudor Manor
House restored by Enfield Council, now used as an
Arts Centre. The finest piece of late-Elizabethan
architecture left in the borough. Two fine panelled
rooms and early painting on plaster.

### St Mary Magdalene Church
🚶 Windmill Hill, Enfield, EN2 7AJ
🕐 Sat 10am–5pm. T·P·D
🚇 Enfield Town, Oakwood
Fine Victorian Gothic church with impressive
windows and painted chancel. Paintings by
Buckeridge and Westlake 1897. Restoration of
chancel paintings was to celebrate the Diamond
Jubilee of Queen Elizabeth II. William Butterfield,
1893

### Winchmore Hill Friends Meeting House & Burial Ground
🚶 Winchmore Hill Quaker Meeting, 59 Church Hill,
N21 1LE
🕐 Sat/Sun 2pm–5pm. T·R·d
🚇 Southgate, Winchmore Hill
Grade II listed, built 1790. A central double door
under a bracketed cornice hood, large sash windows
with delicate glazing bars. Panelled interior. Curved
entrance wall allowed carriages to turn in the
narrow lane. Notable burial ground.

# Greenwich

| | |
|---|---|
| Borough area (km²) | 47.3 |
| Population | 280,100 |
| Average age | 35 |
| First Open House | 1993 |

ROYAL *borough of* GREENWICH

visit **greenwich** time after time

### Blackheath Halls
🏃 23 Lee Road, Blackheath, SE3 9RQ
🕐 Sat 10am–5pm + hourly tours (11am–4pm, max 30) + hourly music performance by community groups. T·R·D
🚇 Greenwich, Lewisham
Part of the oldest surviving purpose-built cultural complex in London, with a magnificent barrel vaulted ceiling in the Great Hall. Today it remains a vibrant arts venue. William Webster, 1895

### Blackheath House
🏃 195 Shooters Hill Road, SE3 8UL
🕐 Sat 1pm–5pm.
🚇 Westcombe Park, Blackheath
Edwardian four-bedroom house, home of an interior designer and his partner. A homage to mid-century modern design with a contemporary extension using bespoke reclaimed bricks.

### Charlton House
🏃 Charlton Road, Charlton, SE7 8RE
🕐 Sun 11am–5pm + historical tour every 90 mins (max 20). T·R·P·D
🚇 North Greenwich, Charlton
London's only surviving great Jacobean mansion, set in Charlton Park, red brick with white stone dressings and beautifully proportioned hall. Each room has a unique fireplace coupled with beautiful strap work ceilings and original features. Norman Shaw, 1607

### Devonport Mausoleum
🏃 National Maritime Museum, Romney Road, SE10 9NF
🕐 Sat/Sun 11am–4pm (max 15, access through National Maritime Museum entrance off Romney Road)
🚇 Maze Hill, Cutty Sark
Handsome mausoleum in former Royal Navy cemetery, restored 1999 by University of Greenwich. Many interesting plaques. Thomas Ripley, 1750

### Eltham Lodge
🏃 Royal Blackheath Golf Club, Court Road, SE9 5AF
🕐 Sat 10am–1pm. T·R·P

🚇 Mottingham
Grade I listed Caroline mansion built for Sir John Shaw. Refurbished 18C with fine plaster, ceilings and staircase. Clubhouse of Royal Blackheath Golf Club since 1923. Hugh May, 1664

### Greenwich Heritage Centre
🏃 Artillery Square, Royal Arsenal, Woolwich, SE18 4DX
🕐 Sat 9am–5pm + tours of the store at 12pm and 2pm (max 8) + drop-in children's drop-in arts and crafts session at 10.30am (max 25). T·D
🚇 Woolwich Arsenal
Housed in a naval store on historic Royal Arsenal, the centre holds information about Greenwich buildings, past and present. James Wyatt, 1783

### Greenwich Reach Swing Bridge
🏃 Glaisher Street, Deptford, SE8 3ER
🕐 Sat 1pm–5pm + opening of bridge at 3.30pm. D
🚇 Deptford, Cutty Sark
Greenwich Reach Swing Bridge, winner of the pedestrian bridge category in the 2015 Structural Awards, forms part of the Thames Path. The bridge delivers a valued and elegant crossing over Deptford Creek in South East London. COWI Ltd, Moxon Architects, 2015

### Greenwich Yacht Club
🏃 1 Peartree Way, SE10 0BW
🕐 Sat/Sun (2pm-5.30pm) ½ hourly tours led by members of the yacht club + Members annual art show at 2pm. T·R·d
🚇 Cutty Sark, Greenwich
Contemporary timber and aluminium building using existing pier, offering unique views of the river, The O2 and Thames Barrier. Frankl + Luty, 2000

### Old Royal Naval College
🏃 Main entry West Gate (King William Walk), or East Gate (Park Row) and Romney Road crossing, SE10 9NN
🚇 Cutty Sark, Greenwich

**Painted Hall, Chapel, Visitor Centre**
🕐 Sat/Sun 10am–5pm + tours Sat 11am, 12.30pm, ↱

1.30pm, 3pm, Sun 11am, 12.30pm, 3pm (max 25)·
'Explore the Jacobean Undercroft' tours, hourly
(11am-4pm, max 15). Meet on Grand Square to
collect tickets ·R·d
Sir Christopher Wren's riverside masterpiece in
Greenwich. Includes Chapel, Visitor Centre, King
Charles Court, Victorian Skittle Alley and the
Jacobean Undercroft. Sir James Thornhill, Sir
Christopher Wren, Nicholas Hawksmoor, 1696

### King William Court
- ⏰ Sat/Sun 11am-4pm hourly tours (max 20), meet
  on Grand Square to collect tickets).
Wren-designed building completed under the
direction of Hawksmoor and Vanbrugh, 1698-1712.
Original wood panelling, refurbished by Dannatt
Johnson in 2001 for University of Greenwich. Sir
Christopher Wren, Nicholas Hawksmoor, Sir John
Vanbrugh, 1698

### Queen Anne Court
- ⏰ Sat/Sun 11.30am-3.30pm hourly tours (max 20),
  meet on Grand Square to collect tickets).
Wren and Hawksmoor building, completed 1749
when Thomas Ripley built the pavilions facing
the river. Highlights include council boardroom,
grand staircase and restored Portland stonework.
Refurbished in 2000 for University of Greenwich. Sir
Christopher Wren, Nicholas Hawksmoor, 1689

### Queen Mary Court
- ⏰ Sat/Sun hourly tours (11.30am-3.30pm, max 20,
  Meet on Grand Square to collect tickets and start/
  finish tours).
Last major building on the site (1751). Original
layout, timber panelling, barrel vaulting and
Portland stone. Refurbished in 2000 by Dannatt
Johnson for University of Greenwich. Sir Christopher
Wren, Thomas Ripley, 1694

### Ravensbourne
- 🏃 6 Penrose Way, Greenwich Peninsula, Greenwich,
  SE10 0EW
- ⏰ Sat 10am–5pm (No access to roof terrace) + hourly
  tours by architecture students and tutors (11am-
  4pm). T·D
- 🚇 North Greenwich
An inspirational learning environment on the
Greenwich Peninsula. It features a series of
interlinked floors around an impressive central
atrium. BREEAM Excellent status. RIBA Award
Winner 2011. Foreign Office Architects, 2010

### Ruins of Garrison Church - RA Barracks
- 🏃 Grand Depot Road, Woolwich, SE18 6XJ
- ⏰ Sat/Sun 10am–5pm. T·R·P·D
- 🚇 Woolwich Arsenal
Built to serve the Royal Artillery community posted
at Woolwich. Bombed in 1944 and now a ruin. It is
the VC memorial for the Royal Artillery and has some
very fine mosaics. Restoration project completed in
2015 with fine new arched roof. Thomas Wyatt, 1863

### Severndroog Castle
- 🏃 Castle Wood, Shooters Hill, Greenwich, SE18 3RT
- ⏰ Sun 11am–4pm (max 30). T·R·P
- 🚇 Welling, Eltham
Grade II* listed triangular brick Georgian tower
sited in Oxleas Woods. Standing 63ft tall it offers
spectacular panoramic views across the capital. It
was built in 1784 by Lady Anne James in memory of
her husband Sir William James. Richard Jupp, 1784

### St Alfege Church, Greenwich
- 🏃 Greenwich Church Street, SE10 9BJ
- ⏰ Sat 10am–4pm/Sun 12pm–4pm (limited access
  after 1pm Sat, 2pm Sun) + tour of St Alfege Crypt,
  every 45 mins (1pm-4pm, max 16) d·T
- ❗ Pre-book only: bit.ly/2ufFAba
- 🚇 Cutty Sark, Greenwich
Magnificent English Baroque church, Grade I listed,
gutted by fire in 1941 and restored by Sir Albert
Richardson to original design. Many original
features. Burial site of Thomas Tallis, organist/
choirmaster (1505-85). Nicholas Hawksmoor, 1714

### Thames Barrier & Information Centre
- 🏃 1 Unity Way, SE18 5NJ
- ⏰ Sat/Sun 11am–3.30pm (max 40, no access onto
  the Thames Barrier structure). T·R·P·d
- 🚇 North Greenwich, Charlton
Information centre sited by the Thames Barrier,
with a working model of the Barrier, films about its
construction and exhibition explaining its past,
present and future. Rendel, Palmer and Tritton, 1984

### The Conservatoire, Blackheath
- 🏃 19-21 Lee Road, SE3 9RQ
- ⏰ Sun 10am–5pm + architect-led tours of spaces,
  (10.30am & 2pm, max 25) + family architecture
  workshop at 11am (max 20). T·R·d
- 🚇 Blackheath
Part of the oldest surviving purpose-built cultural
complex in London, founded by the community
through the purchase of bonds. Arguably the finest
in London, the main art studio possesses generous
space and a magnificent north light. John Edmeston
and Edward Gabriel, 1896

### The Fan Museum
- 🏃 12 Crooms Hill, SE10 8ER
- ⏰ Sat 10am–5pm. T·R·D
- 🚇 Maze Hill, Greenwich
Carefully restored Grade II* listed Georgian town
houses, retaining many principal architectural
features, including elegant façades and panelled
rooms. Now houses the UK's only museum devoted
to the history of fans and craft of fan making. John
Savery, 1721

### The Keep
- 🏃 The Keep, Blackheath, SE3 0AG
- ⏰ Sun resident-led tours of grounds and selected
  houses, hourly (11am-4pm, max 6).
- 🚇 Blackheath

↦

A development of 44 'T2' Span houses built in 1957 by Eric Lyons on the Cator Estate.

## Tump 53 Nature Reserve
🚶 Bentham Road, Thamesmead, SE28 8AS
🕐 Sun 11am–3.30pm + launch of Tump 53. T·d
🚇 North Greenwich, Abbey Wood
A former munitions testing site which has been reclaimed for nature. The site now contains mixed woodland, a glade, and a pond, and is surrounded by a reed-fringed moat.

## University of Greenwich, Stockwell Street
🚶 Stockwell Street, Greenwich, SE10 9BD
🕐 Sat/Sun 10am–4pm (max 20, no access to roof gardens) + hourly tours.
🚇 Cutty Sark, Greenwich
The building features a limestone exterior designed to 'complement but not mimic' the surrounding historical architecture, whilst behind the façade is a 4-storey composition of steel, glass and exposed concrete. Heneghan Peng Architects, 2014

## Woolwich Arsenal Clock Tower
🚶 Duke of Wellington Avenue, SE18 6SS
🕐 Sat/Sun 2pm-5.45pm, Conservation engineer's tour of history and restoration, every 20 mins, (max 20), no access to clock mechanism. D
🚇 Woolwich Arsenal
When the historic clocktower suffered near total destruction, Ramboll's conservation engineers employed rigorous analysis, salvage testing and traditionally detailed replacements allowing over 85% of the original materials to be reinstated.

## Woolwich Town Hall
🚶 Wellington Street, Woolwich, SE18 6PW
🕐 Sat/Sun 10am–5pm (Victoria Hall, council chamber, committee rooms, public hall. Tours Sat only). T·d
🚇 Woolwich Arsenal
Florid Edwardian Baroque. Domed entrance hall, grand staircase and stained glass windows, a great example of civic architecture of the time belonging to the Classical tradition rather than the Gothic Revival favoured outside London. Alfred Brumwell Thomas, 1906

## Walks + Tours

### Emirates Air Line tour
🚶 Meet: Emirates Cable Car Terminal, Edmund Halley Way, SE10 0FR
🕐 Sat/Sun 10am, 11am, 12pm (max 20), includes travel on cable car, entry to Aviation Experience Museum, in-flight guide).
🚇 North Greenwich, Charlton
Tour exploring the civil engineering achievements of the construction of the cable car. Led by the Emirates Air Line engineers and front-of-house team. Wilkinson Eyre Architects, 2011

## Thamesmead's Landscape and Hidden Spaces
🚶 Meet: Tump 53 Nature Reserve, Bentham Road, Thamesmead, SE28 8AS
🕐 Sun 2pm
🚇 North Greenwich, Abbey Wood
A tour through Thamesmead's landscapes, including some less well-known hidden spaces. Led by Peabody's Director of Landscape, Dr Phil Askew.

## The Progress Estate
🚶 Meet: The Progress Hall, Admiral Seymour Road, Eltham, SE9 1SL
🕐 Sun 2pm (max 20).
🚇 Eltham
The first and most spectacular of the garden suburbs built during the First World War (ref: Pevsner), constructed in less than 12 months in 1915 to accommodate some of the senior and skilled workers in the vastly expanded Woolwich Arsenal. HM Office of Works, 1915

The Conservatoire, Blackheath ↘

# Hackney

| | |
|---|---|
| **⊕ Hackney** | |
| Borough area (km²) | 19.1 |
| Population | 274,300 |
| Average age | 33 |
| First Open House | 1993 |

## 24 St John's Church Road
🚶 24 St John's Church Road, E9 6EJ
🕐 Sat 1pm–5pm/Sun 10am–5pm (max 30) + architect-led presentation every 20 minutes. T·R·d
🚇 London Fields, Hackney Downs
Gracefully refurbished Victorian terrace introducing the UK's first heated clay ceiling system. Natural and reclaimed materials complement original features throughout. Modern extension with sedum roof. Silke Stevens, 2014

## 29 Malvern Road
🚶 29 Malvern Road, E8 3LP
🕐 Sat/Sun 11am-5pm, ½ hourly architect-led tours (max 10).
🚇 London Fields, Dalston (Kingsland)
Refurbishment and extension of a Victorian House, featuring a glazed roof rear extension, generous high ceiling new basement with sunken garden and passive energy strategy with air tight construction and well insulated external envelope. Vercelli Cohen Architects, 2016
*www.vercellicohenarchitects.com*

## 30 Crown Place
🚶 30 Crown Place, EC2A 4ES
🕐 Sat/Sun 10am-4pm (max 20) + hourly tours. T·D
🚇 Liverpool Street
Striking 16-storey glass landmark office building with 3 terraces. An unusual form with a distinctive profile. Sustainable features include PV cells at roof level and ground floor geo-thermal heat source. Horden Cherry Lee Architects, 2009

## 52 Whitmore Road
🚶 52 Whitmore Road, N1 5QG
🕐 Sat 10am-5pm (private residential space not accessible). D
🚇 Old Street
This mixed use building on Regent's Canal illustrates capabilities of the cross laminated timber structure. The vast columnless, double height photography studio which stretches 9mx23m will be open, as will the canalside walkway and deck. Waugh Thistleton Architects, 2012

## Adelaide Wharf
🚶 118/120 Queensbridge Road (at junction Whiston Road), E2 8PD
🕐 Sat 10am-2pm (max 15). D
❗ Pre-book only: info@firstbase.com
🚇 Liverpool Street
A mixed tenure residential scheme with some workspace extruded into a prototype block. Façade is layers of larch making reference to warehouses of packing crates that once occupied the site. RIBA Winner 2008. Allford Hall Monaghan Morris, 2008

## Arcola Theatre
🚶 24 Ashwin Street, E8 3DL
🕐 Sat/Sun 10am-5pm + ½ hourly tours (front of house and backstage) with history of site and developments in Sustainability (10am-1pm, max 15). T·R·D
🚇 Dalston (Kingsland), Dalston Junction
Multi-award winning professional theatre housed in the Reeves and Sons 1868 Artist's Colour Works. Renovation focused on sustainability and features include minimal intervention, large scale materials reuse and renewable energy technology. Edward Henry Horne, 1868

## Barge House
🚶 46a DeBeauvoir Crescent, N1 5RY
🕐 Sat 10am-10pm/Sun 10am-5pm (max 50) + 'Print Parlour' Salon Series (max 50). T·R·d
❗ Pre-book only: www.bargehouse.co.uk/whatson
🚇 Liverpool Street, Haggerston
A bijoux venue with Canal Side Bar, Mezzanine & Lounge. On site of an ex-print house, double-height ceilings, natural wood interiors are contrast with heavy industrial steel work to create an impressive contemporary environment. Kyson Design Ltd, 2011

## Barrett's Grove (Spruce Apartments)
🚶 42 Barrett's Grove, N16 8AJ
🕐 Sat hourly architect-led tour (1pm-4pm, max 10).
❗ Pre-book only: bit.ly/2uH8aob
🚇 Dalston (Kingsland)
Six units in a building constructed using Cross-laminated timber, which provides a sustainable alternative to concrete and steel. RIBA London

↪

Award 2017 and RIBA National Award 2017. Amin Taha Architects, 2016

## Black Stone Building
🚶 70a Mountgrove Road, N5 2LT
🕐 Sat/Sun 10am–5pm (architect on site) T·R
🚇 Arsenal, Finsbury Park
The concrete framed structure of this apartment building adjusts to its irregularly shaped corner plot. Exposed beams and columns support lime-washed interiors and a scratched stucco façade forms an abstract expression to the street. 6a Architects, 2016

## Broadway Market Mews
🚶 12 Broadway Market Mews, E8 4TS
🕐 Sat 10am–5pm (max 8) + tours every 90 mins (11am–4pm, max 15).
🚇 Cambridge Heath, Bethnal Green
The conversion, reappropriation and extension of an existing brick warehouse into 3 flats retaining commercial use at ground level. The project includes 3 different roof forms and takes a complementary approach to the existing building. Rivington Street Studio Architecture, 2016

## Bruno Court, The German Hospital
🚶 10 Fassett Square, E8 1BF
🕐 Sun 10am-12.30pm ½ hourly resident-led tours, (max 20, access to lobby, stairwells, roof terrace and communal garden). T
🚇 Hackney Downs, Dalston Junction
Modernist extension to Hackney's German Hospital, closed 1987 and converted into flats in 1999. Burnet, Tait and Lorne, 1935

## Clonbrock Road
🚶 33 Clonbrock Road, N16 8RS
🕐 Sun 10am–1pm (max 20)
🚇 Canonbury, Dalston Junction
Internal reconfiguration, refurbishment and 2-storey front brick cantilevered extension to 1957 yellow stock residence plus new roof extension. Lipton Plant Architects, 2014

## Coal House
🚶 West & Coal House entrance: new river path via Lordship Road, N16 5HQ
🕐 Sat/Sun 9am–4pm (max 20) T·R·D
🚇 Manor House, Stamford Hill
A haven for wildlife and people in Hackney: reed-fringed ponds and dykes with a heritage café. Allen Scott Associates and Kaner Ollette, 2015

## Cut Glass Studio Ltd
🚶 The Briggs Building, 2-4 Southgate Road, N1 3JJ
🕐 Sat/Sun 10am–5pm (max 5).
🚇 Highbury & Islington, Angel
Large factory building adjacent to Regents Canal. London Yellow brick. Constructed early 1800, original use tent manufacturers to Ministry of Defence. Now used as artist studios. Thomas Briggs London Limited, 1815
*www.cutglassstudio.co.uk*

## Dalston Eastern Curve Garden
🚶 13 Dalston Lane, E8 3DF
🕐 Sat/Sun 12pm–10pm + tours about history and design of garden every 90 mins (1pm-5pm). T·R·D
🚇 Dalston (Kingsland), Dalston Junction
Popular community garden in area lacking in green public space, created on abandoned railway land. Wooden pavilion & 'Pineapple House' structures. Hackney Design Award Winner 2010 & 2011, Landscape Institute President's Award 2011. J&LGibbons, EXYZT, Muf Art and Architecture, 2010

## De Beauvoir Road
🚶 92 - 96 De Beauvoir Road, N1 4EN
🕐 Sat 1pm–5pm (max 20, external spaces, rooftop terraces and studios) + architect-led tours, every 40 mins. T·D
🚇 Liverpool Street, Haggerston
De Beauvoir Block is a new development of inspirational workspaces, designed for businesses in the creative industry. Characterful Victorian warehouses with recent addition of rooftop studio/offices and external central courtyard. Henley Halebrown, 2016

## Flat in Hackney
🚶 175 Graham Road, Flat 1, E8 1PD
🕐 Sat 10am–5pm (max 10, ground floor only)
🚇 Hackney Downs, Bethnal Green
New glass side extension that floods the internal accommodation with natural light. Internal patio that allows for ventilation and light into the property. CCASA Architects, 2016

## Frampton Park Baptist Church & Housing
🚶 Frampton Park Road, E9 7PQ
🕐 Sat 10am–5pm/Sun 10am–1pm. T·R·D
🚇 Hackney Central, London Fields
New church and community facilities with three new residential blocks on a post-war council estate. Matthew Lloyd Architects LLP, 2015

## Gallery House Hackney
🚶 12 Chesholm Road, N16 0DR
🕐 Sat 10am–5pm (max 15, no access to loft bedroom) + architect-led tour of extension, every 20 mins.
🚇 Highbury & Islington, Dalston Junction
Side extension to an existing Victorian house with a light filled gallery space and includes a new loft space clad in black zinc. The project has a rich palette of materials which contribute to the warm and unique atmosphere of the home. Neil Dusheiko Architects, 2016
*www.neildusheiko.com*

## Hackney Empire
🚶 291 Mare Street, E8 1EJ
🕐 Sat tour at 9am (max 25, duration 45 mins). T
ⓘ Pre-book only: hackneyempire.co.uk ↱

Here East ↗

Here East, a 1.2 million square foot technology and creativity campus, includes flexible work spaces, large scale studios and large event venue. Explore communal spaces and onsite businesses such as Plexal and UCL. Hawkins\Brown, 2017
*hereeast.com*

### Hoxton Hall
🚶 130 Hoxton Street, N1 6SH
🕐 Sun 11am–6pm. T·R·d
🚇 Liverpool Street, Hoxton
Unique surviving Grade II* listed Victorian saloon-style music hall dating from 1863. Additional rooms and spaces added by Quakers in 1910, with current frontage added 1980. Lovegrove & Papworth, 1863

### Kingsland Basin Moorings (CHUG)
🚶 Kingsland Basin Moorings (via towpath), N1 5BB
🕐 Sun 12pm–5pm (Access to moorings and communal areas, plus individual boats). T·R·d
🚇 Angel, Dalston Junction
Small is beautiful: 6ft narrowboats provide individual design solutions for living and working in confined conditions. The self-managed moorings are a unique community with shared open spaces, offering a glimpse of alternative urban living. 1984

### Macdonald Wright Architects
🚶 Unit EG1, 24 Hertford Road, N1 5QT
🕐 Sat 10am–5pm (max 35) + Caring Wood: Models, drawings and film by MWA and RoA. T·D
🚇 Highbury & Islington, Haggerston
Studio is a fit-out of an historic industrial building on Kingsland Wharf. Bleached redwood joinery is used throughout the interior for both fitted and loose furniture. Macdonald Wright Architects, 2016

### Mossbourne Community Academy
🚶 100 Downs Park Road, E5 8JY
🕐 Sat 10am–1pm (max 50) + student-led tour of the site's special points of interest, every 45 mins + exhibition of current Art and Design Technology student work. T·R·d
🚇 Hackney Downs, Hackney Central
One of the largest timber-framed buildings in the UK, configured as a broad 'V' with access from a covered cloister. Its focus is the generous external space to the North. RIBA Award Winner 2005 and Civic Trust Awards Winner 2006. Rogers Stirk Harbour + Partners, 2004

### Pembury Circus
🚶 Pembury Road, Hackney, E8 1JG
🕐 Sat 10am–4pm hourly architect-led tours (max 20). T·D

🚇 Bethnal Green, Hackney Central
Exuberant Grade II* listed auditorium and the most perfect example of Edwardian variety theatre remaining in London. Refurbishment restored the interiors added to the fly-tower and provided new back-stage areas. Frank Matcham, 1901

### Hackney New School
🚶 317-319 Kingsland Road, E8 4DL
🕐 Sat 10am–1pm (main hall, typical classrooms, music and art rooms, bridges) + architect-led tour of building, every 45 mins (max 20). T·D
🚇 Haggerston
A mixed-ability Free School with a focus on music, combining a 500 pupil secondary school and 200 pupil sixth-form. The brick buildings frame a series of precincts between the neighbouring streets and the canal basin. Henley Halebrown, 2015

### Hackney Town Hall
🚶 Mare Street, E8 1EA
🕐 Sun 11am–5pm (max 20, no access to office space) + hourly tours. T·D
🚇 London Fields, Bethnal Green
Grade II listed Neo-Classical building of Art Deco style, built in 1937 to designs by Lanchester and Lodge. Hawkins\Brown Architects have led the recent refurbishment and restoration programme, completed in 2017. Lanchester & Lodge, 1934

### Haggerston School
🚶 Weymouth Terrace, E2 8LS
🕐 Sat 2pm–6pm + hourly tours (max 10). D
🚇 Hoxton
Grade II listed secondary school, containing some of Goldfinger's boldest and most handsome public interiors. Includes bush hammered concrete and coffered ceilings in the entrance and assembly hall block. Refurbished in 2012. Ernö Goldfinger, 1963

Hackney Downs, Hackney Central
Award-winning car free mixed use development of 268 high quality homes for all ages. Including older peoples accommodation, a vibrant community centre and commercial space, a new public square and play area. Fraser Brown MacKenna, 2015

### Restored Historic Almshouse at the Geffrye Museum
🚶 136 Kingsland Road, E2 8EA
🕐 Sat 10am–4.30pm (max 14) + object handling. T·B·d
🚇 Liverpool Street, Old Street
Grade I listed restored 18C almshouse, which has been taken back to its original condition and offers a rare glimpse into the lives of London's poor and elderly in the 1780s and 1880s. Richard Halsaul and Robert Burford, 1714

### Rio Cinema
🚶 107 Kingsland High Street, E8 2PB
🕐 Sat 10am–12.30pm/Sun 10am–1pm (max 50) + photography exhibition of the cinemas history and other Dalston cinemas. T·R·d
🚇 Dalston (Kingsland), Dalston Junction
Grade II listed Art Deco cinema with stalls and circle created in 1937 within the shell of an Edwardian cinema, retaining many original features. George Coles, 1915

### Rivington Place
🚶 69 Rivington Street, EC2A 3BA
🕐 Sat 12pm–7pm + tour at 2pm (max 20). T·B·D
🚇 Liverpool Street, Shoreditch High Street
First permanent visual arts space dedicated to global diversity, inspired by African art and architecture as well as contemporary art and music. RIBA Award Winner 2008. Adjaye Associates, 2007

### Scenario House
🚶 50 Alconbury Road, E5 8RH
🕐 Sat 10am–1pm/Sun 1pm–5pm + architect-led tours Sat 1pm, Sun 5pm (max 15).
⚠ Pre-book tours only: info@scenariorchitecture.com (please specify which tour)
🚇 Stoke Newington, Rectory Road
Renovation and extension of a Victorian terrace house, adapting it contemporary lifestyle. Architects own home, this house presented them with the opportunity to test their architectural methods and 'practice what they preach'. Scenario Architecture, 2016
scenarioarchitecture.com

### Scoble Place
🚶 25 Scoble Place, N16 7TS
🕐 Sun 1pm–5pm (max 15)
🚇 Hackney Downs, Dalston (Kingsland)
Covered in striking vertical larch cladding, this modern house is sympathetic to surrounding Victorian terraces and 60's apartments. The living area and kitchen are sunken to maximise light without compromising neighbours. Designcubed, 2016

### Shoreditch Town Hall
🚶 380 Old Street, EC1V 9LT
🕐 Sun 10am-4pm, ½ hourly tours (max 20). T·R·d
🚇 Moorgate, Hoxton
A magnificent Grade II listed building housing many contrasting spaces from the grand assembly hall to the untouched rabbit warren of basement rooms. Caesar Augustus Long, 1866

### St Augustine's Tower
🚶 The Narroway, off Mare Street, E8 1HR
🕐 Sat/Sun 11am–5pm. R·B·d
🚇 Hackney Downs, Bethnal Green
Grade I listed, remaining tower of medieval parish church, with working late 16C clock. New exhibition of Hackney's history. Extensive views from roof. (Organised by Hackney Historic Buildings Trust).

### St Mary of Eton Church Mixed Use Development
🚶 95 Eastway, Hackney Wick, E9 5JA
🕐 Sat/Sun 12pm–4pm (no access to apartments). T·D
🚇 Hackney Wick
Refurbished Grade II* listed church with new community facilities and new housing. 2015 RIBA Award, New London Architecture Award, Housing Design Award. Bodley & Garner, Matthew Lloyd Architects LLP, 1892

### Studio Wayne McGregor
🚶 Broadcast Centre, Here East, 10 East Bay Lane, Queen Elizabeth Olympic Park, E15 2GW
🕐 Sat 10am–5pm (max 50). T·D
🚇 Stratford International, Stratford
The home of Wayne McGregor CBE and his creative collaborations, Studio Wayne McGregor comprises three dance studios, including two of the largest in London, and a series of playful spaces in which to collaborate, make and create. We Not I, 2017
waynemcgregor.com

### Suleymaniye Mosque
🚶 212 Kingsland Road, E2 8AX
🕐 Sat/Sun 10am–6pm (max 75, main prayer hall and ladies prayer hall only) + hourly tours. T·R·P·d
🚇 Liverpool Street, Haggerston
6-storey building with Western exterior and traditional Islamic interior, modelled on the Blue Mosque in Istanbul. Networld Project Management, 1996

### Sweetdram
🚶 Unit G1B1, Stamford Works, 3 Gillett Street, N16 8JH
🕐 Sat 10am–1pm (max 10). T·d
🚇 Old Street, Dalston (Kingsland)
A 1000ft² double-height industrial print works transformed into Sweetdram's headquarters. SODA designed a monolithic joinery wall that creates a highly flexible space incorporating workstations, offices, a copper still, and tasting bar. SODA, 2016

### The Antepavilion Rooftop Initiative
🚶 55 Laburnum Street, E2 8BD ↱

Macdonald Wright Architects © Heiko Prigge ↗

### Village Underground
🚶 54 Holywell Lane, EC2A 3PQ
🕐 Sat 11am–6pm (max 50, access via a spiral staircase. No access to venue below). T
🚇 Liverpool Street, Shoreditch High Street
Recycled tube train carriages make affordable artists' studios on reclaimed land on top of an abandoned railway viaduct. Auro Foxcroft & Nicolas Laurent, 2007

### Widebeam Narrowboat - Juniper Island
🚶 Haggerston Wharf, Regents Canal, Kenning Terrace, N1 5PP
🕐 Sat/Sun 11am-4pm hourly tours (max 10), owners on hand for questions.
🚇 Hoxton, Old Street
This Widebeam Narrowboat, moored on the Regents Canal in Hoxton, is a cosy, well-thought out home as well as an example of how this 250yr old format can be approached in a new way using modern technology and materials. Jo Davies & Matthew Booth with Dave Clark Boat Builders Ltd, 2014

🕐 Sat 10am–1pm/Sun 10am–5pm (max 50, access via a staircase to the rooftops). T
🚇 Old Street, Liverpool Street
A canal-side collection of industrial buildings that play host to a series of experimental rooftop architectural structures: The Beach House, Flood House, Wikkel House and this years Antepavilion competition winner HVAC by PUP Architects. The Antepavilion Commission, Shiva Limited, PUP Architects, The Architecture Foundation, 2017

### Vex
🚶 85 Maury Road, N16 7BT
🕐 Sat 1pm–5pm (max 25).
🚇 Rectory Road, Stoke Newington
A new curving fluted concrete house with sound/music by 'Scanner'. Chance de Silva, 2016

## Walks + Tours

### Hackney's Timber Buildings - Walking Tour
🚶 Meet: outside Murray Grove building, near the carpark, N1 7FB
🕐 Sat 10.30am.
🚇 Old Street, Hoxton
Hackney has a cluster of timber buildings just a short walk apart. This is an opportunity to view three of them in the company of Andrew Waugh. The tour will start at Murray Grove, go on to Bridport Place and end at Whitmore Road.

Studio Wayne McGregor © Richard Davies ↘

# Hammersmith & Fulham

| | |
|---|---|
| Borough area (km²) | 16.4 |
| Population | 185,300 |
| Average age | 36 |
| First Open House | 1996 |

h&f
hammersmith & fulham

### 184 Shepherds Bush Road
🚶 184 Shepherd's Bush Road, London, W6 7NL
🕐 Sat 9am–5pm (max 10, ground floor only) +
architect-led tour of 1st floor every 45 mins
(max 10). T·D
🚇 Hammersmith
Once a Ford garage, the Grade II listed building
comprises 115,000 sqft of office space, set over 6
floors. Sensitively designed, the building is housed
in an innovative glass dome, blending heritage and
modern design. McLaren Group, 1916/ColladoCollins
Architects (refurb), 2016

### Bridget Joyce Square, Community Rain Park (SuDS)
🚶 Australia Road, W12 7PH
🕐 Sat/Sun 10am–5pm (max 30) + designer-led
tours of the park and rainwater management
(SuDS) features, ½ hourly + Sustainable
Drainage (SuDS) demonstration model · Live rain
sculpture demonstration · Permeable paving
demonstration. T·R·D
🚇 Shepherd's Bush Hammersmith & City, East Acton
A public landscape with community needs at its
heart that also manages rainwater to reduce flooding
and pollution. Walk the 'wiggly wall' between trees
and grassy basins that store rain or watch the
'rain sculptures' in the raingardens. Robert Bray
Associates, 2015
*www.robertbrayassociates.co.uk*

### Bulwer Yard
🚶 27 Bulwer Street, W12 8AR
🕐 Sat 1pm–5pm (max 6). T·d
🚇 Shepherd's Bush
3-storey courtyard building finished in hydraulic
lime render with recycled blue glass aggregate – a
material discovered on an 18C façade in Prague.
Adams + Collingwood Architects, 2005

### Bush Theatre
🚶 7 Uxbridge Road, W12 8LJ
🕐 Sat 10am–1pm/Sun 10am–5pm (limited access
to backstage areas) + ½ hourly tours of building
with Bush Theatre staff, (max 15) T·B·D
🚇 Shepherd's Bush, Paddington

Former Victorian library designed in the
English Renaissance style and commissioned by
philanthropist John Passmore Edwards - the second
most prolific architect of public libraries prior to
WW1. Redeveloped in 2016 and reopened March 2017.
Maurice B. Adams, 1895

### Colet House
🚶 151 Talgarth Road, W14 9DA
🕐 Sun 10am–5pm (top studio - first floor, east and
west studios - ground floor) + hourly history talk
10.30am–3.30pm. T·R·B·d
🚇 Barons Court, Kensington Olympia
Unique building for artists with three large studios,
all with north light through expansive windows.
Fairfax B Wade-Palmer, 1885

### Emery Walker's House
🚶 7 Hammersmith Terrace, W6 9TS
🕐 Sun 2pm–5pm (max 10, downstairs and garden
only)
🚇 Stamford Brook
The home of Emery Walker, printer, antiquary and
mentor to William Morris. A unique Arts and Crafts
domestic interior. Furnishings by Philip Webb and
William Morris, 1750

### Fulham Palace
🚶 Bishop's Avenue, SW6 6EA
🕐 Sun 11am–5pm (general access to public rooms
only) + garden tour at 2pm (max 15) · Tours of
upstairs offices (10.30am & 11.30am, max 10)·
hourly tours of public rooms & Jessie Mylne
Education Centre (12pm-4pm, max 30). T·R·B·d
🚇 Putney Bridge, Putney
Former residence of the Bishop of London until 1973.
Tudor red-brick courtyard with Georgian additions
and Butterfield Chapel (1867). Walled garden. Two
HLF funded restoration projects completed; a third is
due to commence late 2017. Stiff Leadbetter, 1766

### Greenside Primary School
🚶 Westville Road, W12 9PT
🕐 Sun 12pm–5pm (access to hall, foyer, corridor,
one classroom, playground and garden) +
architectural tours including Gordon Cullen

184 Shepherds Bush Road © Eugene Codjoe ↗

mural, every 20 mins + 'Bouncing off the Wall!' 20C Graphic arts fair· Talk relating to post war Britain at 1pm · James Dunnett on 'Goldfinger after Greenside: the years of fulfilment' at 2pm (James Dunnett is a Goldfinger expert and was his last Architectural Assistant). T·R·D
🚇 Ravenscourt Park, Shepherd's Bush
One of only two schools designed using Ernö Goldfinger's school building system - precast reinforced concrete frame with brick infill. Fine, top-lit mural by Gordon Cullen, restored 2014. Grade II* listed. Ernö Goldfinger, 1952

### Kenneth Armitage Foundation
🚶 22a Avonmore Road, W14 8RR
🕐 Sat 11am–6pm/Sun 11am–2pm + new work by David Murphy and Catherine Aitken. T·d
🚇 West Kensington, Kensington Olympia
House and studio built by Arts and Crafts. Once the residence of sculptor Kenneth Armitage, since 2005 occupancy of the house and studio has been offered as a biennial sculpture fellowship. James M MacLaren, 1888

### Koestler Arts Centre – Former Governor's House of HM Prison Wormwood Scrubs
🚶 168a Du Cane Road, W12 0TX
🕐 Sat 10am–5pm. T·R·P·d
🚇 East Acton, Acton Central

The Koestler Trust is the UK's leading prison arts charity, based in the governor's house in the gates of HMP Wormwood Scrubs. Paintings, drawing and sculpture, all for sale, cover walls and plinths throughout the three-storey building. Edmund Du Cane, 1891

### LAMDA (London Academy of Music & Dramatic Art)
🚶 155 Talgarth Road, W14 9DA
🕐 Sun 10am–5pm + ½ hourly student-led tours (10.30am-4:30pm) T·R·d
🚇 Hammersmith, Barons Court
LAMDA's home since 2003. Victorian building with more recent extensions, including a new £28.2m centre for world-leading drama training which opened in June 2017. Facilities include three theatres, rehearsal studios and technical spaces. John Salmon Quilter, 1894

### Maggie's Centre
🚶 Charing Cross Hospital, Fulham Palace Road, W6 8RF
🕐 Sat 11am–2pm (max 40, downstairs only) T·R·D
🚇 Barons Court, Hammersmith
RIBA award-winning space designed to be welcoming and uplifting. The raised roof allows natural light to enter the whole of the building. Partitions divide ↦

up the structure, placing the kitchen at the heart of the building. Rogers Stirk Harbour + Partners, 2008

### Roca London Gallery
🚶 Station Court, Townmead Road, SW6 2PY
🕐 Sat/Sun 11am–5pm + Sat tour at 12pm, 3pm (max 30) T·D
🚇 Fulham Broadway, Imperial Wharf
A space inspired by the various phases or states of water, offering a unique visual and interactive experience with Roca, the leading global bathroom brand. Zaha Hadid Architects, 2011
*www.rocalondongallery.com*

### The Hurlingham Club
🚶 Ranelagh Gardens, SW6 3PR
🕐 Sat tours 11am & 3pm (meet 15mins before at the main gate. No admittance at any other time). T·d
🚇 Putney Bridge
Last of the grand 18C mansions which once fronted this part of the river, with magnificent interiors and extensive grounds. Dr William Cadogan, 1760

### Tin House
🚶 Smugglers Yard, Devonport Road W12 8PB
🕐 Sat 10am–1pm + furniture exhibition. T·D
🚇 Shepherd's Bush
Making efficient use of an irregular urban site, this house is made up of interconnecting top-lit pavilions arranged to define a serene private courtyard. Henning Stummel Architects, 2015

### White City Place
🚶 201 Wood Lane, W12 7TU
🕐 Sat/Sun 10am–5pm + architect-led tour at 11am (max 30). T·D
🚇 Shepherd's Bush, White City
Buildings built in the 90s and early 00s for the BBC are now being recycled to accommodate multiple new users, from the Royal College of Art to new corporate tenants. Subtle and radical interventions are making the transition possible. Allies and Morrison, 2004

### William Morris Society - Kelmscott House
🚶 26 Upper Mall, W6 9TA
🕐 Sat 11am–5pm (max 50, basement and Coach House only). T·B·d
🚇 Hammersmith, Ravenscourt Park
Residence of Sir Francis Ronalds, George MacDonald and (from 1878-96) William Morris. Organised by William Morris Society.

Roca London Gallery ↘

# Haringey

| | |
|---|---|
| Borough area (km²) | 29.6 |
| Population | 278,000 |
| Average age | 35 |
| First Open House | 1994 |

### 6 Wood Lane
🚶 6 Wood Lane, N6 5UB
🕐 Sat 10.30am–6pm/Sun 10.30am–5.15pm (max 10) + architect led tour, every 45 mins. T
🚇 Highgate
A double height ark floats above the entrance bridge and masonry base. A smoker's balcony off the elevated lounge overlooks the lush garden below. Above a sun-kissed semi circular terrace and winter garden nestles within the tree canopy. Birds Portchmouth Russum, 2016

### 19 Mayfield Road
🚶 19 Mayfield Road, Crouch End, N8 9LL
🕐 Sun 10am–5pm (downstairs and garden only). P
🚇 Finsbury Park, Harringay
This project aimed to open up the kitchen to the garden, creating a seamless transition with minimum impact. Kitchen and garden are intended to feel as one space, enabling greater use of both areas for multiple functions. Luis Trevino, 2012

### 101 Stapleton Hall Road
🚶 101 Stapleton Hall, N4 4RH
🕐 Sat 1pm–5pm (ground floor and garden only).
🚇 Harringay, Finsbury Park
This house has been remodeled and extended on the ground floor, creating a lovely, open plan, light filled, family space, opening out on to the rear garden. Knott Architects, 2016

### 639 Tottenham High Road
🚶 639 Tottenham High Road, N17 8AA
🕐 Sat 11am–2pm. T·D
🚇 Seven Sisters, Bruce Grove
Grade II listed. Former gas showroom built in 1901 in attractive neo Jacobean style. Damaged during 2011 riots, now fully refurbished by GLA and managed by London Youth Support Trust as Enterprise Centre and support for local community. Sergison Bates, 2012

### A kitchen on wheels in Wood Green
🚶 24 Dorset Road, N22 7SL
🕐 Sat 10am–5pm.
🚇 Alexandra Palace
A modest Victorian railway cottage remodelled to give flexibility between cellular rooms for day to day activities and a larger living area when required. Turner Architects, 2016

### Alexandra Palace
🚶 Meet at South Terrace, by Ice Rink Entrance, Alexandra Palace Way, N22 7AY
🕐 Sat 10am–4pm basement tour, ½ hourly (max 15, basement tours do not have step free access. Sturdy shoes required. Visitors over 16 only.) T·P
❗ Pre-book only: bit.ly/2tm83KU
🚇 Wood Green, Alexandra Palace
Alexandra Palace opened in May 1873 as a public centre of recreation, education and entertainment and has had many uses since then. Tours will visit the basement and will focus on WWI, when the Palace was used as an internment camp. John Johnson & A Meeson, 1873

### Allison Road
🚶 53 Allison Road, N8 0AN
🕐 Sat 10am–5pm (max 15).
🚇 Manor House, Harringay
A sensitive renovation of a Victorian terraced house to create a home for a young family, including a generous extension to accommodate a contemporary kitchen/diner with unique utility space/cloak room/WC arrangement. Trevor Brown Architect, 2016

### Blue House Yard
🚶 5 River Park Road, N22 7TB
🕐 Sat 10am–5pm (access to studios and private workspaces at the discretion of tenants. All common areas accessible) T·d
🚇 Wood Green, Alexandra Palace
A collection of new creative workspaces. Framed by a bright blue refurbished studio complex, nine tall, slender standalone worksheds and a double-decker bus café, the Yard will be a much-needed social space in Wood Green. Jan Kattein Architects, 2017

### Bruce Castle Museum
🚶 Lordship Lane, Tottenham, N17 8NU
🕐 Sat/Sun 1pm–5pm (max 25) + ½ hourly tours and specialist talks about refurbishment of Grade I building + hourly bite-sized classical music ↪

performance · children's historical dressing-up activities at 1pm (max 20) + Sun architectural/panorama artist gallery talk at 2.30pm (talk accompanies exhibition by Gabriela Schutz) T·R·P·B·d
🚇 Seven Sisters, Bruce Grove
Tudor Manor House built for Sir William Compton in 1514, substantially altered in 17C and 18C. A museum since 1906 housing local history & exhibitions of Bruce Castle, and Haringey area.

## Furtherfield Gallery
🚶 McKenzie Pavilion, Finsbury Park, N4 2NQ
🕐 Sat/Sun 11am–5pm + exhibition
🚇 Manor House, Harringay Green Lanes
The McKenzie Paviliion is named after landscape designer Alexander McKenzie, who produced plans for Finsbury Park, which opened in 1869. It sits in the centre of the park by the boating pond, playground and Victorian Flower Garden.

## Green Rooms
🚶 13-27 Station Road, Wood Green, N22 6UW
🕐 Sat 1pm–5pm (lobby, bar, restaurant) + tour with architect at 1pm & 3pm. T·R·d
❗ Pre-book only: info@greenrooms.london
🚇 Wood Green, Alexandra Palace

A hotel in a striking early Art Deco building, built in 1925 for The North Metropolitan Power Board. Clean modern lines and expressed copper services contrast with decaying ceiling features, exposed brick and original marble. SODA, 2016

## Hale Village
🚶 Meet: outside Tesco Express N17 9NE
🕐 Sat tour at 11am
🚇 Tottenham Hale
New high-density waterside development with green design features including bio mass and green roofs. Includes residential for sale and rent, student accommodation and range of community facilities. BDP, 2008

## Highgate School Chapel, Big School, Museum & Highgate Junior School
🚶 North Road, N6 4AY
🕐 Sat 11am–2pm. d·T·R
🚇 Archway, Highgate
Highgate is three schools in one: founded by Sir Roger Cholmeley, Lord Chief Justice of England, in 1565, it is governed as a single charitable foundation. F P Cockerell, 1865-7/Architype (junior school), 2016

Blue House Yard © Jan Kattein Architects ↘

Omved Gallery, Gardens ↗

### Lacey House
🕴 11 Hermiston Avenue, N8 8NL
🕐 Sat 10am–1pm (max 15, access to kitchen
extension and garden only).
🚇 Hornsey

Patterned red brick extension to a Georgian terraced house for a textiles designer. Bricks have been laid in a Flemish bond with protruding headers to create the 'lacy Brick' pattern. Pamphilon Architects, 2016

### Markfield Beam Engine and House
🕴 Markfield Road, South Tottenham, N15 4RB
🕐 Sat/Sun 11am–5pm + steam demonstrations
12.30pm, 2pm, 3.30pm. T·R·P·B·D
🚇 Seven Sisters, South Tottenham

Grade II listed Victorian industrial building set within a park and next to the River Lea, with the original Wood Bros beam pumping engine in situ, as originally installed. Recently restored Engine and Engine House.

### Omved Gardens, Gallery
🕴 Townsend Yard, Highgate, N6 5JF
🕐 Sat 10am–5pm (max 60) T·d
🚇 Archway, Highgate

The project aims to explore the possibilities of this forgotten piece of the city, and how it could be rediscovered and re-appropriated by introducing a series of small scale interventions. HASA Architects, 2017

### Oxford Road
🕴 27 Oxford Road, Stroud Green, N4 3HA
🕐 Sat 1pm–5pm/Sun 10am–1pm (max 25). T
🚇 Crouch Hill, Finsbury Park

Rear/infill extension with a sequence of uses, each defined by changes in ceiling pattern: exposed larch beams shift orientation from the rooflit dining space to window seat/living area, and flow externally to a sheltered pergola space. Chance de Silva, 2017

## St Augustine of Canterbury
🚶 Corner Archway Road & Langdon Park Road, N6 5BH
🕐 Sat/Sun 10am–5pm + ½ hourly tours. R·D
🚇 Archway, Upper Holloway
High Victorian church with early 20C additions, restored after fire in 1924. Fine Hunter organ plus case. Imposing, sculptured west front and features stained glass by Margaret Aldridge Rope. J D Sedding, Henry Wilson, J Harold Gibbons, A G Scott, 1888

## St Paul's, Harringay
🚶 Wightman Road, N4 1RW
🕐 Sun 2pm–6pm (max 50, access to organ gallery only when accompanied by a volunteer. No access to sacristy/crypt) + children's history trail at 2pm (max 50, Informal history trail. Sheets available to pick up from the welcome desk.). T·R·P·d
🚇 Harringay Green Lanes, Manor House
Extraordinary building, based on a Mycenaean 'megaron' design, contains work by Stephen Cox (altar, font, reredos), John Makepeace (alms box) and Danny Clahane and Anton Wagner (statues). Inskipp and Jenkins, 1993

## The Old Schoolhouse
🚶 Hornsey Historical Society, 136 Tottenham Lane (corner Rokesly Ave), N8 7EL
🕐 Sun 11am–4.30pm (max 15, main school room) + The Victorian Infants' School exhibition. B·d
🚇 Finsbury Park, Hornsey
Small, early Victorian infant school, closed in 1934, and after conversion and some demolition re-opened in 1981 as HQ of Hornsey Historical Society. Sir John Taylor, 1848

## Tottenham Town Hall
🚶 Approach Road, N15 4RY
🕐 Sat 11am–6pm.
🚇 Seven Sisters, South Tottenham
Complete refurbishment of Grade II listed town hall, rescued from English Heritage 'at risk' register, now returned to its former glory. Restored grand foyer and Moselle Room with stunning Moorish-Jacobean style ceiling. AS Taylor & AR Jemmett, 1904

## Tower and Churchyard of St Mary's Hornsey
🚶 High Street Hornsey, N8 7NT
🕐 Sun 2pm–5pm (max 15) + tour of the tower from crypt to roof/self guided tomb and tree tours in the Churchyard, every 15 mins. R
🚇 Turnpike Lane, Hornsey
Grade II* listed tower with restored chapel remaining from Medieval parish church. Tour includes crypt, ringing chamber & main roof with excellent extensive views in all directions. Organised by Friends of Hornsey Church Tower.

# Walks + Tours

## Muswell Hill Walk
🚶 Meet: Queen's Avenue, beside Muswell Hill Library, N10 3PE
🕐 Sat 2pm (max 45). T·R
🚇 Highgate, Alexandra Palace
Tour takes in early and late Victorian, Edwardian and 1930s buildings, and gives an historical interpretation of how a rural enclave changed into a unique Edwardian suburb. Finishes North Bank, Pages Lane, with an illustrated talk.

## Tottenham Green Conservation Area
🚶 Meet: Sun 11am outside Old Tottenham Town Hall, Town Hall Approach Road, N15 4RY
🕐 Sun 11am. T
🚇 Seven Sisters, Tottenham Hale
External tour of buildings including 18C Georgian houses, 19C Jewish Hospital, Prince of Wales Hospital and Holy Trinity Church, ancient High Cross Monument, Edwardian Town Hall complex, housing developments and Bernie Grant Arts Centre.

## Tottenham High Road Regeneration Tour
🚶 Meet: Seven Sisters station (outside exit 1), N15 4RR
🕐 Sat 11am (max 30)
🚇 Seven Sisters
Completed and planned public realm improvements and reuse of vacant sites along Tottenham High Road - part of the Tottenham Regeneration Programme. You & Me Architects, Adams and Sutherland Architects, Landolt & Brown, Tom Ebdon Architects, 2014

Lacey House © Vicky Bamforth Photography ↘

# Harrow

| | |
|---|---|
| Borough area (km²) | 50.5 |
| Population | 252,300 |
| Average age | 38 |
| First Open House | 1996 |

*Harrow*COUNCIL
LONDON

BUILDING A **BETTER**
HARROW

## Canons Park
🚶 Donnefield Avenue entrance, Edgware, HA8 6RH
🕐 Sun 10am–5pm (max 20) + hourly tours led by a member of the Friends of Canons Park. T·R·D
🚉 Edgware, Mill Hill Broadway
Grade II listed historic park landscape containing several listed buildings, including an 18C 'temple' building, bothy and compound, and walled kitchen garden, converted in 1937 to an informally planted garden by Harrow Council.

## Church of St Lawrence, Little Stanmore
🚶 Whitchurch Lane, Edgware, HA8 6RB
🕐 Sun 1pm–5pm. P·d
🚉 Edgware, Canons Park
Unique Continental Baroque church rebuilt in 1715 by James Brydges, first Duke of Chandos. Painted walls and ceiling with trompe-l'oeil effect. Wood carvings by Grinling Gibbons and the organ on which Handel played. John James, 1715

## Former Grosvenor Cinema, now Zoroastrian Centre For Europe
🚶 440-442 Alexandra Avenue, Harrow, HA2 9TL
🕐 Sat 11am–5pm + hourly tours + ½ hourly talks on Zoroastrian heritage. T·R·P
🚉 Rayners Lane
Grade II* listed Art Deco building with well-preserved interior. Auditorium with deep coved ribs; proscenium arch flanked by fluted columns. F E Bromige, 1936

## Harrow School: Old Schools, Fourth Form Room
🚶 Old Schools, Church Hill, Harrow-on-the-Hill, HA1 3HP
🕐 Sun 2pm–5pm + tours every 20 mins (max 35).
🚉 South Harrow, Harrow & Wealdstone
Best preserved 17C schoolroom in the country. Wainscot panelling, benches, tables and chairs. Original fireplace replaced in 1730, oriel window inserted in 1820. Walls carved with names of every Harrow pupil until 1847. Sly, 1615

## Harrow School: Old Speech Room Gallery
🚶 Old Schools Church Hill, Harrow-on-the-Hill, HA1 3HP
🕐 Sun 2pm–5pm (max 35)
🚉 South Harrow, Harrow & Wealdstone
Purpose built room intended for the teaching of public speaking which figured prominently in the classical curriculum. Converted 1976 by Alan Irvine into modern gallery with mezzanine floor.
C R Cockerell, 1819

## Paxfold House
🚶 47 Elizabeth Gardens, Stanmore, HA7 4UG
🕐 Sat 10am–4pm (max 15) + hourly tours (11am-3pm, max 10). T·R·P·D
🚉 Stanmore
A low energy sheltered scheme and affordable housing scheme for older people. Owned and managed by Harrow Churches Housing Association (HCHA). Includes solar thermal and PV panels.
TM Architects, 2015

## Pinner House
🚶 Church Lane, Pinner, HA5 3AA
🕐 Sat 10am–4pm (downstairs and first floor communal rooms). T·R·d
🚉 Pinner
Grade II* listed early Georgian house with pilastered front and magnificent oak-panelled dining room. Former rectory of the vicar of Harrow and Nell Gwynne's daughter by Charles II.

## Seven Acre Lake, Canons Park Estate
🚶 Rose Garden Close, off Canons Drive, Edgware, HA8 7RF
🕐 Sun ½ hourly resident-led tours (1pm-4.30pm, max 6). P·d
🚉 Canons Park, Edgware
Private 18C Seven Acre Lake, part of the dismantled Canons Mansion grounds, now surrounded by 1930s character housing. Wildlife includes Canada geese, swans and ducks. William Kent, 1720

## St Alban Church
🚶 The Ridgeway, North Harrow, HA2 7PF
🕐 Sat 9.30am–12.30pm/Sun 12pm–5pm. T·P·D
🚉 North Harrow, Harrow On The Hill
Notable 1930s Grade II listed church with Swedish and German influences externally. Landmark tower. ↥

Stepped tunnel - vault with arches to side aisle walls giving a light lively interior. Marquetry panelling to Lady Chapel. Arthur Kenyon, 1936

### St Panteleimon Greek Orthodox Church
🚶 660 Kenton Road, Harrow, HA3 9QN
🕐 Sat/Sun 11am–6pm. T·P·B·D
🚇 Kingsbury
Built in traditional Byzantine style with dome and cross shape, the materials and form reflect a past era whilst meeting current building and thermal efficiency requirements. Internal superstructure including mezzanine floor and dome. Neo Architects, 2011

## Walks + Tours

### Harrow Civic Centre Regeneration Walk and Talk
🚶 Meet: at benches outside 140 Station Road, Harrow, HA1 2RH

🕐 Sat hourly tours (10am-4pm, max 30).
🚇 Harrow On The Hill, Harrow & Wealdstone
Harrow Council's £1.75bn Heart of Harrow Regeneration Programme is underway. There will be a 60min walking tour of key sites including a workshop held by public realm designers We Made That and an exhibition at Whitefriars artist studios. *www.buildingabetterharrow.co.uk*

### Modernism in Metroland
🚶 Meet: outside Stanmore tube station, London Road, Stanmore, HA7 4PD
🕐 Sat 10am & 2pm
🚇 Stanmore
A walking tour of Stanmore's Art Deco and modernist homes, from the birth of metro-land to the post-war era. Douglas Wood/Gerald Lacoste/Owen Williams/R.H Uren/Rudolf Frankel

Paxfold House ↘

# Havering

| | |
|---|---|
| Borough area (km²) | 112.3 |
| Population | 254,300 |
| Average age | 40 |
| First Open House | 1998 |

**64 Heath Drive**
- 🚶 64 Heath Drive, Gidea Park, Romford, RM2 5QR
- 🕐 Sat/Sun 2.30pm–5.30pm (max 12, guided tours of whole house). T·R·P·d
- 🚉 Hornchurch, Gidea Park

Model modernist villa now completely refurbished with modern garden by Dan Pearson. Grade II listed. Unsuitable for children under 7. Lubetkin & Tecton, 1934

**Bower House**
- 🚶 Orange Tree Hill, Havering-atte-Bower, Romford, RM4 1PB
- 🕐 Sat 10am–4pm + tours every 15 mins from 11am. T·R·P·B·d
- 🚉 Romford

Grade I listed country house commanding the most extensive southerly views over Essex. Staircase mural by Sir James Thornhill, a painter notable for the 'Painted Hall' at the Royal Naval Hospital at Greenwich. Set in grounds with a pond. Henry Flitcroft, 1729

**Elm Park Primary School**
- 🚶 Elm Park, South End Road, Hornchurch, RM12 5UA
- 🕐 Sat/Sun 1pm–5pm. T·R·P·D
- 🚉 Elm Park

Bright, spacious award winning school, providing flexible spaces to accommodate a range of activities. The 2-storey building has a sedum grass roof with classroom spaces opening onto a double-height shared 'heart' space. Walters & Cohen Architects, 2011

**Havering Museum**
- 🚶 19-21 High Street, Romford, RM1 1JU
- 🕐 Sat 10am–5pm. T·B·D
- 🚉 Dagenham East, Romford

A cultural centre in part of the old Romford Brewery building near to the historic market place. Permanent and temporary exhibition displays tell the story of the London Borough of Havering from Bronze Age to present day. TTSP Architects, 2010

**Ingrebourne Valley Visitor Centre**
- 🚶 Hornchurch Country Park, Sqaurdrons Approach, Hornchurch, RM12 6DF
- 🕐 Sat/Sun 9am–5pm + Historical/Military Weekend. T·R·P·d
- 🚉 Romford, Elm Park

The centre is a partnership project between Essex Wildlife Trust and Havering Council. Built on a former RAF base in Hornchurch Country Park. The centre overlooks the River Ingrebourne Valley.

**Langtons House**
- 🚶 Billet Lane, Hornchurch, RM11 1XJ
- 🕐 Sun 10am–5pm (max 25, downstairs only) + tours of the house & gardens. T·D
- 🚉 Hornchurch, Emerson Park

Grade II listed neo-Georgian house with later additions. Landscaped garden with lake, orangery and gazebo.

**Noak Hill Sports Complex**
- 🚶 Noak Hill Road, Romford, RM3 7YA
- 🕐 Sat/Sun 10am–5pm (no access to staff areas). T·R·P·D
- 🚉 Hornchurch, Romford

Opened in January 2017 on the old Broxhill school site, the New Noak Hill sports complex was built by Havering Council and managed by everyone active. The main building has been refurbished and extended to a high standard.

**Rainham Hall**
- 🚶 The Broadway, Rainham, RM13 9YN
- 🕐 Sat 11am–4pm (max 15, ground and first floor access only). T·R·B
- 🚉 Rainham

Grade II* listed 18C house and garden built for a merchant. The Hall features fine wrought-iron gates, carved porch, and interior paneling. Opened fully in 2015 following renovation project, with a new café and exhibition programme.

**Romford Town Hall**
- 🚶 Main Road, Romford, RM1 3BD
- 🕐 Sat 12pm-3.30pm, ½ hourly tours (max 20, main rooms on the first floor of the building). T·D
- 🚉 Hornchurch, Romford

Grade II listed. Unique fittings using Bath stone, red cedar wood and Tasmanian oak, with full-height entrance hall and tall central staircase window and flagpoles. HR Collins & AEO Geens, 1935

## Thames Chase Forest Centre
🏃 Broadfields, Pike Lane, Upminster, RM14 3NS
🕐 Sat/Sun 10am–5pm + Sunday craft market at
   10.15am . T·R·P·B·D
🚇 Upminster
Distinctive award-winning visitor centre of modern timber sustainable construction forming an A-frame building roofed with cedar shingles, attached to 17C listed barn - one of the best preserved in the London area. Laurie Wood Architects, 2005

## The Queen's Theatre
🏃 Billet Lane, Hornchurch, RM11 1QT
🕐 Sat 1pm–5pm + hourly backstage tours (2pm-4pm,
   max 25) · Childrens backstage treasure hunt
   (ages 4-10) at 2pm & 4pm (max 20). T·R·P·d
❗ Pre-book only: 01708 443333
🚇 Hornchurch, Emerson Park
Opened by Sir Peter Hall, a robust example of 1970s civic architecture and a vibrant and successful producing theatre. Norman Brooks, 1975

## The Round House
🏃 Broxhill Road, Havering-atte-Bower, Romford,
   RM4 1QH
🕐 Sun tours at 10.30am, 12pm, 2pm, 3.30pm
   (max 15). T·P

❗ Pre-book only: michaelheap26@googlemail.com
🚇 Romford
Grade II* listed late Georgian elliptical 3-storey stuccoed villa. Attributed John Plaw, 1792

## Upminster Old Chapel
🏃 The Old Chapel, Saint Marys Lane, RM14 2QR
🕐 Sun 3pm–6pm. T·R·P·d
🚇 Upminster Bridge, Upminster
Grade II timber-framed former Dissenters' Meeting House (1800) with pedimented façade. Two blank windows flank the Doric entrance porch.

## Upminster Tithe Barn Museum
🏃 Hall Lane, Upminster, RM14 1AU
🕐 Sat/Sun 10.30am–4pm. P·D
🚇 Upminster
15C box-framed, 9-bay, aisled barn, weatherboarded with crown-post, collar-tie reed-thatched roof. Ancient monument. Kent Barn Builders, 1450

## Upminster Windmill Visitor Centre
🏃 Mill Field, St Mary's Lane, Upminster, RM14 2QL
🕐 Sat/Sun 10am–5pm (max 20, Workshop viewing
   only). T·P·D
🚇 Upminster, Upminster Bridge
Modern visitor centre with a living green roof. The building contains an education room and workshop. The visitor centre was built over the the old mill house.

64 Heath Drive ⬊

# Hillingdon

| | |
|---|---|
| Borough area (m²) | 115.7 |
| Population | 301,000 |
| Average age | 36 |
| First Open House | 1995 |

### Battle of Britain Bunker & Visitor Centre
- Wren Avenue, Uxbridge, UB10 0RN
- Sat/Sun 10am–5pm. T·P
- Pre-book only: 11gpenquiries@btconnect.com
- Hillingdon, Uxbridge

The Bunker, built in 1939 and today restored to its wartime state, controlled the RAF fighters that won the Battle of Britain. Its new visitor centre is due to open in early 2018 but visitors will be able to have a 'sneak preview'.

### Cranford Stable Block & St Dunstan's Church
- Cranford Park, The Parkway, Cranford, TW5 9RZ
- Sat 10.30am–4.30pm/Sun 11.30am–4.30pm (max 20, church open between 12.30-4.30pm only). T·R·P·d
- Hounslow West, Hayes & Harlington

Restored 18C stable block of now demolished Cranford House, former seat of the Earl of Berkeley. The front has arches with stone keystones facing a cobbled yard.

### Eastcote House Gardens
- High Road Eastcote, Eastcote, HA5 2FE
- Sun 11am–6pm (no access to gallery in stables) + Classic Car Rally. T·R·d
- West Ruislip, Eastcote

Restored timber-framed 17C stables, 18C brick dovecote and large walled garden, all set in parkland of the former Eastcote House (dem. 1964). Family home of the Hawtrey family from 1527 to 1930. Interiors largely as originally constructed.

### Manor Farm Site, Manor House
- Manor Farm Site, Bury Street, Ruislip, HA4 8BD
- Sat/Sun 10am–5pm, entry Manor House, Great Barn (Sunday only) + tour at 2pm (max 15) + Norman settlement T·P·d
- West Ruislip, Ruislip

Oldest heritage site in Hillingdon, occupied since 11C. 16C Manor Farm House, with a modern interpretation centre. Grade II listed 13C Great Barn, second largest in the country. 16C Little Barn, now a library. Listed monument Norman Motte.

### St Martin's Church, Ruislip
- High Street, Ruislip, HA4 8DG
- Sat 10am–5pm/Sun 1pm–5pm. T·P·D
- Ruislip, West Ruislip

Church dates from 1250 with 15C additions and Victorian restorations. Grade II listed. Fine late medieval wall paintings and funeral hatchments.

### St Mary the Virgin Church
- High Street, Harmondsworth, UB7 0AQ
- Sat 10am–5pm (no access to church tower)/Sun 12pm–5pm. T·R·D
- West Drayton

Parts of the building date back to 11C, a fine Norman doorway and a Saxon sundial outside.

### St Mary's Church, Harefield
- off Church Hill, Harefield, UB9 6DU
- Sat 10am–5pm/Sun 1pm–5pm (max 75). T·R·P·d
- Uxbridge

Exceptionally fine 12C medieval church, surrounded by large country churchyard, including Anzac Cemetery from WWI. Notable monuments including Lady Spencer, Countess of Derby. Fine 18C 3-decker pulpit. Grade I listed. The Newdigate Family, 1180

### St Peter & St Paul Harlington
- St Peter's Way, High Street, Harlington, UB3 5AB
- Sat/Sun hourly tours (11am-4pm, max 10) + history exhibition.
- Hatton Cross, Hayes & Harlington

Grade I listed church 16C with Norman font and Norman stone arch carved with cats' heads. Interesting monuments including Easter sepulchre. Ancient yew tree in churchyard. Good restoration between 1830 and 1860.

### Swakeleys Estate
- Swakeleys Road, Ickenham (access from Milton Road) UB10 8LD
- Sat/Sun 10am–5pm (house Sat only, grounds open both days).
- Uxbridge, West Ruislip

A most important house in Ickenham an outstanding example of Jacobean architecture built in the 1630s. Red brick construction laid in English bond on an H plan. Great Hall includes the 1655 Harrington Screen, 18C marble fireplace panelling.

The Great Barn, Harmondsworth ↗

### The Great Barn, Harmondsworth

🚶 Manor Court, High Street, Harmondsworth, UB7 0AQ
🕐 Sat/Sun 10am–5pm. P·B·D
🚇 West Drayton

The timbers of this great medieval barn (1426-7), over 190 feet long and nearly 40 feet high, are 95% original. Displays include the conservation/repairs carried out in 2014 and its place in the agricultural history of the village.

### Uxbridge Lido

🚶 Hillingdon Sports and Leisure Complex, Gatting Way, Uxbridge, UB8 1ES
🕐 Sat/Sun 10am–5pm (lido, Clive Hamilton suite). T·R
🚇 Uxbridge

This 1930s 'Moderne Art Deco' designed lido was refurbished in 2010 to include a £33m sports complex. It has closed down multiple times throughout its history but is currently much enjoyed by the public. G. P Trentham, 1935

### Uxbridge Quaker Meeting House

🚶 York Road, Uxbridge, UB8 1QW
🕐 Sat 10am–5pm/Sun 1pm-5pm (max 20) + ½ hourly tours by Uxbridge Quaker guides (max 10) + exhibition. T·R·D
🚇 Hayes & Harlington, Uxbridge

An early 19C meeting house, with a little-altered large meeting room, set within a garden, retains much of its original character and fabric, full-height shutters and the fixed seating in the elders' stand. Hubert Lidbetter, 1818

# Hounslow

| | |
|---|---|
| Borough area (km²) | 55.9 |
| Population | 274,200 |
| Average age | 36 |
| First Open House | 1995 |

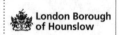

**London Borough of Hounslow**

## Adobe Village Hounslow Heath Infant and Nursery School

🏃 Martindale Road, TW4 7HE
🕐 Sat 12pm–4pm (grounds of school). T·R·P·D
🚇 Hounslow West, Hounslow

A unique striking playscape and adobe home structure that integrates outside learning with innovative earth forms. Construction is 'rammed' earth made from earth filled tubes. Adobe construction is recognised for sound reducing properties. Small Earth, 2011

## Boston Manor House

🏃 Boston Manor Road, Brentford, TW8 9JX
🕐 Sat/Sun 12pm–5pm + tours 12.30pm, 2pm, 3.30pm.
🚇 Boston Manor, Brentford

Jacobean Manor House set in parkland with lake and ancient trees. Richly decorated 17C plaster ceilings in State Rooms. Donald Insall, 1623

## Brentford Canal Toll House and Gauging Lock

🏃 Access off High Street, Brentford, TW8 8EE
🕐 Sat/Sun 10am–5pm.
🚇 Brentford

Single-storey canal toll house where tolls were collected for passing through the lock. Grand Junction Canal connected the Thames at Brentford to the Industrial Midlands in 1794 at the height of the industrial revolution.

## Chiswick House

🏃 Burlington Lane, W4 2RP
🕐 Sat 10am–6pm + tours (11am-3pm, max 20)/Sun tours (11am-3pm, max 20). T·R·P·B
🚇 Turnham Green, Chiswick

One of the earliest and finest examples of neo-Palladian design in the UK, Chiswick House is an 18th century villa in west London. The 65 acres of Grade I listed gardens are the birthplace of the English Landscape Movement. Lord Burlington, William Kent, 1727

Chiswick House © Richard Bryant ↘

## Fuller's Griffin Brewery
🏃 Chiswick Lane South, W4 2QB
🕐 Sun 10am–5pm (max 15, Brewery & Hock Cellar only) + pre booked guided tours, hourly (11am-3pm, max 15). T·R
❗ Pre-book only: 020 8996 2063
🚇 Turnham Green, Stamford Brook
The brewery has existed in its present form for almost 200 years and there has been a brewery on the site since the 17C.

## Gunnersbury Park & Museum
🏃 Gunnersbury Park, Popes Lane, W3 8LQ
🕐 Sat guided tours 10am & 12.30pm (max 30, Duration 90 mins) of the Large Mansion and heritage area of Gunnersbury Park. T·P
❗ Pre-book only: visitgunnersbury.org/open-house
🚇 Acton Town
Former home to the Rothschild family, now a local history museum set in beautiful 19C mansion on an elevated terrace overlooking lawns and parkland. Major restoration project is under way. Alexander Sedgley, 1802

## Hogarth's House
🏃 Hogarth Lane, Great West Road, W4 2QN
🕐 Sat/Sun 12pm–5pm (max 10) + hourly tours (1pm-4pm, max 10). T·d
🚇 Turnham Green, Chiswick
Early 18C red brick home of artist William Hogarth extended significantly c1749-1764. Delightful walled garden containing famous ancient mulberry tree. A unique oasis in modern west London.

## Kempton Great Engines Trust
🏃 Kempton Park Water Treatment Works, Snakey Lane, Hanworth, TW13 7ND
🕐 Sat/Sun 10am–5pm + ½ hourly tours (max 8). T·R·P·B
Magnificent Art Deco building (1927) housing two 1,000-ton triple expansion steam pumping engines, one restored and working. Also on site are two steam turbines and one of the UK's only working pair of Mercury Arc Rectifiers plus other equipment.

## Osterley Park House
🏃 Jersey Road, Isleworth, TW7 4RD
🕐 Sat/Sun 11am–5pm. T·R·P·B·d
🚇 Osterley, Isleworth
Osterley Park and House is one of the last surviving country estates in London. Late 18C redesign by Robert Adam for the Child family. It was a party palace for entertaining friends and clients, fashioned for show. Robert Adam, 1761

## Spring Grove House (West Thames College)
🏃 London Road, Isleworth, TW7 4HS
🕐 Sat 10am-4pm (ground floor rooms only) + tour every 45 mins. T·R·P·D
🚇 Hounslow East, Isleworth
Example of late Victorian architecture and interior design, including stained glass windows and mosaics.

Grade II listed. Previous owners include Pears 'Soap' family and Sir Joseph Banks. Restored and refurbished 2011-12. Sir John Offley, 1754

## St Mary's Convent
🏃 10 The Butts, Brentford, TW8 8BQ
🕐 Sat guided tours at 10am, 12pm, 3pm of the historic sections, modern chapel, and heritage rooms (max 8, duration 1.5 hours; includes historical talk). T·P·d
❗ Pre-book only: 0208 568 7305
🚇 Northfields, Brentford
Convent in 18C Grade II listed house, c1764-1792, with original features including fine decorative plasterwork. Various additions including west wing (1913-15), and harmonious care home facilities and chapel by PRP Architects (1998-2001).

# Walks + Tours

## Bedford Park
🏃 Meet: at Victorian Society (garden), 1 Priory Gardens, W4 1TT
🕐 Sun 2.30pm.
🚇 Turnham Green
Bedford Park is known as the first garden suburb. Buildings by R Norman Shaw, E J May, Maurice B Adams, and CFA Voysey. Some 400 houses, in Queen Anne Revival style. A landmark in suburban planning. Norman Shaw, EW Godwin, EJ May and Maurice B Adams, 1875

## Hounslow Open House Guided Cycle Tour
🏃 Meet: Turnham Green Station, W4 1LR
🕐 Sat 12.45pm (max 25). T·P·d
❗ Pre-book only: hounslow@lcc.org.uk
🚇 Turnham Green
Guided architectural bike tour led by local Hounslow Cycle Campaign (HCC) group around Open House buildings in West London.

## Pauper to Patient - the Buildings
🏃 Meet: All Saints' Church, Church Street, Isleworth, TW7 6BE
🕐 Sun 3.30pm (max 25). T·R
🚇 Syon Lane, Hounslow East
Walking tour giving insight into the lives of wealthy and poor. From old cottages disguised by a Strawberry Gothic façade, 18C mansions, 19C charity school to decade old hospital with former work house block still in use.

## Spring Grove Estate Walk
🏃 Meet: at Isleworth Station, London Road, TW7 4BX
🕐 Sat 2.30pm.
🚇 Osterley, Isleworth
Planned as the first local speculative housing development by Henry Daniel Davies who in 1850 purchased the Spring Grove House estate, former home to botanist Sir Joseph Banks (now West Thames College, see separate entry).

# Islington

| | |
|---|---|
| Borough area (km²) | **14.8** |
| Population | **231,200** |
| Average age | **35** |
| First Open House | **1995** |

👑 ISLINGTON

## 56 Whistler Street
🚶 56 Whistler Street, N5 1NJ
🕐 Sat/Sun 10am–1pm.
🚇 Highbury & Islington, Arsenal
A transformation of a typical two-up, two down terrace into a modern, urban living space with a number of spaces within a small footprint and a passive environmental design. Coffey Architects, 2007

## AL_A Studio
🚶 14a Brewery Road, N7 9NH
🕐 Sat 10am–5pm (downstairs only). d
🚇 Caledonian Road, Caledonian Road & Barnsbury
AL_A, the architects for the V&A Exhibition Road Quarter, Central Embassy in Bangkok and MAAT, Lisbon, open their top-lit studio, formerly an Islington Council transport depot. AL_A, 2012

## Bennetts Associates Architects
🚶 1 Rawstorne Place, EC1V 7NL
🕐 Sat 10am–4pm + '30 images from 30 Years in Practice' exhibition . T·D
🚇 Farringdon, Angel
RIBA Award-winning architects' office combining a revitalised group of redundant industrial buildings and an 18C barn with new contemporary elements. Bennetts Associates with Baynes & Mitchell, 2002
www.bennettsassociates.com

## Bevin Court
🚶 Cruikshank Street, WC1X 9HA
🕐 Sat 10am-4pm tours every 90 mins (max 15). D
ⓘ Pre-book only: bit.ly/2twBw93
🚇 King's Cross St Pancras, Farringdon
One of London's hidden Modernist gems. Lubetkin's motto 'Nothing is too good for ordinary people' resonates through this building. Skinner, Bailey and Lubetkin, 1954

## Bunhill Heat and Power Energy Centre
🚶 Central Street, EC1V 8AB
🕐 Sat 10am-5pm (max 20) + tours every 20 mins (max 20). d
🚇 Barbican, Old Street
A ground-breaking decentralised energy scheme located in the south of the borough and part of Islington's wider strategy to reduce fuel poverty and yield financial and environmental benefits to the community. Tim Ronalds Architects, 2012

## Caledonian Park Clocktower
🚶 Market Road, N7 9PL
🕐 Sat 10am-3pm hourly tours (max 12, duration approx 50 mins. NB tower has very steep wooden stairs. High heels and flip-flops not allowed).
ⓘ Pre-book only: bit.ly/2twWa9q
🚇 Caledonian Road, Caledonian Road & Barnsbury
Opened in 1855 as centrepiece of the Metropolitan Cattle Market. The seven storey clock tower offers magnificent views over London. The original working clock mechanism by John Moore of Clerkenwell adds further interest. J.B. Bunning, 1850

## City, University London
🚶 Northampton Square, London, EC1V 0HB
🕐 Sat 10am-5pm + hourly tours of new main entrance and historic College Building (11am-4pm). T·R·D
🚇 Barbican, Farringdon
Grade II listed building in the Arts and Crafts style. College building has been prominent in Islington life throughout its history, surviving bomb damage in WW2 and a major fire in 2002. The refurbished 1960s main building will also open. EW Mountford, 1896
www.city.ac.uk

## Clay House
🚶 Flat 3, 14 Monnery Road, N19 5RZ
🕐 Sat 11am-2pm architect led-tours, every 45 mins (max 8). R
🚇 Archway, Gospel Oak
5 storey Victorian townhouse with top two floors created into a masionette. Interiors made from clay. Simon Astridge Architecture Workshop, 2016

## Finsbury Town Hall
Rosebery Avenue, EC1R 4RP
🕐 Sun 10am-5pm (max 10, ground and first floor only) + ½ hourly tours. T·D
🚇 Angel, Farringdon
Opened by Lord Rosebery, an ornate building with elegant décor influenced by the Art Nouveau ↑

movement. Notable rooms including the Great Hall with unique stained glass, antique mirrors and Clerkenwell Angel statuettes. C Evans Vaughan, 1895

### Florence Street
🏃 24 Florence Street, N1 2DX
🕐 Sat 10am–1pm (max 10, basement and ground floor only).
🚇 Highbury & Islington, Angel
A darkened brick tower and a glass volume create a kitchen and living room extension with garden views. Brick arches above the openings and the blind window are a playful reference to the Victorian residence. Gundry and Ducker Architecture, 2016

### Hugh Myddelton Primary School
🏃 Myddelton Street, EC1R 1YJ
🕐 Sat/Sun 2pm–6pm (max 18) + ½ hourly tours (max 6). T·D
🚇 Farringdon, Angel
Classrooms have been refurbished and external areas redesigned to maximise space for learning. A first floor cantilevered extension, gold timber cladding and contrasting cobalt blue render create a light and vibrant learning environment. Julian Sofaer, 1966

### Ironmonger Row Baths
🏃 1 Norman Street, EC1V 3AA
🕐 Sat/Sun 9am–6pm. T·R·P·D
🚇 Old Street
Grade II listed building, refurbished from May 2010 to November 2012. Original features, Turkish baths, laundry, swimming pool. Historical details of 1931 bath, maps and photos in a purpose built history room. AWS & KMB Cross, 1930

### Islington Micro Flat
🏃 Flat B, 23 Islington Park Street, N1 1QB
🕐 Sat 3pm–6pm + architect-led tour at 4pm/Sun 11am–2pm + architect-led tour at 1pm (max 4).
🚇 Highbury & Islington, Angel
A small open plan flat with bespoke furniture that adapts to space and function to accomodate the occupant's needs. Kitchen, dining, bathroom, two double beds, living, office & plenty of storage in 35 m2. Creative Ideas & Architecture Office (CIAO), 2016

### Islington Town Hall
🏃 Upper Street, N1 2UD
🕐 Sun tours at 12pm, 2pm. T·D
❗ Pre-book only: bit.ly/2uoBLAu
🚇 Angel, Essex Road
Grade II listed. Original Art Deco style interiors, staircases and the impressive council chamber. Original clocks, paintings and decorative panels have survived for nearly a century in this lovely municipal building. ECP Monson, 1922

### London Metropolitan Archives
🏃 40 Northampton Road, EC1R 0HB
🕐 Sat 10am–5pm (First floor public areas, visitor lounge and cloakrooms) + Archivist led tour of strong rooms and conservation studio, hourly (10.30am–4.30pm, max 10) + 'Building the archives' exhibition. T·d
❗ Pre-book only: openhouselma.eventbrite.co.uk
🚇 Farringdon, King's Cross
LMA's older building was built in the late 1930s for the Temple Press and has many original features. Purpose built extension in early 1990s for archival storage. Public rooms remodelled by Bisset Adams in 2000s. F W Troup, H R Steele, 1939

### Moreland Primary School
🏃 Moreland Street, Goswell Road, EC1V 8BB
🕐 Sat 10am–4pm architect-led tours of new build primary school, ½ hourly (max 20). D
🚇 Angel, Old Street
New built school to accommodate a 2-form intake (420 pupils in total), 56 place nursery and children's centre. The school includes recreation, training and support facilities, designed and mapped to meet the needs of the local community. Haverstock, 2016

### Newington Green Primary School
🏃 N16 8NP
🕐 Sat 10am–2pm + hourly tours.
🚇 Dalston (Kingsland), Canonbury
Reconfiguration and complete refurbishment of a 1950's school to create a new Early Years Wing, rationalise teaching spaces and significantly improve the thermal performance of the building.

### Oak Room, New River Head
🏃 New River Head, 173 Rosebery Avenue, EC1R 4UL
🕐 Sat/Sun 10am–5pm (max 15).
❗ Pre-book only: bit.ly/2uQa5az
🚇 Angel, Farringdon
Formerly boardroom of the 17C water house, the Oak Room is a fine late Renaissance room demonstrating the New River Company's wealth. 1697 carved oak interior, attributed to Grinling Gibbons, including overmantel and panels over the doors.

### Paxton Locher House
🏃 8-9 Clerkenwell Green, EC1R 0DE
🕐 Sat/Sun 10am–5pm. T·d
🚇 Farringdon
A unique modern courtyard house making brilliant use of a restricted site. A retractable glass roof gives wonderful natural light and opens the house to the sky in dry weather. Richard Paxton Architects, 1995

### Pollard Thomas Edwards (Diespeker Wharf)
🏃 Diespeker Wharf, 38 Graham Street, N1 8JX
🕐 Sat 11am–6pm. T·d
🚇 Angel, Essex Road
Conversion of a canalside Victorian warehouse, formerly a timberyard, into spacious offices, garden and glazed extension with one of the best waterside views in London.

### Priory Green
🏃 Hugh Cubitt House, 48 Collier Street, N1 9QZ

↦

Clay House © Nicholas Worley ↗

🕐 Sat 10am–4pm (no access to flats) + hourly tours (max 10, tours will start from The Secret Café.). T·D
🚇 King's Cross St Pancras, King's Cross
Modern movement estate, received Conservation Area status after extensive refurbishment by Peabody. Pioneering in use of concrete and some of the most sculptural stairways ever designed for social housing. Tecton & Lubetkin, 1957

### Sun Rain Room
🚶 5 Wilmington Square, WC1X 0ES
🕐 Sat 10am–12.30pm (max 25, ground floor, basement and garden only) + hourly architect-led tours of the building.
❗ Pre-book only: kate@tonkinliu.co.uk (Please put 'Open House London' as the subject line)
🚇 Euston
Set in a Grade-II listed Georgian townhouse, the Tonkin Liu Studio has been extended. Designed and built by the practice, an innovative timber roof and reflecting pool gathers the bouncing rain make this a good place to be on a bad day. Tonkin Liu, 2017

### The Bower Phase 1
🚶 207 Old Street, EC1V 9NR
🕐 Sat 10am–1pm (common parts and estate only) + ½ hourly architect-led tour. D
🚇 Old Street
Reinvention of a collection of underperforming 1960s buildings to create a coherent mix of workspace, ground floor retail/restaurants and new public realm. Allford Hall Monaghan Morris, 2016

### The Charterhouse (Chapel and Museum)
🚶 Charterhouse Square, EC1M 6AN
🕐 Sun 2pm–5pm. T·D
🚇 Farringdon, Barbican
Founded as a Carthusian Monastery in 1371, later sold as a Tudor mansion. Elizabeth I and James I both spent time here. In 1611 endowed as a school (now in Godalming) and almshouse, which it remains to this day.

### The Institution of Structural Engineers
🚶 47-58 Bastwick Street, EC1V 3PS
🕐 Sat/Sun 10am–5pm + activities for kids. T·R·D
🚇 Angel, Farringdon
The headquarters for the Institution of Structural Engineers celebrates a spirit of collaboration between architect, engineer and client, showcasing retrofit as a sustainable solution. Hugh Broughton Architects, 2015

### Union Chapel
🚶 Compton Terrace, N1 2UN
🕐 Sat 10am–4pm/Sun 11am–4pm + hourly historian-led tours of chapel (max 12). T·B·d
🚇 Angel, King's Cross
An architectural Grade I treasure that is home to a working church, an award winning venue, a unique organ and The Margins Project for those homeless and in crisis in London. James Cubitt, 1877

## Vantage Point

🚶 2 Junction Road, Archway, N19 5RQ
🕐 Sat/Sun 10am-6pm, tours every 2 hours (max 10). T·D
⚠ Pre-book only:
residentsteamvp@essentialliving.co.uk
🚇 Archway, Upper Holloway

A landmark new rental apartment building in north London. Designed for sharing, it boasts a range of communal areas, including a duplex penthouse social space on the top two floors providing panoramic views of London. GRID Architects, 2014
*www.essentialliving.uk.com*

## W. Plumb Family Butchers

🚶 493 Hornsey Road, N19 3QL
🕐 Sat 10am-7pm/Sun 10am-5pm (max 25, access to former shop only). D·R
🚇 Archway, Upper Holloway

Grade II listed, magnificent former Victorian butcher's shop c1900 with elaborate Art Nouveau wall tiling, geometric tiled floor, scrolled meat rails and mahogany cashier's booth with etched and brilliant cut glass. Very well preserved.

## White Collar Factory

🚶 1 Old Street Yard, Old Street, EC1Y 8AF
🕐 Sat/Sun 10am-5pm. T·R·D
🚇 Farringdon, Old Street

New office space that combines the wisdom of well-built industrial spaces with innovative design, sustainable principles, future-proof flexibility and panoramic views. It has achieved BREEAM Outstanding. Allford Hall Monaghan Morris, 2016

## four23 Studio

🚶 Berry House, Berry Street, EC1V 0AA
🕐 Sat/Sun 10am-5pm (access to studio space on 2nd floor only). T·d
🚇 Liverpool Street, Farringdon

Former precious metals workshop has been re-imagined by interior designer Harriet Paterson into a unique work and exhibition space for leading communication design studio four23. Frederick J Gibbons, 1937

# Walks + Tours

## Caledonian Park: Meat, Murder & Mayhem

🚶 Meet: Caledonian Park, Market Road, N7 9PL
🕐 Sat tours 11am, 2pm (max 20, meet at the base of the clocktower). D
⚠ Pre-book only: bit.ly/2gQwRcv
🚇 Caledonian Road, Caledonian Road & Barnsbury

Tour showing how Copenhagen Fields became Caledonian Park and how diplomacy gave way to debauchery and agitation and then butchery and commerce. J B Bunning, 1850

Moreland Primary School © John Kees Photography ↘

# Kensington & Chelsea

| | |
|---|---|
| Borough area (km²) | 12.1 |
| Population | 159,000 |
| Average age | 39 |
| First Open House | 1994 |

THE ROYAL BOROUGH OF
KENSINGTON
AND CHELSEA

## 3floor-in2 Apartment
🏃 17 Elgin Crescent, W11 2JD
🕐 Sun 3pm–6.45pm (max 33) + architect-led tour and introduction, every 20 mins.
🚇 Holland Park, Shepherd's Bush
This project unites two flats with the insertion of dramatic full height vertical space: a stair rises through three new minor levels that shape this new tall atrium. Sunlight beams diagonally through the previously shaded spaces. Andrew Pilkington Architects, 2013
*andrewpilkington.com*

## 18 Stafford Terrace – The Sambourne Family Home
🏃 18 Stafford Terrace, W8 7BH
🕐 Sat/Sun 3pm-6.30pm (max 30) + tour at 12pm (Saturday). T·B
🚇 High Street Kensington, Kensington Olympia
From 1875, the home of the Punch cartoonist Edward Linley Sambourne, his wife Marion, their two children and their live-in servants. Recognised as the best surviving example of a late Victorian middle-class home in the UK. Joseph Gordon Davis, 1871

## 155 Holland Park Avenue
🏃 155 Holland Park Avenue, W11 4UX
🕐 Sat/Sun 10am-4pm, tours every 45 mins (max 10, visitors may be asked to remove shoes)
🕐 Pre-book only: 02076022489
🚇 Holland Park, Shepherds Bush
An idiosyncratic tour of art and design as each room depicts different styles, ranging from Victorian Gothic to a maharaja's loo. A place of fabulous effects and fun, drawing inspiration from world travel.

## 264 Westbourne Park Road
🏃 264 Westbourne Park Road, W11 1EJ
🕐 Sat/Sun 10am-5pm (max 8, closed 12noon-3pm. Shoes off).
🚇 Westbourne Park, Paddington
New building as an urban accent – two independent houses atop each other. It draws from the tectonic composition of adjacent Victorian houses. Features include rain water harvesting, roof garden, solar water heating. Studio Bednarski, 2011

## Chelsea Academy
🏃 Lots Road, SW10 0AB
🕐 Sat 10am–1pm (max 30) + tour every 45 mins. T·d
🚇 Fulham Broadway, Imperial Wharf
One of a new generation of schools on a very tight urban space. The architectural language is classical, formal and restrained. Numerous energy-saving measures are incorporated. RIBA Award Winner 2011. Feilden Clegg Bradley, 2010

## Dana Research Centre and Library, Science Museum
🏃 Wellcome Wolfson Building, 165 Queen's Gate, SW7 5HD
🕐 Sat 11am–6pm (max 15, NB no access from the Science Museum itself. No access to the rest of the building). T·D
🚇 Gloucester Road, South Kensington
A world-class environment for academic research into the Museums' collections. A double layer of steel-perforated panels lines the double-height glazing that dominates the reading room, dappling sunlight to create an inspirational space. Coffey Architects, 2016

## Embassy of Slovakia
🏃 25 Kensington Palace Gardens, W8 4QY
🕐 Sat/Sun 10am–5pm (ground floor and mezzanine).
🚇 Notting Hill Gate
Modern Brutalist-style awarded by RIBA in 1971. The building of former Czechoslovak Embassy is made out of reinforced concrete panels, long glass rows of window with wooden partitions separating the interior spaces. Jan Bocan, Jan Sramek and Karel Stepansky, 1970

## Embassy of the Republic of Estonia
🏃 44 Queen's Gate Terrace, SW7 5PJ
🕐 Sat 10am-12pm, hourly tours (max 40, photo ID required for entry.) + Estonian design presentation and pop-up shop at 10am (max 40, Open 10am-1pm to those booked on tours). T·d
🕐 Pre-book only: rsvp.london@mfa.ee
🚇 Gloucester Road, High Street Kensington
Representing Neo-Classicist style characteristic of the mid-19C, many of the details of the house

Hidden House ↗

have been restored to their original splendour. The interior design is inspired by Estonian nature: swamps, lakes and forests. William Harris, James Matthews, 1859

### Goldfinger Factory, Trellick Tower
🏃 13-15 Golborne Road, W10 5NY
🕐 Sat 10.30am–6pm/Sun 11am–5pm. T
🚇 Ladbroke Grove, Paddington
Design, build and teaching social enterprise based in the ground floor of the Grade II* listed, Brutalist Trellick Tower. Combines a furniture showroom and a café on one floor and a woodworking workshop and teaching academy underneath. Ernö Goldfinger, 1972

### Grand Union Studios - The Ladbroke Grove
🏃 332 Ladbroke Grove, London, W10 5AD
🕐 Sat 10am–2pm (full access to commercial building. Access to common parts of residential building only, plus courtyard). D
🚇 Ladbroke Grove
Mixed use development on the former Grand Union Centre site in west London, including commercial and retail space, mixed-tenure residential units and shared amenity space with a striking public art piece by Martin Richman. Allford Hall Monaghan Morris, 2016

### Hidden House
🏃 39 Russell Garden Mews, W14 8EU
🕐 Sun 10am–5pm (max 15).
🚇 Kensington Olympia
A new build 2600 sq ft mews house as featured on Grand Designs. Four floors with a large basement living space and night club dance floor wrapped around a courtyard with a pond and waterfall. Sustainable features. Hogarth Architects, 2011

### Holy Trinity Church
🏃 146 Sloane Street (just off Sloane Square), SW1X 9BZ
🕐 Sat/Sun 10am–5pm + Arts and Crafts Festival. T·R·B·D
🚇 Sloane Square, Victoria
A sumptuous feast of Victorian stained glass and bold sacred sculpture at what Sir John Betjeman called the 'cathedral of the Arts and Crafts movement.'Work by William Morris, Edward Burne-Jones, William Blake and Christopher Whall. J D Sedding, Henry Wilson, 1888

### Institut francais du Royaume-Uni
🏃 17 Queensberry Place, SW7 2DT
🕐 Sat/Sun 11.45am–6pm (max 25) + hourly tours of the Art Deco building + exhibition. T·d ↦

🚇 Gloucester Road, South Kensington
1939 Art Deco listed (Grade II) building refurbished in 1950, then restructured and modernised in 2014. Contains an authentically classic cinema, private salons, multimedia library and bistro. Patrice Bonnet, 1939

## Moravian Close
🚶 381 Kings Road, SW10 0LP
🕐 Sat/Sun 1pm–5pm (max 100) + illustrated walk and talk (max 40) · Children's exploration activity of the Close. T·R·B·D
🚇 South Kensington, Clapham Junction
A former stable yard of Sir Thomas More's Chelsea estate, now an 18C Chapel, other buildings, and Burial Ground. Parts of the enclosing walls are Tudor in origin. E and M Gillick enhanced the grounds in the 20C.

## Peter Jones
🚶 Sloane Square, SW1W 8EL
🕐 Sat 10am–5pm/Sun 12pm-4pm + hourly tours (max 20) + exhibition. T·d
🚇 Sloane Square
Grade II* listed building, involving complex mix of new build and restoration. Britain's first ever curtain walling and listed features such as spiral staircase. Sloane Room has one of best views over Chelsea. RIBA Award Winner 2005. Crabtree, Slater & Moberley, 1936

## Royal Brompton Centre for Sleep
🚶 The Old Fire Station, South Parade, SW3 6EJ
🕐 Sat 11am–5pm (max 40) + hourly tours by Steven Appleby, hourly (11am-4pm, max 25). T·R·D
⚠ Pre-book only: bit.ly/2vs4CUv
🚇 South Kensington
Located within the refurbished old Brompton Fire Station. Artist Steven Appleby was commissioned to create a series of new artworks for the building's 'day' and 'night' areas. Robert Pearsall, 1892

## Royal Hospital Chelsea
🚶 Royal Hospital Road, SW3 4SR
🕐 Sat tours at 10am, 1pm, 2pm/Sun tours at 1pm, 2pm (max 40, duration 90-120 mins). T·R·d
⚠ Pre-book only: 020 7881 5493 (tours manager)
🚇 Sloane Square, Victoria
The hospital buildings are one of England's architectural glories, built in brick in the decades after the Great Fire of London and sitting in 66 acres of beautiful gardens. Sir Christopher Wren, Nicholas Hawksmoor, Sir John Vanbrugh, 1682

Grand Union Studios - The Ladbroke Grove © Rob Parrish ↘

Walmer Yard © Hélène Binet ↗

## Serpentine Pavilion 2017
🏃 Kensington Gardens, W2 3XA
🕐 Sat/Sun 10am–6pm. P·T·R·B·D
🚇 Lancaster Gate, South Kensington
Francis Kéré has been commissioned to design the Serpentine Pavilion 2017, responding to the brief with a bold, innovative structure that brings his characteristic sense of light and life to the lawns of Kensington Gardens. Diébédo Francis Kéré, 2017

## Silchester Estate
🏃 Freston Road, W10 6TT
🕐 Sat/Sun 10am–12pm hourly architect-led tours, (max 8). D
🚇 Latimer Road
New development of 112 mixed tenure homes, community and retail facilities delivered by Peabody and RBKC. Designed around a communal garden and integrating an existing 20-storey tower within a new urban block. Sculpture by Nathan Coley. Haworth Tompkins, 2016

## Sunbeam Studios, Ladbroke Hall
🏃 79 Barlby Road, W10 6AZ
🕐 Sat 1pm–5pm (max 30) + guided tours, hourly D·T
❗ Pre-book only: events@sunbeamstudios.com
🚇 Latimer Road, Ladbroke Grove
The showpiece of Clement-Talbot Automobile Works, the building housed the offices and turbine hall for the factory that built the first car in the world to go 100 miles in one hour. It stayed open through WW1 and WW2 as part of war efforts.

## The Ismaili Centre
🏃 1-7 Cromwell Gardens, SW7 2SL
🕐 Sun 10am–4pm + ½ hourly architectural tours of the building. T·d

🚇 South Kensington
Part of an international family of Ismaili Centres, a religious, cultural and social space for the Shia Ismaili Muslim community. The serenity of the entrance fountain to the roof garden reflects Muslim traditions in architecture and design. Casson Conder Partnership, 1983

## The Roof Gardens & Babylon Restaurant (formerly Derry & Toms)
🏃 6th Floor, 99 Kensington High Street (entrance on Derry Street), W8 5SA
🕐 Sun 9am–11am. T·R·D
🚇 Paddington, High Street Kensington
A fine example of 1930s architecture, now home to 1.5 acres of beautifully themed gardens with Spanish Garden, Tudor Garden and English Woodland Garden. The space has served as an escape from London for over 75 years. Bernard George, 1938

## Victoria and Albert Museum (V&A)
🏃 Cromwell Road, SW7 2RL
🕐 Sat/Sun tours 11am, 1pm (max 20). T·R·B
❗ Pre-book only: 02079422000
🚇 South Kensington, Victoria
Introducing the varied architecture of the V&A, allowing access to some areas usually closed to the public. New display 'Designing the V&A'. The latest building and restoration projects including Exhibition Road Quarter by architects AL_A. Francis Fowke, Henry Scott, Sir Aston Webb, 1856

## Walmer Yard
🏃 235 - 239 Walmer Yard, W11 4EY
🕐 Sat 10am-4pm tours every 2 hours (max 20). T
❗ Pre-book only: check website for details
🚇 Shepherd's Bush
The first residential building by architect and academic Peter Salter, developed by Crispin Kelly. The discreet and private set of four interlocking houses is the product of a decade of learning, thought and inspiration. Peter Salter, 2016

# Walks + Tours

## World's End Estate Walk
🏃 Meet: 16 Blantyre Street, World's End Estate, SW10 0DS
🕐 Sun tours 2.30pm, 4.30pm (max 50, access to all communal parts of the building and gardens. Access to view a residential property on the estate is not guaranteed). T·R·D
🚇 Earl's Court, Imperial Wharf
Designed by Eric Lyons and built in the 1970s the World's End Estate is a deliberate attempt to overcome many of the issues of previous high-rise developments and eliminate monotonous bland façades through alternative designs and materials. Eric Lyons, 1969

# Kingston

| | |
|---|---|
| Borough area (km²) | 37.3 |
| Population | 175,400 |
| Average age | 37 |
| First Open House | 2017 |

THE ROYAL BOROUGH OF
KINGSTON
UPON THAMES

## All Saints' Church
🚶 Market Place, Kingston Upon Thames, KT1 1JP
🕐 Sat 10am–4pm (max 200) + 2014 Restoration of All Saints (max 10, Images of the restoration project 2014-16). T·R·D
🚇 Kingston
Large church on site dating back 1000 years, where the first 7 Kings of England were crowned.

## Chestnut Road
🚶 26 Chestnut Road, Kingston upon Thames, KT2 5AP
🕐 Sat/Sun 10am–5pm (max 20, downstairs only). D
🚇 Kingston
This contemporary family home incorporates a 'Miami' inspired pink kitchen and dining area, complete with a gold, sparkly drinks bar, green tiles, and hidden planters. The WC is by far the smallest in the world. Lost and Found Architects, 2015

## Clover House
🚶 Kingston Hill, Kingston upon Thames, KT2 7JP
🕐 Sat 10am–2pm (max 10, ground floor and new bedroom) + tours every 20 mins. d
🚇 Norbiton
Extension to and renovation of 1964 house by Robert Stille. New 2 storey wing containing kitchen and master bedroom, bedroom added over living room. Internal re-arrangement + refurbishment to create warm and light-filled five bedroom home. Robert Stille, 1964

## Dorich House Museum
🚶 Kingston University London, 67 Kingston Vale, SW15 3RN
🕐 Sat 11am–5pm + Tour at 11.30am. T·P
🚇 Kingston, Putney
The former studio home (1936) of the Russian sculptor Dora Gordine and her husband the Hon. Richard Hare, a scholar of Russian art and literature.

## Fredrick W Paine Funeral Directors
🚶 24 Old London Road, Kingston upon Thames, KT2 6QG
🕐 Sat 10am–5pm/Sun 1pm–5pm (ground and first floor only). R
🚇 Kingston
The town's oldest firm of funeral directors has conducted funerals from these premises since 1908. The original interior is Grade II listed. The building also contains the Frederick W Paine Museum and the firm's archive.

## Guildhall and History Centre
🚶 High Street, Kingston upon Thames, KT1 1EU
🕐 Sat 10am–5pm (access to the History Centre) + History of Guildhall and the Magistrates Courts at 2.30pm (max 15). T·D
🚇 Kingston
Built in the Georgian style, the Guildhall brought together Kingston's administrative functions. Purpose built Magistrates Courts were included in the building, part of which are now home to Kingston History Centre. Maurice Webb, 1935

## Hillcroft College
🚶 South Bank, Surbiton, KT6 6DF
🕐 Sat/Sun Guided tour at 10.30am (max 10). T·P
🚇 Surbiton
A Victorian mansion house built in the 1860s for Frederick Bryant of Bryant and May Matches. The building is very typical of its time and retains many of its original features. Rowland Plumbe, 1877

## Ivy Conduit
🚶 Holy Cross Preparatory School George Road, Kingston upon Thames, KT2 7NU
🕐 Sat 11am–2pm.
🚇 Norbiton
Ancient conduit house built around the beginning of the 16C. Constructed by Cardinal Wolsey to help supply fresh water to Hampton Court Palace. Cardinal Wolsey, 1515

## Kingston Ancient Market Place
🚶 Market Place, Kingston upon Thames, KT1 1JS
🕐 Sat 10am–5pm/Sun 10am–1pm (pick up a hand-out at the Market House, the centrepiece of Kingston Ancient Market Place). d
🚇 Kingston
The RIBA award-winning design has diversified the use of the Kingston Ancient Market Place.

New perforated, cross-laminated timber market stalls are transformed into lanterns at night, together with high-quality, durable granite pavers. Tonkin Liu, 2014

### Kingston Museum
🚶 Wheatfield Way, Kingston upon Thames, KT1 2PS
🕐 Sat 10am–5pm + tour and history of the building at 10.30am. T·B
🚇 Kingston
A Carnegie-funded building attached to Kingston Library. Grade II listed. Holdings range from ceramics to topographical drawings. Alfred Cox, 1904

### Light play
🚶 29 St Georges Road, Kingston upon Thames, Surrey, KT2 6DL
🕐 Sat 1pm–5pm (max 5, downstairs only). T
🚇 Norbiton

A contemporary extension to a Victorian villa, connecting to the garden through pocket glass sliding doors and a slot roof light to filter light. Subtle lighting in niches and ceilings add warmth at night to the space and garden.

## Walks + Tours

### Surbiton History
🚶 Meet: outside Surbiton Train Station, Station Approach, Victoria Road, Surbiton, KT6 4PE
🕐 Sun 2.30pm (max 15).
ⓘ Pre-book only: local.history@kingston.gov.uk
🚇 Surbiton
Guided tour of historic Surbiton.

Kingston Ancient Market Place © Anthony Hurren ↘

# Lambeth

| | |
|---|---|
| Borough area (km²) | 26.81 |
| Population | 328,900 |
| Average age | 34 |
| First Open House | 1993 |

Lambeth

## 15b Herne Hill Road
🏃 15b Herne Hill Road, SE24 0AU
🕐 Sat/Sun 11am–5pm.
🚇 Brixton, Loughborough Junction
Renovation of flat in Victorian terrace house, creating new living area within restructured roof space using unusual and reclaimed materials, and retrofit of substantial insulation. Colin MacInnes, 2011

## 1a Woodland Road
🏃 1a Woodland Road, Crystal Palace, SE19 1NS
🕐 Sat 10am–5pm (max 6, access to whole flat plus Victorian yard with workshops made from found materials). R
🚇 Crystal Palace
Borrowed light streams into a compact 26m2 flat from unusually high roof windows. The interior is inspired by found or free materials, yet there has been no compromise on design or the need for functionality within the restricted space. Melinda Styles and Jon Storey, 2016
*www.swiftsyard.co.uk*

## BFI Mediatheque
🏃 BFI Southbank, Belvedere Road, South Bank, SE1 8XT
🕐 Sat 10.30am–5pm (max 30) + Talk by architect. T·D
🚇 Southwark, Blackfriars
BFI Mediatheque is the free digital service that provides curated storytelling of National Archive collections in a unique location. Dramatically transformed in 2017, the Mediatheque facility is accessible, colourful and welcoming to all. Cullinan Studio, 2017

## Brixton Windmill
🏃 Windmill Gardens, West end of Blenheim Gardens, SW2 5EU
🕐 Sat/Sun ½ hourly tour 1pm-4.30pm, (max 3, Duration 40 mins) · Short tours to first floor, every 20 mins (max 6) + Harvest Festival at 1pm Sunday. T·R·B
❗ Pre-book only: brixtonwindmill.org/visit
🚇 Streatham Hill, Brixton
One of very few windmills in London. Built 1816 when Brixton Hill was open fields and a working mill until 1934. Restored to working order 2011. NB. steep ladders, low beams, heavy machinery and confined spaces.

## Brockwell Lido, Brockwell Park
🏃 Dulwich Road, SE24 0PA
🕐 Sat 10am–1pm/ Sun 1pm–5pm (max 30) + ½ hourly tour (10.15am-12.45pm, max 30). T·P·D
🚇 Brixton, Herne Hill
Classic 1930s open air swimming-pool restored to former glory with addition of a single story extension replicating the original design. H A Rowbotham & T L Smithson, 1937

## Build Studios
🏃 203, Westminster Bridge Road, SE1 7FR
🕐 Sat/Sun 2pm–6pm (max 50) + 'The Decorated City' children's activity (max 10, design and create your own model building). T·D
🚇 Waterloo, Waterloo (East)
New co-working and event space for businesses working in the built environment sector.
Work spaces created by adapting a classic British-made industrial shelving system, and partitions added through fabric and cork display panels. Allford Hall Monaghan Morris, Carver Haggard Architects, 2015

## Central Hill Estate
🏃 Corner of Central Hill and Vicars Oak Road (next to Gipsy Hill Police Station), SE19 1DT
🕐 Sun 11am–6pm + Resident/Architects for Social Housing tours every 2 hours (11.30am-5pm) + Alternative People's Plan exhibition· Talk at 1.30pm (max 50).
❗ Pre-book only: bit.ly/2umn9D8
🚇 Crystal Palace, Gipsy Hill
Tree-lined housing estate on the ridge of Central Hill, Crystal Palace incorporating open spaces, views over London, gardens and sense of community. Rosemary Stjernstedt/Ted Hollamby 1970s

## Christ Church, Streatham
🏃 3 Christchurch Road, SW2 3ET
🕐 Sat 10am–5pm (All areas except bell tower)/Sun 1pm–5pm. T·R·d

🚇 Tulse Hill, Brixton

Grade I listed pioneering brick polychromy. Designed with early Christian, Italian, Ottoman, Alhambran, Mamluk, Sevillean and Ancient Egyptian influences with fine mosaics and stained glass by Walter Crane, JF Bentley and John Hayward.

## City & Guilds of London Art School

🏃 124 Kennington Park Road, SE11 4DJ
🕐 Sat/Sun 10am–5pm. T·D
🚇 Kennington, Elephant & Castle

A not for-profit, higher education institution located in Kennington since 1879, training the artists, carvers and conservators of tomorrow from Georgian houses and Victorian studios on Cleaver Square. Adrian Searle, 1780
*www.cityandguildsartschool.ac.uk*

## Clapham Library

🏃 Mary Seacole Centre, 91 Clapham High Street, SW4 7DB
🕐 Sat 10am–5pm/Sun 1pm–5pm (no access to staff areas). T·D
🚇 Clapham Junction, Clapham North

The building is based around a spiral theme that allows a building of multiple uses to feel like one space to reinforce a sense of community spirit. Studio Egret West, 2012

## Cressingham Gardens

🏃 Cressingham Gardens Rotunda, Tulse Hill SW2 2QG
🕐 Sat/Sun 10am–5pm. T·R·D
🚇 Tulse Hill, Brixton

Low-rise high density leafy estate located next to beautiful Brockwell Park noted for its innovative design, incorporating pioneering architectural elements and echoing the natural topography. Under threat of demolition by Lambeth council. Ted Hollamby, 1967

## Feilden Fowles Studio and Oasis Farm

🏃 8 Royal Street, SE1 7LL
🕐 Sat 10am–5pm (max 30) + hourly architect-led tour of the farm and office (11am-4pm, max 30) d·T
🚇 Westminster, Waterloo (East)

The Waterloo Community Farm is run by two charities: Jamie's Farm and the Oasis Community Hub. Feilden Fowles have been working on the design and delivery of the farm and its associated office and educational spaces. Feilden Fowles, 2016

## Lambeth Palace

🏃 Lambeth Palace Road, SE1 7JU
🕐 Sat (9am-2pm tours every 15 mins (max 20). T·d
ⓘ Pre-book only: lambethopenhouse.eventbrite.com
🚇 Waterloo, Vauxhall

For nearly 800 years Lambeth Palace has been the London residence of the Archbishop of Canterbury. ↪

Feilden Fowles Studio and Oasis Farm ↘

Streatham and Clapham High School © Anthony Coleman ↗

Oldest remaining parts date back to the 13C with buildings added and altered over time to suit changes in fashion and purpose.

## Mrs Custard's House
🏃 41A Lambert Road, SW2 5BB
🕐 Sat 10am-4.30pm architect-led tours of building and gardens, ½ hourly (max 20).
🚇 Brixton
Contemporary refurbishment, extension and landscaped garden and light well with blurred boundaries between inside and outside with the enigmatic feline, Mrs Custard, wandering between the two. Mustard Architects, 2016
*mustardarchitects.com*

## National Theatre
🏃 South Bank, SE1 9PX
🕐 Sat 10am–4.30pm/Sun 1.15pm-6pm + tour of Workshops and Max Rayne Centre, ½ hourly (max 12. Meet at Cottesloe Room ( Dorfman Theatre) + Archive handling (max 10) T·R·P·B·D
🚇 Waterloo
A key work in British Modernism (Grade II* listed) with three theatres, designed with workshops and theatre-making all on-site. RIBA Award Winner. Denys Lasdun and Partners, 1976

## Pullman Court
🏃 Streatham Hill, Streatham Hill, SW2 4SZ
🕐 Sun 11am–6pm (no access to roof). d
🚇 Brixton, Streatham Hill
Grade II* listed buildings, modern movement style with balcony walkways and period internal features. Frederick Gibberd, 1936

## Rambert
🏃 99 Upper Ground, SE1 9PP
🕐 Sat 11am-5pm hourly tours (max 15). T·D
🚇 Charing Cross, Waterloo
RIBA National Award winner 2014, Rambert's home provides the company with state of the art facilities for the creation of new choreography and music for dance. It enables the company to unlock the riches of the Rambert archive. Allies and Morrison, 2013

## Royal Festival Hall, Southbank Centre
🏃 Belvedere Road, SE1 8XX
🕐 Sat/Sun 10.30am-2.30pm behind the scenes tour, every 2 hours (max 20). T·R·B
🚇 Waterloo, Embankment
Grade 1 listed building, originally built for the 1951 Festival of Britain. Following the successful refurbishment in 2007, millions of people visit each year to enjoy the cultural/festival programme. RIBA Award Winner 2008. LCC Architects Department 1951/ Allies and Morrison Architects (refurb), 2007

## Sail Street
🚶 8 Sail Street, SE11 6NQ
🕐 Sat 10am–2pm + ½ hourly tour (max 10). D
🚇 Lambeth North, Waterloo
A building of affordable homes (sold at a 35% discount) for local first time buyers in Lambeth from Pocket Living. 27 one bedroom homes, 1 wheelchair accessible home & 3 two bedroom homes. There is a shared roof terrace for all residents. HKR Architects, 2017

## Streatham and Clapham High School, new sixth form centre
🚶 42 Abbotswood Road, SW16 1AW
🕐 Sat 10am–1pm. D
🚇 Balham, Streatham Hill
New sixth form centre extension on the top floor of the existing school building including sixth form common room, study room and classrooms. Cottrell & Vermeulen Architecture, 2016

## The Clockworks
🚶 6 Nettlefold Place, SE27 0JW
🕐 Sat 11am–6pm + Tour led by the curator, hourly + Workshop demonstrations (may involve 3d printing, wheel-cutting, lathe work etc). T·d
🚇 West Norwood
Internationally pre-eminent museum and integral workshops devoted to electrical timekeeping and the distribution of accurate time (1840-1970). Practical education and conservation in action. Michael Crowley Architect, 2012

## The Edible Bus Stop Studio
🚶 Arch 511, Ridgway Road, SW9 7EX
🕐 Sun 2pm–6pm (max 15) P·d
🚇 Brixton, Loughborough Junction
A former mechanics garage, refurbished utilising reclaimed and recycled materials to create a functional design studio and workshop. The team will be available to discuss an exhibition of their Urban Design work. The Edible Bus Stop Studio, 2014

## The Old Vic
🚶 103 The Cut, SE1 8NB
🕐 Sat ned's behind the scenes tour at 9am, 10.45am (max 20). T·R·d
❗ Pre-book only: bit.ly/2eFCKs0
🚇 Southwark, Waterloo (East)
World-famous playhouse, Grade II* listed, with Georgian exterior and restored Victorian interior. Only London theatre of the time still open. Rudolph Cabernel, 1818

## The South London Botanical Institute
🚶 323 Norwood Road, SE24 9AQ
🕐 Sun 1pm–5pm + Cyanotype Photography of Herbarium Specimens and Plant Drawing Evening's Fruit and Veg Collection at 1pm (max 50). T·R·d
🚇 Brixton, Tulse Hill
Brick-built Victorian villa with sweeping drive.

Few interior changes since 1910 when A O Hume founded the SLBI. Lecture Room with bespoke wallpaper designed around plants and herbarium specimens with a nod to Hume's Indian connections.

## West Norwood Cemetery
🚶 Norwood Road, adjacent corner Robson Road, SE27 9JU
🕐 Sat 1pm–5pm + Tour at 2pm, 2.30pm, 3pm (Meet inside main cemetery gate. Duration 90 mins). T·P·B
🚇 Tulse Hill, Brixton
Opened 1837, with monuments to famous Victorians (Doulton, Tate, Reuter, Mrs Beeton). 69 Grade II/II* listed structures, including Greek Chapel c1872, architect uncertain, mausolea by EM Barry and GE Street and entrance arch by W Tite. Sir William Tite, 1837

## Wheatsheaf Community Hall
🚶 Wheatsheaf Lane, SW8 2UP
🕐 Sat 10am–5pm/Sun (max 10, no access to small hall (upstairs). T
🚇 Vauxhall
Grade II listed. The earliest reference to a building on the present site of Wheatsheaf Hall is in 1880, when there was a small villa standing in its own gardens. Williams, Messers Higgs and Hill, 1880

# Walks + Tours

## Clapham Old Town and Venn Street
🚶 Meet: by the Clock Tower next to Clapham Common tube, SW4 0BD
🕐 Sun 2pm (max 25). D
🚇 Clapham Common
This guided walk around Clapham's Old Town looks at a radically redesigned public realm which re-balanced the street environment in favour of the pedestrian and cyclist. Urban Movement + LB Lambeth, 2011

## Southbank Place
🚶 Meet: Canary Wharf Contractor's Site Office, Elizabeth House, 39 York Road, SE1 7NQ
🕐 Sat site tours at 10am, 12pm, 2pm (max 25, duration 2 hours.). T
❗ Pre-book only: openhouse@canarywharf.com (state Southbank Place in subject with names and preferred time)
🚇 Waterloo
A 5.25 acre mixed-use development on the site formerly known as the Shell Centre. Developers Braeburn Estates, the partnership between Canary Wharf Group and Qatari Diar, will deliver 1.4 million sq ft of new accommodation and public realm. Patel Taylor, Squire & Partners, GRID Architects, KPF, Adamsons , Townsend, 2019

# Lewisham

| | |
|---|---|
| Borough area (km²) | 35.2 |
| Population | 303,400 |
| Average age | 35 |
| First Open House | 1994 |

Lewisham

### 2 Eco Vale
🏃 2 Eco Vale, rear of 270-332 Wood Vale, SE23 3DL
🕐 Sat 10am–5pm (max 25, access to one house). T·d
🚇 Honor Oak Park
Three new eco-houses: biodiversity roof, exhaust air heat pump, timber clad, triple glazed modern eco-house on backland site. Chance de Silva, 2015

### 35 Lutwyche Road
🏃 35 Lutwyche Road, Lewisham, SE6 4EP
🕐 Sun 11am–6pm (max 20). T·d
🚇 Bellingham, Catford Bridge
A new build, triangular courtyard house, set in an end of terrace infill site. This two bed home, designed for Julia and her daughters, has burnt timber cladding, timber beams and soffit, front and rear gardens, and a series of skylights. Studio Bam, 2017

### Boone's Chapel
🏃 Lee High Road, SE13 5PQ
🕐 Sat/Sun 1pm–5pm (max 30, Excludes access to adjacent almshouse garden) + The almshouses of southeast London. d
🚇 Hither Green, Lewisham
Grade I listed former almshouse chapel (1682) restored in 2008 as a studio and exhibition space. Brick and Portland stone chapel with contemporary service building and small garden in grounds of the Merchant Taylors' Almshouses.

### End House
🏃 87a Manwood Road, SE4 1SA
🕐 Sun 10.30am–1.30pm (max 10). d
🚇 Lewisham, Brockley
A fresh, contemporary end of terrace house that makes clever use of a small site by using a simple form to offer privacy combined with open plan living. Sustainable features include recycled newspaper insulation and breathable walls. Edgley Design, 2010

### Forest Mews
🏃 Rockbourne Mews, SE23 2AT
🕐 Sat 10am-4pm architect-led tour of the mews including one of the houses, hourly (max 25).
⚠ Pre-book only: events@stolon.co.uk
🚇 Forest Hill

Three bespoke houses, each with a studio and courtyard, set around a communal courtyard. Inspired by views of ivy growing over trees in wintertime - all three houses are clad with striking green walls, trained to a geometric pattern. Stolon Studio, 2014

### Goldsmiths Centre for Contemporary Art
🏃 St James's, New Cross, SE14 6AD
🕐 Sat 10am–5pm (max 30, access is via organised tours every 2 hours only).
⚠ Pre-book only: bit.ly/2vybPm2
🚇 New Cross, New Cross Gate
A new contemporary art gallery at Goldsmiths, providing a landmark space which will host high-profile public exhibitions. The gallery will give new use to a Grade-II listed, Victorian-era water tank, which once fed the Laurie Grove Baths. Thomas Dinwiddy, 1898/Assemble (refurb), 2017

### Horniman Museum and Gardens
🏃 100 London Road, SE23 3PQ
🕐 Sat 11am-2pm, Horniman Architecture: Then and Now, every 90 mins (max 15, Duration 45-60 mins.). T·D
⚠ Pre-book only: www.horniman.ac.uk/visit/events/open-house-weekend
🚇 Forest Hill
The Horniman Museum moved into its current building with its landmark Clocktower in 1901. Since then the site has been expanded with a number of architecturally-significant developments, including green-roofed education space and library. Charles Harrison Townsend, 1901

### Lewisham Arthouse
🏃 140 Lewisham Way, SE14 6PD
🕐 Sun 10am–5pm + Interactive Children's activity. T
🚇 St.John's, Deptford Bridge
Former library, converted to studios. Grade II listed building in classical Renaissance style with curved glass vaulted roof. A Brumwell Thomas, 1914

### Louise House
🏃 Dartmouth Road, Forest Hill, SE23 1DL
🕐 Sat 10am–5pm (max 10) + Hourly tour. T·R ↱

Forest Hill
A Grade II listed purpose-built former industrial school within a setting of municipal buildings and a modern newly created garden. Thomas W Aldwinckle, 1891

## Manor House Gardens Ice House
🏃 Manor House Gardens (Old Road), SE13 5SY
🕐 Sat/Sun 12pm–5pm (max 8).
Ⓜ Hither Green, Lewisham
Grade II listed ice well and underground chambers in Manor House Gardens park, which provided ice for nearby Manor House (see separate entry). Cited in 2002 Civic Trust Awards. 1770

## Manor House Library
🏃 34 Old Road, SE13 5SY
🕐 Sat 10am–5pm (max 10) + Hourly tour. T·R·d
Ⓜ Blackheath, Hither Green
Grade II listed classical design with 5 bay façade, 4 column portico and two Adam-style plaster work ceilings on the ground floor. Now a library with restored fixtures and fittings illustrating the elegance of the original design. Richard Jupp, 1771

## Mary Evans Picture Library
🏃 59 Tranquil Vale, Blackheath, SE3 0BS
🕐 Sat 10am-4.30pm, history and context tour, ½ hourly (max 16). T ↪

2 Eco Vale © Dennis Gilbert ↘

Blackheath

An Arts and Crafts-style former parish hall built in 1928 after houses were destroyed by a First World War Zeppelin raid, now housing the Mary Evans Picture Library. Charles Canning Winmill, 1928

## PLACE/Ladywell

- 261 Lewisham High Street, SE13 6NJ
- Sat 10am–3pm + architect-led tour of the housing, hourly (10am-2pm).
- New Cross, Ladywell

Winner of the Mayor's Prize for innovation, and the New London Architecture temporary building award, PLACE/Ladywell is a 24-unit housing development for homeless families. It also includes workshops and a café at ground level. Rogers Stirk Harbour + Partners, 2016

## Sayes Court

- Sayes Court Park, Grove Street, Deptford, SE8 3LN
- Sat 1pm–5pm.
- New Cross, Deptford

Birthplace of the National Trust and home of John Evelyn FRS. Lost but now to be reborn in the heart of Deptford.

## Segal Close Self-build Houses

- 4 & 7 Segal Close, Honor Oak Park, SE23 1PP
- Sun 10am–1pm (max 20, external and internal viewings with talks, some areas will be restricted access on the day) + Talk with Alice Grahame and Jon Broome at 11am.
- Forest Hill, Honor Oak Park

A short cul-de-sac consisting of seven 'Segal Method' houses. This modular timber frame self-build system, advocated by the architect, is reminiscent of 19C American and traditional Japanese architecture. Walter Segal, 1984

## South East London Combined Heat & Power Energy Recovery Facility

- Landmann Way, off Surrey Canal Road, SE14 5RS
- Sun 10am–3pm. T·R·d
- Surrey Quays, New Cross Gate

Energy Recovery Facility providing long-term sustainable solution for waste treatment, producing National Grid electricity & heat for Southwark residents. Designed to minimise visual impact whilst remaining a high quality landmark building. Alan J Smith Partnership, 1993

## Spring Gardens

- Ennersdale Road, Arlington Close, SE13 6JQ
- Sat 1pm–5pm. T·R·d
- London Bridge, Hither Green

Purpose-built hostel for 65 homeless residents, offering high-quality accommodation in buildings arranged around a beautiful garden with mature trees, light, open and airy with training spaces. Sustainable features include solar panels. Peter Barber Architects, 2010

## The Mansion and homesteads at Beckenham Place Park

- Beckenham Hill Road, BR3 1SY
- Sun 11am–9pm + tours of mansion house including open house studios on first floor, ½ hourly (11am-4pm, max 40) · tours of fire damaged homesteads, ½ hourly (11am-4pm, max 15) · tours of parkland highlighting historic features and planned restoration, ½ hourly (12pm-3pm, max 40) · Film showing at 7pm. T·R·P·d
- Pre-book only: beckenhamplace.org
- Beckenham Junction, Beckenham Hill

Tours of this Palladian mansion and unprecedented access to the fire damaged homestead to be restored over the next two years. Georgian performances, workshops and an evening film showing in the mansion.

## The Master Shipwright's House

- Watergate Street, SE8 3JF
- Sat 10am–5pm/Sun 10am–1pm (selected rooms and garden) + The Lenox Project (restored cannon and exhibition trailer on site). R·d
- Greenwich, Deptford

The oldest upstanding building of the former Deptford Royal Dockyard - home and office of the master shipwright since 1513 - remodelled in early 18C. Gardens & river frontage. "Hidden London at its delightful best" - The Telegraph.

## The Seager Distillery Tower

- 1 Mill Lane Deptford, SE8 4HN
- Sat/Sun 10am–5pm (max 8, viewing gallery). D
- Deptford Bridge, Deptford

Regeneration project by Galliard Homes on site of former Seager distillery, includes refurb of a 19C warehouse, conversion of former 19C Holland House, a new Crescent building, Pavilion and 27-storey residential tower with viewing gallery. Dannatt Johnson Architects, 2005

## Trinity Laban Conservatoire of Music and Dance

- Creekside, SE8 3DZ
- Sun 10am–1pm (max 50). T·D
- Pre-book only: tours@trinitylaban.ac.uk
- Deptford Bridge, Deptford

The largest purpose-built contemporary dance centre in the world. A gently curving façade with richly coloured plastic-cladding leads into spaces filled with vivid colour and dynamic form. Herzog & de Meuron, 2003

## Unit 3 Studio

- Unit 3, 7 Coulgate Street, Brockley, SE4 2FA
- Sun 10am–1pm (max 15). T·d
- Brockley

A characterless volume transformed into stimulating workspace which engages with its surroundings. A perforated, cork lined pod forms a studio, whilst the space outside the pod acts as the social and support space. Selencky///Parsons, 2016

Unit 3 Studio © Richard Chivers ↗

**Walter Segal Self-build Houses (see other entry)**
🚶 Multiple houses, Walters Way, Honor Oak Park, SE23 3LH
🕐 Sun 1pm–6pm (max 20, access to downstairs only for most properties, one upstairs room in one property. NB two steps to each house) + Various info available, plus videos at 1pm (max 20). T·R
🚇 Honor Oak Park

A close of 13 self-built houses. Each is unique, built using method developed by Walter Segal, who led the project in the 1980s. Houses have been extended and renovated. Sustainable features include solar electric, water & space heating. Walter Segal, 1987

## Walks + Tours

**Blackheath Village Walk**
🚶 Meet: on the Heath opposite 74 Tranquil Vale SE3, 74 Tranquil Vale, SE3 0BW
🕐 Sat/Sun 9am (max 30).

! Pre-book only: via self-addressed envelope to Blackheath Society, 11 Blackheath Village, SE3 9LA)
🚇 Blackheath

Walk through the 250 year-old Blackheath Village, a rare rural survival within the urban sprawl of SE London. A spread of architectural interest from the 1780s onwards. Led by historian Neil Rhind MBE FSA for the Blackheath Society.

**Ladywell Fields**
🚶 Meet: Sat 11am at northern entrance of Ladywell Fields, Ladywell Road, SE13 7XB
🕐 Sat 11am
🚇 Ladywell

A river and park restoration project 10 years on. River channels, backwaters, pools and riffles, improved habitats within the river corridor along with improved access and educational benefits. Led by Mehron Kirk, landscape architect. BDP,

# Merton

| | |
|---|---:|
| Borough area (km²) | 37.6 |
| Population | 208,100 |
| Average age | 37 |
| First Open House | 2001 |

## 9 Parkside Avenue
🚶 9 Parkside Avenue, SW19 5ES
🕐 Sun 1pm–5pm + talk by the architect. d
🚇 Wimbledon
Complex series of interlocking spaces within a simple overall volume, with references to the dramatic and hidden sources for lighting spaces seen in Baroque churches and the work of Sir John Soane. Sustainable features included. Holden Harper, 1999

## 106 Gladstone Road
🚶 106 Gladstone Road, Wimbledon, SW19 1QW
🕐 Sat/Sun 10am–5pm (max 12, tours from project architect, shoes off).
❗ Pre-book only: daniel@studio1architects.co.uk
🚇 Wimbledon
Contemporary refurbishment with additional rear and roof extensions. Seamless skylights, concrete floors, exposed brickwork, projecting glass box, whitewashed ash slats and oak ribs create an enthralling new take on a period house. Studio 1 Architects, 2015
www.studio1architects.co.uk

## Baitul Futuh Mosque
🚶 Ahmadiyya Muslim Association, 181 London Road, Morden, SM4 5PT
🕐 Sat/Sun 10am–5pm + ½ hourly tours. T·R·P·B·D
🚇 Morden, Morden South
Largest purpose-built mosque in Western Europe accommodating 13,000 worshippers. The building is a blend of Islamic and modern British architecture and incorporates much of the structure of an old dairy site. Sutton Griffin Architects, 2003

## Brenley Park
🚶 Aventine Avenue, Mitcham, CR4 1GF
🕐 Sat/Sun 11am–1pm + architect-led tour at 12pm.
🚇 Mitcham Eastfields

Supported by

CLARION
HOUSING GROUP

Designed with sustainability and energy efficiency in mind, these double aspect homes edge the landscaped park perimeter so residents enjoy balcony views and peace and quiet whilst creating natural security in the public park. Hunters, 2012
hunters.co.uk

## Buddhapadipa Temple
🚶 14 Calonne Road, Wimbledon Parkside, SW19 5HJ
🕐 Sat/Sun 10am–5.30pm (max 50). R·B·T·P
🚇 Wimbledon
Complex of buildings on 4 acres of land with Buddhist Theravada Temple in Thai style – one of only two outside Asia. Interior mural paintings by Thai artists, depicting aspects of the Buddha's life. Sidney Kaye Firmin Partnership, 1980

## Cannizaro Studios
🚶 The old Potting sheds, Cannizaro Park, SW19 4UW
🕐 Sat/Sun 11am–5pm (open studios) + Sun guided tour of park at 11.30am (Duration 1 hour) T·d
🚇 Wimbledon
Victorian Potting sheds converted to artists' studios set within grounds of Grade II listed Cannizaro Park.

## Donhead Preparatory School
🚶 33 Edge Hill, SW19 4NP
🕐 Sat 10am–5pm. T·D
🚇 Raynes Park, Wimbledon
School (1867) updated and extended to incorporate four new classrooms, a 150 seat auditorium, a double height art room and a 50 seat chapel. Phillips Tracey Architects, 2016

## Elliott Wood
🚶 241 The Broadway, SW19 1SD
🕐 Sun 10am–5pm + hourly engineer-led tours (11am–4pm). T·R
🚇 South Wimbledon, Wimbledon
A Victorian villa with impressive 2-storey vaulted steel and glass office space with mezzanine for structural engineers Elliott Wood. Richard Paxton Architects, 2004

## New Studios, Wimbledon College of Arts
🚶 Merton Hall Road, SW19 3QA
↱

○ Sat/Sun 10am–5pm (max 80). T·D
🚇 Wimbledon, Wimbledon Chase
This 2-storey studio building is an exemplar building of sustainable design, providing simple, flexible workspace for Wimbledon College of Arts students. In 2017 it received the RIBA London Award and RIBA London Sustainability Award.
Penoyre & Prasad, 2014
*www.arts.ac.uk/wimbledon* · *@WimbledonUAL*

## New Wimbledon Theatre
🏃 93 The Broadway, SW19 1QG
○ Sun 11am–6pm + tours (12pm-5pm). T·R·d
🚇 Wimbledon
Striking Edwardian theatre with beautiful main auditorium in classic three-tier design, seating 1652. Recent major refurbishment. Cecil Masey & Roy Young, 1910

## Wimbledon Windmill
🏃 Windmill Road, Wimbledon Common, SW19 5NR
○ Sat 2pm–5pm/Sun 11am–5pm + ½ hourly tours. T·R·P·B·d
🚇 Putney, Wimbledon
Rare example of a hollow post mill. Grade II* listed, it now contains a museum depicting the history and development of windmills in Britain. Many working models, windmill machinery, equipment and tools.
Charles March, 1817

106 Gladstone Road ↘

# Newham

| | |
|---|---|
| Borough area (km²) | 36.2 |
| Population | 342,900 |
| Average age | 32 |
| First Open House | 1995 |

Newham London

## Abbey Mills Pumping Station
🏃 Abbey Lane, E15 2RW
🕐 Sat/Sun 10am–5pm (max 15). T
ⓘ Pre-book only: bit.ly/2uNnYp8
🚇 Road, Bromley By Bow
Abbey Mills pumping station 'A', built by engineer Joseph Bazalgette, Edmund Cooper and architect Charles Driver. Built between 1865 and 1868 it has been described as the cathedral of sewage.

## House Mill
🏃 Three Mill Lane, Bromley by Bow, E3 3DU
🕐 Sat/Sun 11am–4pm (max 18, ground and 1st floors only) + ½ hourly tours (max 18). T·R·P·B·d
🚇 Devons Road, Bow Road
The Worlds largest tidal mill. 5-storey, timber-framed, brick-clad timber watermill with four waterwheels, originally built 1776 to mill grain for distillery trade. Operational until 1940. On historic 3 Mills Site.

## Old Ford Water Recycling Plant
🏃 Dace Road (site is accessed from the Greenway), E3 2NW
🕐 Sat 10am–5pm (beekeeper on site am).
🚇 Stratford International, Stratford
UK's largest community-scale wastewater recycling facility converting sewage to non-potable water to supply Olympic Park venues. Clad in timber, gabion baskets and corten steel to blend within the environment. Lyall Bills & Young Architects, 2012

## Old Manor Park Library
🏃 835 Romford Road, E12 5JY
🕐 Sat 10am–5pm (max 75) + OOMK printing press sessions (max 10, studio artists may also offer workshops and demonstrations). T·R·d
🚇 Manor Park, East Ham
A Grade II listed Carnegie building, unused for three years, has been transformed into a new centre for publicly accessible workspaces for artists, makers and a resource for the enjoyment of the local community. AH Campbell, 1904

## Royal Docks Adventure
🏃 1012 Dockside Road, E16 2QT
🕐 Sat/Sun 10am–5pm (max 20). T·P·d

🚇 Royal Albert
2-storey building with glass façade overlooking the Royal Dock, formerly London Regatta Centre. Boathouse & Clubhouse, including changing rooms, gym & restaurant. Designed to act as a focus for community activities in the area. Ian Ritchie Architects, 2015

## Salmen House
🏃 53a Salmen Road, Plaistow, EJ3 0DT
🕐 Sat/Sun 10am–5pm + hourly architect-led tours (max5)
ⓘ Pre-book only: office@officesandm.com
🚇 Plaistow, West Ham
An end of terrace new build house, of textured render with terrazzo details. It contains generous vertical spaces, such as double height bedrooms, exposed beam ceilings and a triple height staircase on a contrained corner site. Office S&M, 2017

## Silvertown
🏃 Meet: Gate 3, Mill Road, E16 2BE
🕐 Sat hard-hat site tours at 10.30am & 12.30pm (max 20, Please ensure suitable footwear. Not suitable for people with mobility restrictions)
ⓘ Pre-book only: hello@silvertownlondon.com (please state number of people)
🚇 Custom House
A 62-acre development in London's Royal Docks. At the heart lies Millennium Mills, an iconic former flour mill which has been derelict for decades. A section of the Rank Hovis Premier Mill remains with a restored Grade II listed grain silo. Fletcher Priest Architects, 2018

## St Mary Magdalene Church & Nature Reserve
🏃 High Street South/Norman Road, E6 3PG
🕐 Sat 10am–4pm (max 15) + ½ hourly tours. T·R·d
🚇 East Ham, Beckton
Grade I listed 12C church, with London's largest churchyard and one of the best-preserved Norman archways in the country, as well as other interesting features, including 750-year-old wall paintings.

## St Mary the Virgin
🏃 Church Road, Manor Park, Little Ilford, E12 6HA

① Sat 10am–5pm / Sun 1pm–5pm. T·d
🚇 East Ham, Manor Park
Small Grade I listed 12C chapel in lovely churchyard setting, it retains original architectural features and has interesting brasses, monuments and stained glass windows.

### The City of London Cemetery and Crematorium at Aldersbrook
🚶 Aldersbrook Road, E12 5DQ
① Sat/Sun 10am–5pm + history tour at 10am (max 30). T·R·P·d
⚠ Pre-book only: 02085302151
🚇 Wanstead, Manor Park
A stunning Grade I listed 200 acre landscape designed and landscaped in 1856 to deal with the environmental/health/space issues of London's cramped and over-used churchyards. Rich in architecture from the Victorian era. William Haywood & William Davidson, 1855

### Three Mills Lock
🚶 Prescott Channel, Three Mills Island, Bromley-by-Bow, E3 3DY
① Sat/Sun 10am–5pm.
🚇 Bromley By Bow, Stratford
Positioned at the mouth of the Olympic site, this state-of-the-art structure offered a sustainable transport link for the 2012 games. The dock, weir, fish belly gates and fish pass control the water level in the Bow back rivers. VolkerStevin, 2009

## Walks + Tours

### Beyond the Olympic Park - the real Lea Valley from industry to art
🚶 Meet: The White Building, White Post Lane, E9 5EN (10am tour); House Mill E3 3DU (2pm tour)
① Sat 10am from Hackney Wick to Three Mills (tour ends at House Mill E3 3DU), 2pm from Three Mills to Leamouth. Each walk is about 2-3 miles long.
⚠ Pre-book only: ralphward@blueyonder.co.uk
🚇 Stratford, Hackney Wick
A riverside stroll in two parts exploring the river Lea from Hackney Wick to the Thames.

### ICE Engineering Highlights Cycle Tour of the Queen Elizabeth Olympic Park
🚶 Meet: outside the Timber Lodge Café, Honour Lea Avenue, Queen Elizabeth Olympic Park, E20 3BB
① Sun 2pm (max 30)
🚇 Stratford, Stratford International
Tour will explore the Olympic Park's enabling works and the construction of the venues, through to the utilities and their supporting infrastructure. Organised by the Institution of Civil Engineers.

### Jubilee Line Night Tour
🚶 Meet: West Ham Underground Station Ticket Hall, Manor Road, E15 3BN
① Tour starts at 11.59pm Friday 15 September). d
⚠ Pre-book only: bit.ly/2tLvVqV
🚇 West Ham
With a focus on the architecture and the operations of the Jubilee line extension stations which created a new design style, this tour takes advantage of Night Tube and showcases the excellent illumination at these stations.

Abbey Mills Pumping Station ⬊

# Redbridge

| | |
|---|---|
| Borough area (km²) | **56.4** |
| Population | **304,200** |
| Average age | **36** |
| First Open House | **1996** |

## Bancroft's School
🚶 611-627 High Road, Woodford Green, IG8 0RF
🕐 Sat 12pm–3pm (max 20, entry to chapel,
Great Hall, library, Dining Hall, tower, and
quad). T·d
🚇 Buckhurst Hill, Chingford
A dignified and impressive design with later
additions. Spiral staircase leads to the top of the
tower, giving excellent views. Formerly a Drapers'
Company charitable school in Mile End Road,
Bancroft's moved to its present site in 1889. Sir
Arthur Blomfield, 1889

## Box Theatre Redbridge College
🚶 Barley Lane, Romford, RM6 4XT
🕐 Sun 10am–5pm (max 30) + hourly tours (11am–
4pm, max 15). T·P·d
🚇 Newbury Park
An award-winning performing arts centre. Conceived
as an elevated translucent box, the building is clad
in coloured glazing to create a vibrant façade. Ayre
Chamberlain Gaunt, 2016

## Fullwell Cross Library
🚶 140 High Street, Barkingside, Ilford, IG6 2EA
🕐 Sat 9.30am–4pm + 'The History of Fairlop Fair'
talk by Jef Page at 2pm. T·D
🚇 Fairlop, Barkingside
The library was built on an open site in Barkingside
High Street. Circular library design copies nearby
roundabout. Complex is set back from the pavement,
to form a new local civic centre with a public space.
Refurbished 1990 and 2011. Coombes & Partners,
Frederick Gibberd, H C Connell, 1958

## Ilford War Memorial Hall
🚶 Ilford War Memorial Gardens, Eastern Avenue,
Newbury Park, IG2 7RJ
🕐 Sat/Sun 11am–4.30pm.
🚇 Newbury Park
Grade II listed memorial hall in the War Memorial
Gardens. Panels in the building show names of the
Ilford men killed during WWI. The Hall was designed
as the entrance to the now demolished children's
ward of the Ilford Emergency Hospital. C J Dawson
& Allardyce, 1927

## Quaker Meeting House, Wanstead
🚶 Bush Road, E11 3AU
🕐 Sun 1pm–5pm + hourly tours (1.30pm-4.30pm) +
Local Quaker History. T·P·D
🚇 Leytonstone
Four hexagon Modernist building within an Epping
Forest setting. A sunny meeting room for Quaker
worship faces onto a wooded burial ground of
simple headstones, including those of Elizabeth Fry,
William Mead and Norman Frith. Norman Frith, 1968

## Redbridge Town Hall, Council Chamber
🚶 128-142 High Road, Ilford, IG1 1DD
🕐 Sat 10.30am–2.30pm (ground and first floors only)
+ ½ hourly tours (max 15). T·D
🚇 Gants Hill, Ilford
Built in 3 stages consisting of the Old Town Hall
(1901) with façade in free classic style and some
original decorations, library (1927) and additional
buildings (1933). B Woolard, 1901

## Repton Park (former Claybury Asylum)
🚶 Repton Park, Manor Road, Woodford Bridge,
IG8 8GG
🕐 Sat 10.30am-12.30pm/Sun 1.30pm-4.30pm hourly
Residents Association led tours (max 15). P·d
🚇 Chigwell, Woodford
Former mental asylum includes 17C Claybury Hall with
Adam staircase. Original asylum (Hall, Chapel, Water
Towers, Gate Lodges, Ward Blocks, Airing Shelters) all
Grade II listed. Private parkland originally designed
by Sir Humphrey Repton. George T Hine, 1889

## Sukkat Shalom Reform Synagogue
🚶 1 Victory Road, Wanstead, E11 1UL
🕐 Sun 10am–4pm. T·R·P·d
🚇 Snaresbrook
Grade II* listed, originally the Merchant Seaman's
Orphan Asylum Chapel, acquired by the synagogue
in 1995 and restored with Heritage Lottery Fund
grant. Timber work and windows installed from a
synagogue in Tottenham which has closed down.
Somers Clarke, 1863

## The Hospital Chapel of St Mary & St Thomas
🚶 48 Ilford Hill, Ilford, IG1 2AT

Box Theatre Redbridge College © Andy Matthews ↗

🕐 Sat 10am–4pm/Sun 1pm–4.30pm + ½ hourly tours
    T·R·B·D
🚇 Gants Hill, Ilford
Founded c1145 by the Abbess of Barking as a hospice
for thirteen old and infirm men, the present building
is 12C and 19C. Grade II* listed with many interesting
monuments, including Burne-Jones windows.

### The Temple
🚶 Wanstead Park, E11 2LT
🕐 Sun 12pm–5pm + talk by local historian Dr
    Richard Arnopp at 12.30pm.
🚇 Wanstead
18C garden feature in style of a Doric temple c1760,
surviving from the magnificent grounds of Palladian
Wanstead House, whose rise and fall is told in the
museum within.

### Uphall Primary School Nursery
🚶 Uphall Road, Ilford, IG1 2JD
🕐 Sat/Sun 10am–1pm (max 10). D
🚇 Barking, Ilford
Unusual 1930s ship-shaped school building,
converted to nursery. Grade II listed. Civic Trust
commendation 2000. Ilford Borough Architects, 1934

### Valentines Mansion
🚶 Emerson Road, Ilford, IG1 4XA
🕐 Sun 12pm–4pm. T·R·P·D
🚇 Gants Hill, Ilford
Large, late 17C Grade II* listed house with
fine staircase and Venetian window and
Georgian additions, used as a family dwelling
until the early 1900s. Reopened to the
public in Feb 2009 following extensive
restoration works. Richard Griffiths
Architects, 1696

## Walks + Tours

### Wanstead Heritage Walk
🚶 Meet: outside Wanstead Station,
    21 The Green, Wanstead, E11 2NT
🕐 Sun 10am (Duration 2 hours)
🚇 Wanstead
A guided walk from Wanstead Station to
The Temple, Wanstead Park, highlighting
St Mary's Church and the remnants of the
historical landscape that formed the grounds
of Wanstead House.

# Richmond

| | |
|---|---|
| Borough area (km²) | 57.4 |
| Population | 197,300 |
| Average age | 39 |
| First Open House | 1995 |

LONDON BOROUGH OF
RICHMOND UPON THAMES

## 8WR
🚶 8 Waldegrave Road, Teddington, TW11 8GT
🕐 Sat 10am–5pm. T·R·D
🚇 Teddington
The home of multi-award winning South-West
London housing provider RHP Group. Rated BREAAM
excellent, the building has innovative features
throughout, including a revolutionary modular home
in the back garden. bptw partnership, 2010
*www.rhp.org.uk/rhpui*

## 110 North Road
🚶 Richmond, TW9 4HJ
🕐 Sun 11am–4pm (max 20). R
🚇 Kew Bridge, Kew Gardens
A bespoke structural frame replaces all internal
structure in this quirky 3-storey home, creating
a series of split section spaces and multi-storey
voids. Hempcrete provides breathable insulation
with original solid wall/lime mortar fabric. MW
Architects, 2016

## Bushy House
🚶 National Physical Laboratory, Queens Road,
   Teddington, TW11 0EB
🕐 Sun 10am–5pm (access to gardens and ground
   floor only) + interactive science show at 12pm
   (max 30, hourly 12pm-4pm). T·R·P·d
🚇 Teddington
Originally built for Edward Proger. From 1797 the
residence of William, Duke of Clarence (later William
IV) and his mistress Dora Jordan. Now part of the
National Physical Laboratory. William Samwell, 1663

## Foundry Mews
🚶 58 Barnes High Street, Richmond, SW13 9AZ
🕐 Sat/Sun 10am–5pm (access to individual units
   may vary). d
🚇 Barnes Bridge
A surreptitious mixed-use, new-build development
making sustainable use of a highly constrained
brownfield backland site. It comprises of seven
dwellings above studio workspaces running along a
communal access courtyard. Project Orange, 2016

## Garrick's Temple to Shakespeare, Hampton
🚶 Garrick's Lawn, Hampton Court Road, Hampton,
   TW12 2EJ
🕐 Sun 1pm–5pm (max 12, full access) + tour/talk
   at 11am (max 12, light refreshments) · ½ hourly
   tours by Temple Trustee, (1pm-4pm, max 12).
   T·R·d
🚇 Hampton Court, Richmond
Grade I listed Georgian garden building. Tribute to
Shakespeare built in the Ionic style by actor David
Garrick. Arcadian Thames side setting in restored
18C gardens thought to be by Capability Brown.

## Grove Gardens Chapel
🚶 Richmond Cemetery, Grove Gardens, off Lower
   Grove Road, TW10 6HP
🕐 Sun 2pm–5pm. d
🚇 Richmond
Small, charming Gothic chapel of imaginative design
with plate tracery and mosaic triptych. Former
cemetery chapel, now restored for mixed community
use. Thomas Hardy was apprenticed to the architect.
Sir Arthur Blomfield, 1873

## Ham House and Garden
🚶 Ham Street, Ham, Richmond, TW10 7RS
🕐 Sat 10am–5pm (house and below stairs open
   12pm-4pm. Last entry 3.30pm). T·R·B·D
🚇 Richmond, Kingston
Built in 1610, Ham House was greatly extended
in the 1670s. One of a series of grand houses and
palaces built along the Thames, an unusual complete
17C survival. Fine interiors and historic gardens.

## Kew House
🚶 10 Cambridge Road, Kew, TW9 3JB
🕐 Sun 10am–5pm (max 30) + owner and engineer
   led tours of house) T·R·d
🚇 Kew Gardens, Kew Bridge
A contemporary family home formed of two
weathering steel buildings inserted behind the
retained façade of a 19C brick stables, set within a
conservation area on the doorstep of Kew Gardens.
Shortlisted for RIBA House of the Year 2015. Piercy &
Company, 2014

Foundry Mews © Jack Hobhouse ↗

### Kilmorey Mausoleum
🏃 275 St Margaret's Road (opposite Ailsa Tavern), TW1 1NJ
🕐 Sun 1pm–5pm (max 5, access to grounds and mausoleum). d
🚇 Richmond, St.Margaret's

Egyptian-style, pink and grey mausoleum created for the second Earl of Kilmorey. The form relates to the shrines at the heart of Egyptian Temples. HE Kendall, 1854

### Langdon Down Centre
🏃 2a Langdon Park, TW11 9PS
🕐 Sun 12pm–4pm + hourly tours (12.30pm-2.30pm) + children's Trail · James Henry Pullen exhibition of ships and artefacts. T·R·P·B·D
🚇 Hampton Wick

Grade II* listed Normansfield Theatre and Langdon Down Museum of Learning Disability. Gothic proscenium arch and elaborate stage and scenery. Built as part of the Normansfield Hospital for patients/students with learning disabilities. Rowland Plumbe, 1877

### Marble Hill Playcentres
🏃 Marble Hill Park, Richmond Road, Twickenham, TW1 2NL
🕐 Sat 12pm–6pm + guided tour by Senior Playworker Esther Pattenden at 2.30pm + '40 years of play at Marble Hill Playcentres' exhibition. T·P·D
🚇 Richmond, Twickenham

An example of DIY, child-led play architecture, Marble Hill Adventure Playground comprises giant rope swings, climbing frames and an aerial runway. Greater London Council, 1975

### Mortlake Crematorium
🏃 Kew Meadow Path, TW9 4EN
🕐 Sun 11am–6pm + hourly tours (max 20). T·P·d
🚇 Kew Gardens, Mortlake

A rare and distinctive example of Art Deco design, with exceptional quality and character. Italianate style cloisters with discreet brick detailing. F Douglas Barton, 1939

### Parish Church of St Anne
🏃 Kew Green, TW9 3AA
🕐 Sat 10am–4.30pm + tours at 11am, 3pm (max 30, duration 1 hour). T·R·P·d
🚇 Kew Gardens, Kew Bridge

Grade II* listed, originally built as a chapel under the patronage of Queen Anne in 1714 and subsequently enlarged. Many notable memorials including to scientist William Jackson Hooker and tombs of Thomas Gainsborough and Johan Zoffany.

### Pope's Grotto and Radnor House School
🏃 Radnor House School, Pope's Villa, Cross Deep, TW1 4QG
🕐 Sat hourly tours (10am-12pm, max 25). T·R·P·B
ⓘ Pre-book only: bit.ly/2tuJorK (password Grotto2017. If you experience problems email swood@radnorhouse.org)

↦

### Strawberry Hill, Twickenham
Grotto with mineral decoration is last remaining part of Alexander Pope's villa built 1720, demolished 1808 and replaced and redeveloped many times in following years.

### Richmond Adult Community College Scheme
🕴 Parkshot, Richmond, TW9 2RE
🕐 Sat 10am–5pm + Hourly tour (11am-4pm). T·R·D
🚇 Richmond
A centre of excellence for adults, providing learning, training and personal development. As a beacon for adult learning, this project facilitates an accessible, effective teaching environment that is substantially more sustainable. Duggan Morris Architects, 2015

### Richmond Lock Building (Surrey Side)
🕴 The Towpath, Richmond, TW9 2QJ
🕐 Sun 10am–5pm (max 30, crew room and staff office out of bounds) + talks from Lock keeper (max 30). T·d
🚇 St.Margaret's (Greater London), Richmond
Example of good-quality late-Victorian functional design. Francis Goold Morony Stoney, 1891

### Royal Botanic Gardens, Kew: Herbarium, Library, Art and Archives
🕴 Main Herbarium, Kew Green, Richmond, TW9 3AE
🕐 Sat/Sun 10am–5pm + Herbarium tour every 20 mins (max 15) + Tropical Nursery – 50 free tickets, see kew.org for details. T·R·P·D
🚇 Kew Gardens, Kew Bridge
Meet the Kew scientists and archivists and learn about the architectural design and history of both the historic and contemporary buildings.
www.kew.org

### Royal School of Needlework
🕴 RSN Shop, East Front Gardens, Hampton Court Palace, KT8 9AU
🕐 Sat/Sun 10am–5pm (Two RSN Embroidery Studios located within Hampton Court Palace) + Tour of RSN Education Studios: rooms not usually open to Palace visitors at 11am, 2pm + Embellishment in Fashion Exhibition & Hand Embroidery Demonstration. T·B·D
🚇 Hampton Court
Baroque palace built for King William III and Mary II. The Tudor towers and chimneys were replaced by grand and elegant exteriors that dominate the buildings today. Sir Christopher Wren, 1689
www.royal-needlework.org.uk

### Sheen House
🕴 37 Berwyn Road, Richmond, TW10 5BU
🕐 Sun ½ hourly architect-led tours (12pm-4pm, max 8).
🚇 North Sheen, Richmond
Contemporary refurbishment and extensions to a 1920s house in North Sheen conservation area, featuring a living roof and a large open-plan space with frameless all-glass façade overlooking a mature garden.

### Sir Richard Burton's Mausoleum
🕴 St Mary Magdalen's RC Church, 61 North Worple Way, Mortlake, SW14 8PR
🕐 Sun 2pm–5pm. d
🚇 Richmond, Mortlake
Grade II* listed mausoleum in the form of an Arab tent with ripples in the stone imitating canvas. Interior is embellished with oriental lamps, devotional paintings and camel bells. Isabel Arundell Burton, 1890

### The Boat and the Pavilion
🕴 11 Orchard Road, St Margarets, TW1 1LX
🕐 Sat/Sun 11am–6pm + Art Exhibition: Gerardo Di Fiore. d
🚇 St.Margaret's, Richmond
Ground floor rear extension for a family of sailors. The open plan layout is defined by curved, floating walls (the boat) and a sculpted ceiling (the pavilion), playfully combining compressed and expanded spaces. Unagru, 2016
www.unagru.com

### The Boathouse Design Studio
🕴 27 Ferry Road, Teddington, TW11 9NN
🕐 Sat/Sun 10am–1pm (max 18). T·R·d
🚇 Kingston, Richmond
Originally built to house the Royal Barge in 1862 and then used for boat building for three generations, The Boathouse is now office space for the creative industries.

### The Darke House
🕴 25 Montpellier Row, TW1 2NQ
🕐 Sun 11am–6pm (max 20) + ½ hourly talk/tour led by owner (max 20). T
🚇 Richmond, St.Margaret's
Designed by celebrated architect Geoffrey Darke as his own home. Described in Grade II listing as 'the ↱

The Boat and the Pavilion © Ståle Eriksen ↘

country's finest example of modernist house in a Georgian setting'. Nearly all original features and many fittings remain. Geoffrey Darke (of Darbourne & Darke), 1968

### The National Archives
🏃 Ruskin Avenue, Kew, Richmond, Surrey, TW9 4DU
🕐 Sat 10am–5pm + ½ hourly tours (10am-3.30pm, repository behind the scenes; roof top and sub-basement; collection care department) + talks and film screenings throughout the day. T·R·P·B·d
ⓘ Pre-book only: bit.ly/2tupGwi
🚉 Kew Gardens, Kew Bridge
South West London's hidden Brutalist masterpiece. McMaster/Clavering/Miller/O'Reilly, 1977
*www.nationalarchives.gov.uk*

### The Old Town Hall, Richmond
🏃 Meet at War Memorial in Riverside Gardens, at end of Whittaker Avenue, TW9 1TP
🕐 Sat 11am–4.30pm (max 12). T
🚉 Richmond
Red brick and Bath stone grand 'Elizabethan Renaissance' style building altered by war, political changes and reflecting Richmond's history. Overlooking the war memorial and the Thames. W J Ancell, 1893

### Velehrad London
🏃 39 Lonsdale Road, Barnes, SW13 9JP
🕐 Sun 10am–5pm. T·d
🚉 Hammersmith, Barnes Bridge
A newly refurbished and extended Victorian house and garden, Velehrad London is a gathering place for Czechs and Slovaks living in and visiting London. It hosts cultural, social and religious events for the community.

### York House
🏃 Richmond Road, TW1 3AA
🕐 Sun 10am–5pm. T·d
🚉 Richmond, Twickenham
Mid-17C house, a scheduled ancient monument, with fine staircase and 18C additions.

## Walks + Tours

### Hampton Court Palace Gardens
🏃 Meet: Hampton Court Palace, East Molesey, KT8 9AU
🕐 Sat/Sun 10am–5pm (some tours involve steps) T·R·B·d
🚉 Hampton Court
A range of tours of the formal gardens at Hampton Court Palace.

Velehrad London © David Grandgorge ⬊

# Southwark

| | |
|---|---|
| Borough area (km²) | 28.9 |
| Population | 314,300 |
| Average age | 34 |
| First Open House | 1994 |

Southwark
Council

### 15 and a half Consort Road
🏃 15 and a half Consort Road, SE15 2PH
🕐 Sat 10am–5pm (max 24) + ½ hourly tours (11am–4pm, max 6, designers on hand).
🚇 Queen's Road Peckham, Peckham Rye
As per Grand Designs, the opening roof and sliding bed-bath typify this extraordinary response to constraints of a tight budget on a brownfield site. Shortlisted RIBA Awards 2006. Voted as one of nation's favourite Grand Designs houses. Richard Paxton Architects, 2005

### 49 Camberwell Grove
🏃 49 Camberwell Grove, SE5 8JA
🕐 Sat/Sun 10am–5pm. T
🚇 Elephant & Castle, Denmark Hill
A Georgian fronted terrace house, remodelled to create an 'L' shaped modern eco house. Open and private living spaces designed horizontally on the ground floor, relaxation spaces designed vertically. John Eger Architects, 2009/Harriet Paterson, 2016

### Alex Monroe Workshop
🏃 42 Tower Bridge Road, SE1 4QT
🕐 Sat 10am–1pm (max 10). T
🚇 London Bridge
This new 4-storey workshop presents an enigmatic and finely crafted storefront. The façade's horizontal metal blades establish, harmony with the composition and articulation of the immediate street, giving it a moiré-like visual effect. DSDHA, 2016

### Allies and Morrison
🏃 85 Southwark Street, SE1 0HX
🕐 Sat 10am–5pm (general access to reception only) + architect-led tour of whole building, every 15 mins T·D
🚇 Blackfriars, Southwark
A tour of Allies and Morrison Studios complex - the original RIBA award winning studio, a converted Grade II listed warehouse and a new timber building. Allies and Morrison, 2003

### Anise Gallery / AVR London
🏃 13a Shad Thames, SE1 2PU
🕐 Sat 10am–5pm + exhibition of RIBAJ Eyeline Drawing Competition. T·D
🚇 Tower Hill, London Bridge
A Victorian spice warehouse, re-invented to house an architectural artwork gallery and an architectural illustrator's studio. The design focuses on flexibility and workspace collaboration. Tate Harmer, 2013

### Bankside Apartment
🏃 100 Tooley Street, SE1 2TH
🕐 Sun 10am–1pm (max 5)
🚇 London Bridge
White interior walls and bleached timber floor create light, generous spaces. There is a clarity in light and volume, relieving the occupant of any distraction and allowing for calm and meditative spaces. Hasa Architects, 2015

### Brunel Museum
🏃 Railway Avenue, SE16 4LF
🕐 Sat/Sun 10am–5pm + ½ hourly guided floodlit tour of shaft. T·R·B·d
🚇 Rotherhithe
Museum tells the story of the great engineering dynasty. Dramatic new staircase leads from sculpture garden to underground chamber. Use train ticket to view Thames Tunnel portico, travel through first underwater shopping arcade. Sir Marc Brunel, 1842

### Canada Water Library
🏃 21 Surrey Quays Road, SE16 7AR
🕐 Sat 9am–5pm/Sun 12pm–4pm + Sat hourly tours of roof space, theatre and meeting rooms (10am–4pm, no tour at 1pm) T·D
🚇 Surrey Quays, Canada Water
A civic centrepiece for the regeneration of the area around Canada Water. Its inverted pyramid form is an innovative response to providing an efficient single large library floor on a smaller footprint site. CZWG, 2011

### Cicely Saunders Institute - King's College London
🏃 Bessemer Road, SE5 9PJ
🕐 Sat 1pm–5pm (access to ground floor and atrium) + hourly tours of building & roof garden (max 15) + exhibition. T·R·D

! Pre-book only: bit.ly/2tkBKvQ
🚇 Loughborough Junction, Denmark Hill
The institute houses clinical, education and research staff from the Department of Palliative Care, Policy & Rehabilitation, and a Macmillan information centre. A contemporary building with artworks and a roof garden. LTS Architects, 2009

## City Hall
🚶 The Queen's Walk, More London, SE1 2AA
🕐 Sat 10am–6pm + City of 1000 Architects children's activity at 11am (in London's Living Room) T·R·D
🚇 London Bridge, Tower Hill
Home of the Mayor of London and London Assembly, an environmentally-aware building with innovative spiral ramp and fine views across London. Foster + Partners, 2002

## Courtyard House
🚶 35 Dovedale Road, SE22 0NF
🕐 Sat 1pm–5pm (max 20). d
🚇 Honor Oak Park
Single-storey courtyard house on constrained site, built out to the perimeter whilst providing light and private views to the interior and avoiding overlooking neighbours. Bathrooms to the street façade provide a buffer to the pavement. Design-Cubed, 2012

## Dawson's Heights
🚶 Bredinghurst, Overhill Road, SE22 0PL
🕐 Sat 10am–4pm, hourly tours (max 10, many stairs) + special architect-led tour with Kate Macintosh (check website for details).
🚇 Pre-book only: bit.ly/2eFIbqV
! East Dulwich, Peckham Rye, Forest Hill
Split between 2 blocks consisting of nearly 300 flats, all with private balconies, a fantastic example of beautifully designed social housing with uninterrupted views of the London skyline. Kate Macintosh for Southwark Council Architects Dept, 1966

## Employment Academy
🚶 29 Peckham Road, SE5 8UA
🕐 Sun 2pm–6pm + ½ hourly tours. T·R·D
🚇 Denmark Hill, Peckham Rye
The Employment Academy is a Grade II listed, late Victorian 'Baroque' building that has now become a local asset to the Southwark community. Edwin T Hall, 1904/Peter Barber Architects, 2013

## Flag Store
🚶 11 The Flag Store, Jubilee Yard, 23 Queen Elizabeth Street, SE1 2LP
🕐 Sat 10am–5pm (max 15, entrance up three flights of stairs).
🚇 Tower Hill, London Bridge
The historic tent factory was converted 25 years ago. No11 has been refitted out as a 2 bed 'loft' apartment. The rough beauty of the warehouse has been complemented with a new timeless contemporary interior. Waterhouse Architects, 2017

## Kaymet Factory
🚶 52 Ossory Road, SE1 5AN
🕐 Sat/Sun 11am–6pm (max 40) + ½ hourly proprietor-led tours of the main factory shed, packing area and showroom (max 12). T·R·d
🚇 Bermondsey, Peckham Rye
The operational factory of Kaymet, a maker of trays and trolleys since 1947. A hidden 1960s building with a small yard, originally a printing works. It is brick built, with clear-storey glazing and tubular truss north-light main shed roof.

## Kingswood House
🚶 Seeley Drive (by car approach only from Kingswood Drive), Kingswood Estate, SE21 8QR
🕐 Sun 12.30pm–4.30pm + ½ hourly tours (1pm–3.30pm). T·R·P·B·d
🚇 Sydenham Hill
Substantial villa built in form of stone-faced baronial castle for the founder of Bovril. Now library and community centre. HV Lanchester, 1892

## Livesey Exchange
🚶 135 Bird in Bush Road, Ledbury Estate, SE15 1NF
🕐 Sat 11am–6pm (max 60) + Old Kent Road industries guided walks 2pm (max 30) + Livesey Exchange hands-on workshops. T·R·D
! Pre-book only: ulrike@what-if.info
🚇 New Cross Gate, Queen's Road Peckham
Transformation of 60 garages below the unusually sculpted podium of the Ledbury Estate into an arcade of workshops and spaces for socialising. The estate is a great example of overlooked post-war architecture. GLC Architects' Department, 1960

Flag Store © Dransfield ↘

Bankside Apartment © James Whitaker ↗

## Lyndhurst Primary School
🚶 Denmark House, Grove Lane, SE5 8SN
🕐 Sat 10am–5pm. D
🚇 Denmark Hill
A partial refurbishment, demolition and extension for an existing school allowing an expansion from a 1.5 to 2 form entry. Cottrell & Vermeulen Architecture, 2015

## Nunhead Cemetery
🚶 Linden Grove, Nunhead, SE15 3LP
🕐 Sat/Sun 1pm–5pm. T·P·B·d
🚇 New Cross Gate, Nunhead
Magnificent Victorian cemetery with Gothic chapel and ruined lodge. One of London's wildest cemeteries. Restored with the help of a lottery grant. 52 acres of woodland, complete with bats, owls, foxes and squirrels. Thomas Little & JB Bunning, 1840

## Old Operating Theatre Museum & Herb Garret
🚶 9a St Thomas Street, SE1 9RY
🕐 Sun 10.30am–5pm (max 57, entry via 42 step spiral staircase).
🚇 London Bridge
St Thomas' Church attic, once part of old St Thomas' Hospital, houses the Herb Garret and Britain's only surviving 19C operating theatre. Thomas Cartwright, 1703

## Old Waiting Room at Peckham Rye station
🚶 Station Arcade, Rye Lane, SE15 5DQ
🕐 Sat/Sun 10am–5pm (max 50) + 'Peckham Streets' photography exhibition + Sun architect-led tour of restoration work at 1pm, 3pm (max 30). R·B
🚇 Peckham Rye
Originally the waiting lounge for passengers at Peckham Rye Station, designed in high Victorian style by Charles Henry Driver in 1865. Benedict O'Looney Architects, 2017

## One Blackfriars
🚶 1-16 Blackfriars Road, SE1 9PB
🕐 Sat/Sun guided tours of development at 10am, 1pm and 4pm (max 15, basement, presentation lounge, show apt, level 32) · Guided tours of executive lounge at 11am, 1pm, 3pm, 5pm (max 50, level 32 only) . T·d
⚠ Pre-book only: bit.ly/2eG9523
🚇 Farringdon, London Bridge, Waterloo, Southwark
The development comprises three distinct buildings linked by a landscaped public piazza. The centrepiece is a 50 storey (170m) residential tower in a unique, softly curved sculptural form. The tower will provide panoramic views of London. Simpson Haugh and Partners, 2017

## ORTUS
🚶 82-96 Grove Lane, Denmark Hill, SE5 8SN
🕐 Sat 10am–5pm + 'Open Moves' by Shane Waltener, an artistic response to a dance project exploring and developing new approaches to working holistically with adults with mental health.T·R·D
🚇 Denmark Hill
A sustainable, environmentally sensitive space; a 1,550sqm pavilion housing learning and event facilities, café and exhibition spaces. Duggan Morris Architects, 2014

## Passivhaus project
🚶 139 Grove Lane, Camberwell, SE5 8BG
🕐 Sat 10am–5pm (max 10) + hourly tours (11am-4pm, max 5). P
🚇 East Dulwich, Denmark Hill
A new build house forming part of an established mews lane. The client wanted the architects to design a Passivhaus within her rear garden. As she is getting older she wanted an accessible home which was very energy efficient. RDA Architects, 2017

## Pear Tree House, Friern Road, East Dulwich
🚶 190a Friern Road, East Dulwich, SE22 0BA
🕐 Sat 10am–5pm + hourly architect-led tours of the house, (11am-4pm). T·d
🚇 East Dulwich, North Dulwich
A contemporary self-build architect's house designed around a 100-year old pear tree, constructed of board-marked concrete and timber cladding featuring crafted joinery and light fittings. RIBA London award winner 2015. Edgley Design, 2014

## Peckham Library
🚶 122 Peckham Hill Street, SE15 5JR
🕐 Sat 10am–5pm (max 15). T·D
🚇 Queen's Road Peckham, Elephant & Castle
A dramatic design resembling an upside-down 'L' of coloured glass and green copper. A pure 21C building. RIBA Award Winner 2000. Alsop and Stormer, 2000

## Pitch Perfect
🚶 20 Daniels Road, SE15 3LR
🕐 Sat 11am–6pm (downstairs only) + hourly architect-led tour of extension (11am-4pm). R·P
🚇 Peckham Rye, Nunhead
One of a terrace of identical houses built in the 1960s for stone masons who worked on Nunhead Cemetery. nimtim proposed a sunken living space with an ↱

exposed timber structure, a playful sawtooth roof and rooflights. nimtim Architects, 2017

**Quay House**
🚶 2c Kings Grove (Queens Road end), SE15 2NB
🕐 Sat 12pm–5pm. T·R·P·B·d
🚇 Queen's Road Peckham
As seen on BBC4 & C5 TV, conversion of 1930s milk depot. Access to ground floor 'beach huts' and residence. Top flat under the 'wavy' roof specially open for 25th Anniversary Year. Exhibition in m2 gallery by Anna Heinrich & Leon Palmer. Quay 2c, 2001

**RDA Architects Studio**
🚶 16 Forest Hill Road, SE22 0RR
🕐 Sat 10am–5pm (max 10). T·R·P
🚇 East Dulwich, Peckham Rye
A 19C building forming part of a small parade of shops, refurbished to an extremely high standard. The front of the building has been restored to replicate the original Victorian façade. RDA Architects, 2015

**Sacred Heart RC Secondary School**
🚶 Camberwell New Road, SE5 0RP
🕐 Sat 10am–1pm. T
🚇 Oval, Denmark Hill
School's complete redevelopment includes a 4-storey teaching block, assembly block and sports block centred around a playground courtyard. Cottrell & Vermeulen Architecture, 2014

**Sands Films Studios & Rotherhithe Picture Research Library**
🚶 82 St Marychurch Street, Rotherhithe, SE16 4HZ
🕐 Sat/Sun hourly tours (9am-4pm, max 40) + library exhibition. T·R·P·B·d
🚇 Canada Water, Rotherhithe
Grade II listed riparian granary built with reclaimed timbers felled in 1700s. Converted in 1970s to picture library, film studios, prop and costume workshops. Oscar-winning international costume house for film, TV, theatre, opera, ballet.

**Sea Containers House**
🚶 22 Upper Ground, SE1 9PD
🕐 Sat 10am–1pm (max 15, exterior and WeWork floors). T·R·D
🚇 Blackfriars, Southwark
Conversion of 1970s Sea Containers building, with double-height entrance hall. Home to WeWork South Bank, a community of creators spanning 5 floors. T.P.Bennett & Son, 1978

**South Bank Tower**
🚶 55 Upper Ground, London, SE1 9PL
🕐 Sat 10am–4pm (max 20, 39th floor viewing gallery). T·D
ⓘ Pre-book only: bit.ly/2u009i1
🚇 Southwark, Blackfriars
A new landmark in a prime position on the South Bank. A redevelopment of a 1970s tower by Richard Seifert, the 41-storey tower features a spectacular 39th floor viewing gallery with far-reaching views across London. KPF, 2016

**South London Gallery**
🚶 65 Peckham Road, SE5 8UH
🕐 Sat/Sun 11am–8pm (architects on site). T·R·B·D
🚇 Elephant & Castle, Peckham Rye
Public contemporary art gallery housed in listed Victorian building. Top-lit gallery, contemporary extension and refurbishment exposing original structural features. Gabriel Orozco designed garden, shop, café and exhibitions open both days. Maurice Adams, 1896/KPF, 2016

**Southwark Integrated Waste Management Facility**
🚶 43 Devon Street, off Old Kent Road, SE15 1AL
🕐 Sat 10am–4pm + ½ hourly tours (max 40) + waste experts Q&A · wild bird display · children's crafting workshop drop in) T·R·d
🚇 Elephant & Castle, Queen's Road Peckham
One of Europe's most advanced recycling facilities, comprising of many sustainable features including grey water, solar panels and green roof. Designed for the purpose of turning waste into a resource. Thorpe Wheatley, 2012
*www.veolia.co.uk*

**Springbank**
🚶 81a Grove Park, SE5 8LE
🕐 Sun 2pm–6pm. T·d
🚇 Peckham Rye, Denmark Hill
One of a pair of modern houses on a sensitive site in a conservation area. A triple-height staircase atrium brings light into the heart of the house, and ground floor areas open onto courtyard gardens on three sides. Niki Borowiecki, 2013

**St Paul's, Newington**
🚶 Lorrimore Square, SE17 3QU
🕐 Sat 10am–1pm/Sun 11am–1pm. T
🚇 Kennington                                          ↦

Southwark Integrated Waste Management Facility ↘

The Music Box © Taylor Wimpey Central London ↗

1960s church with large copper and lead roof and concrete, brick and stained glass external structure. Church also has marble, wood and plaster interior and boasts artwork by Sculptor Freda Pinto and Gerald Holtom. Woodroffe Buchanan & Coulter, 1955

### Stuart Road

45 Stuart Road, SE15 3BE
Sat 1pm–5pm.
Peckham Rye, Nunhead
Originally a victorian house and shop, bombed in 1944 and repaired after the war. Almost entirely rebuilt as a 3-storey house, with a top floor living room overlooking the Nunhead Allotments.

### The Green, Nunhead

5 Nunhead Green, SE15 3QQ
Sat 10am–5pm ('living room,' upstairs, downstairs and garden)
Nunhead, Queen's Road Peckham, Brockley
Built by Southwark Council and run by local resident's charity Nunhead's Voice this new community centre has a family of discrete meeting rooms orientated around a publc living room which opens directly off the street. AOC Architecture Ltd, 2015

### The Music Box

235 Union Street, SE1 0LR
Sat/Sun 10am–5pm + project exhibition and film.
London Bridge, Blackfriars
A place for living; a space for learning. A mixed use campus for the LCCM – the erosion of its cubic form creates a longitudinal distinction between the music college and the residential apartments above. SPPARC Architecture, 2017
*www.spparcstudio.com*

### The Old Mortuary

St Marychurch Street, SE16 4JE
Sat/Sun 10am–5pm + short tour of building with historical background, every 10 mins. T·R·D
Canada Water, Rotherhithe
Retains many original features including original doors, vaulted ceiling in Russell Hall, lantern skylight & iron girder in Varney Room (former post-mortem room), wooden panelling in chapel. Now community centre. Norman Scorgie, 1895

### The Pyramid

Jubilee Yard, 31 Queen Elizabeth Street, SE1 2LP
Sat 10am–5pm (max 20) + exhibition. T·R·d
Tower Hill, London Bridge
New architect's studio, a contemporary pyramid clad in stainless steel and glass. A hidden gem newly arrived in a cobbled courtyard. Dransfield Design Architects, 2007

### The School of Historical Dress

52 Lambeth Road, SE1 7PP
Sat/Sun 10am–6pm + ½ hourly tours (10am-5pm, max 10). T·R·B·d
Elephant & Castle, Waterloo (East)
Now home to the School of Historical Dress, the building was originally built in 1841 as the 'Royal South London Dispensary' for the working poor. Sydney Smirke, 1841
*theschoolofhistoricaldress.org.uk*

### The View from The Shard

Joiner Street, SE1 9EX
Sat/Sun 10am–10pm.
Entry by public ballot ONLY: openhouselondon.open-city.org.uk/listings/2738 (50 places available to use at any point over the weekend)
London Bridge
The highest accessible point of the building at Level 72, an open-air viewing gallery 800ft/244m above ground, exposed to the elements, where guests are surrounded by the shards of glass forming the pinnacle of the building. Renzo Piano, 2013
*www.theviewfromtheshard.com*

### Unicorn Theatre

147 Tooley Street, SE1 2HZ
Sat 11am–6pm (max 12) + hourly tours (12pm-4pm, max 12) + 'Up Club' children's activity 12pm-2pm (max 15) T·R·d
London Bridge
The first professional, purpose-built theatre for young audiences in UK. Described as an asymmetric pavilion, the building has transparent elevations revealing its core, and was designed in consultation with young people. RIBA Winner 2006. Keith Williams Architects, 2005

## Weston Street
🚶 83 & 85 Weston Street, SE1 3RS
🕐 Sat 11am–6pm + ½ hourly tours (11am-5.30pm). d
🚇 London Bridge
Eight tessellating apartments built from in-situ concrete. Arranged over half levels, they incorporate the Solidspace DNA, generating a double-height void linking the eating, living and working spaces of the home. Simon Allford (Allford Hall Monaghan Morris), 2016

## Weston Williamson Architects Offices
🚶 12 Valentine Place, SE1 8QH
🕐 Sat/Sun 10am–5pm. T·R·d
🚇 Southwark, Waterloo
Architects' studio within a 19C warehouse building in the Valentine Place conservation area. Many original features have been restored, celebrated and coupled with contemporary fittings and furniture. Weston Williamson + Partners, 2013

## White Cube Bermondsey
🚶 144-152 Bermondsey Street, SE1 3TQ
🕐 Sat 10am–6pm/Sun 12pm–6pm. Tours of exhibition, archive room and private viewing area Sat 12pm, 2.30pm, Sun 1pm, 2.30pm (max 15). T·B·D
🚇 London Bridge, Bermondsey
White Cube Bermondsey incorporates more than 58,000 sq ft of interior space. The building, which dates from the 1970s, was renovated and designed by London and Berlin-based architects Casper Mueller Kneer in 2011. Casper Mueller Kneer Architects, 2011

## William Booth College
🚶 Champion Park, SE5 8BQ
🕐 Sat 10am–5pm + ½ hourly campus and tower tours. T·R·d
🚇 East Dulwich, Denmark Hill
This monumental Grade II listed college with massive brick tower gives commanding views to the City and Docklands. Sir Giles Gilbert Scott, 1929

## Yellow House
🚶 282a Croxted Road, SE24 9DA
🕐 Sat 10am–5pm + hourly architect-led tours of extension (11am-4pm). R
🚇 Herne Hill
The client wanted an additional bedroom that could be rented temporarily and might later be used by them as a guest/spare/baby room. A limited budget meant a focus on creating large, flexible spaces using simple, characterful materials. nimtim Architects, 2016

## Young Vic
🚶 66 The Cut, SE1 8LZ
🕐 Sun backstage tours at 12.30pm, 1.30pm, 3pm (Foyer open to the public as normal). T·d
🚇 Waterloo, Waterloo (East)
Theatre producing classics, new plays, forgotten works, musicals and opera. It has deep roots in its neighborhood and co-producing relationships with leading theatres all over the world. Haworth Tompkins, 2007

The Shard © The View from The Shard ↘

# Walks + Tours

## Bankside Urban Forest
🚶 Meet: Bankside Community Space, 18 Great Guildford Street, SE1 0FD
🕐 Sat 3pm (max 15). D
❗ Pre-book only: vb@betterbankside.co.uk
🚇 Borough, Blackfriars
Guided walk of Bankside Urban Forest, an ongoing public space project, about recent & emerging public space and greening projects in one of London's oldest neighbourhoods.

## The Low Line: Bankside
🚶 Meet: cycle hire docking station, behind Southwark tube station, Blackfriars Road, SE1 8JZ
🕐 Sat 12pm (max 15)
❗ Pre-book only: vb@betterbankside.co.uk (with 'Low Line Walk / Open House' in subject)
🚇 London Bridge, Southwark
Guided walking tour of the Low Line in Bankside. An emerging pedestrian walkway along the mighty Victorian rail viaduct linking Southwark tube with London Bridge. Gort Scott, 2008

# Sutton

| | |
|---|---|
| Borough area (km²) | 43.8 |
| Population | 202,600 |
| Average age | 39 |
| First Open House | 2006 |

Sutton

**All Saints Carshalton**
High Street, Carshalton, SM5 3AQ
Sat 12pm–5pm/Sun 12.45pm–5pm. T·d
Carshalton
12C south aisle and former chancel. Blomfield nave, chancel, baptistry. Kempe glass, Bodley reredos and screen, spectacular Comper decorations, monuments and brasses, award-winning lighting scheme, fine modern benches. A & R Blomfield, 19C

**Carew Manor**
Church Road, Beddington, SM6 7NN
Sun hourly tours (11am-2pm, max 20). P·D
Pre-book only: 020 8770 4297
Hackbridge
Origin c1510, Grade I listed great hall with its timber hammerbeam roof built for Richard Carew about 1510. 18C and Victorian alterations. Site of important Elizabethan garden created by Sir Francis Carew.

**Carshalton Boys Sports College**
Back gate, Wigmore Road, Carshalton, SM5 1RH
Sat 10am–1pm (max 10). T·D
Morden, Carshalton
New dedicated English department in 2-storey, 10 classroom teaching facility. Clad in dark brick, with floor to ceiling windows, it has a unique identity in a campus-like setting. Maths classroom building clad in Cor-Ten Steel mesh panels. Fraser Brown MacKenna, 2014

**Carshalton Water Tower and Historic Gardens**
West Street, Carshalton, SM5 2QG
Sat/Sun 1pm–5pm + 'Dodgy Bankers' exhibition. T·R·d
Morden, Carshalton
Early 18C Grade II listed building incorporating plunge bath with Delft tiles, orangery, saloon and pump chamber with part-restored water wheel. Hermitage and sham bridge in grounds.

**Honeywood**
Honeywood Walk, Carshalton, SM5 3NX
Sat/Sun 10am–5pm + children's Honeywood window trail and Honeywood colouring sheets + 'The Kirks at Honeywood in the Victorian and Edwardian period' hourly tours (Sat 2pm-4pm,

max 25) + T·R·P·B·d
Carshalton
Chalk and flint house dating to 17C with additions including extensions of 1896 and 1903 when owned by John Pattinson Kirk. Rich in period detail and the interior restored and stairs opened up with funding from the Heritage Lottery Fund.

**Little Holland House**
40 Beeches Avenue, Carshalton, SM5 3LW
Sun 11am–5pm (max 50). T·d
Morden, Carshalton Beeches
Grade II listed building whose interior was created by Dickinson, inspired by the ideals of John Ruskin and William Morris and contains Dickinson's paintings, hand-made furniture, furnishings, metalwork and friezes, in Arts & Crafts style. Frank Dickinson, 1902

**Nonsuch Gallery and Service Wing at Nonsuch Mansion**
Nonsuch Park, Ewell Road, Cheam, SM3 8AP
Sun 11am–4pm + ½ hourly Service Wing tours (2pm-4.30pm, max 4). T·R·P·B·d
Cheam
Gothic style Georgian mansion built for Samuel Farmer. Restored Service Wing includes dairy, kitchen, scullery, larders & laundries. Gallery has model of Henry VIII's Nonsuch Palace, archaeological dig artefacts and mansion stained glass. Jeffrey Wyatt, 1806

**Russettings**
25 Worcester Road, Sutton, SM2 6PR
Sun 10am–1pm (max 20, Downstairs only). T·P·D
Sutton
A double-fronted red brick upper-middle class house, and one of a few Victorian villas to survive in Sutton. The well-preserved interior includes an entrance hall with a mosaic tiled floor and an oak galleried staircase. Frederick Wheeler, 1899

**St Nicholas Church**
St Nicholas Way, Sutton, SM1 1ST
Sat 10am–1pm/Sun 10am–5pm + 'History, tradition and legend' exhibition. T·R·d
Sutton, West Sutton
Built in the Gothic style with dressed flint and stone ↱

dressings. There are monuments to Joseph Glover (1628), to Lady Dorothy Brownlow (1699), to William Earl Talbot (1782) and to Isaac Littlebury (1740). Edwin Nash, 1864

### Subsea 7
🚶 40 Brighton Road, Sutton, SM2 5BN
🕐 Sun tours at 11.15am, 10am, 12.30pm (max 10) T·R·D
① Pre-book only: sally.halsey@subsea7.com
🚇 Sutton
A BREEAM 'Excellent' high quality, contemporary and flexible office building with central atrium, exhibition space, restaurant, café, gym and terraces providing a dynamic and exciting workplace environment for staff and visitors. ESA, 2016

### The Circle Library
🚶 Green Wrythe Lane, Carshalton, SM5 1JJ
🕐 Sat 10am–1pm. T·P·D
🚇 Morden, Carshalton
An inviting, accessible contemporary social space. Full of natural light with spacious free-flowing areas, the building incorporates a range of environmental features including ground-source heating, sedum roof and rainwater harvesting. Curl la Tourelle Architects, 2010

### The Sutton Life Centre
🚶 24 Alcorn Close, SM3 9PX
🕐 Sat 10am–5pm + tour at 11am (max 25) + crafts for children. T·R·P·D
🚇 Morden, Sutton Common
Multi-purpose community building awarded BREEAM Excellent for its use of sustainable energy. Key features include a unique learning facility for children aged 10-13, library, eco-garden, sports pitch and climbing wall. Curl la Tourelle Architects, 2010

## Walks + Tours

### Carshalton Walking Tour
🚶 Meet: at the entrance to Carshalton Train Station, Station Approach, SM5 2HW
🕐 Sun 10am (max 30). T·R
① Pre-book only: 020 8770 4297
🚇 Carshalton
Walk following the verdant banks of the River Wandle, which flows past a number of unique heritage buildings and a world-renowned eco-building. Includes watermill sites, Carshalton Chuch, 18C Water Tower, Honeywood Museum. 80% is off road.

### Sutton Walk: A Suburban Ramble from Russetings to St.Nicholas Church
🚶 Meet: Russetings, 25 Worcester Road, Sutton, SM2 6PR
🕐 Sun 12.30pm (max 30)
① Pre-book only: 020 8770 4297
🚇 Sutton
Walk looking at early suburban development and the changes that have taken place in 19C and 20C. Ends at St Nicholas Church, Sutton.

### Sutton's Urban Beginnings: a walk through Victorian Newtown
🚶 Meet: junction of Lind Road and Lower Road, Sutton, SM1 4PP
🕐 Sun 3pm (max 30)
① Pre-book only: 020 8770 4297
🚇 Sutton
A walk through Victorian Newtown exploring the early suburban development of Sutton.

Subsea 7 © Matt Clayton ↘

# Tower Hamlets

| | |
|---|---|
| Borough area (km²) | 19.8 |
| Population | 304,000 |
| Average age | 31 |
| First Open House | 1992 |

**TOWER HAMLETS**

## 133 Whitechapel High Street
🚶 133 Whitechapel High Street, E1 7QR
🕐 Sat 10am–5pm. T·d
🚇 Whitechapel, Aldgate East
Sensitive refurbishment of a 1930s style Art Deco building, using eye-catching Miami-inspired pastel colours with the white masonry walls, and restored wood-block polished floors showcasing the building's original atmosphere. Morrow + Lorraine Architects, 2016

## Bow Church - St Mary's and Holy Trinity
🚶 Bow Road, E3 3AH
🕐 Sat 11am–5pm/Sun 12pm–5pm + tour at 1pm, 3pm (max 20) + Art workshop: painting stained glass windows · Wildlife trail (3-14 years · max 15)
🚇 Mile End, Stratford
Medieval village church, restored in late 19C and after bomb damage in WWII. 15C font and memorials from five centuries. Grade II* listed. Refurbished for 700th anniversary in 2011; bell tower and cupola currently being restored. C R Ashbee (refurb), 1900/H S Goodhart-Rendel (restoration), 1945

## Chrisp Street Market
🚶 The Clocktower, Chrisp Street Market, E14 6AQ
🕐 Sat/Sun 10am–1pm (max 20).
🚇 All Saints
Marketplace including a beautiful Modernist 'practical folly' designed as part of the site for the 1951 Festival of Britain live architecture exhibition. Sir Frederick Gibberd, 1951

## Christ Church Spitalfields
🚶 Commercial Street, E1 6LY
🕐 Sat 10am–5pm (access crypt and café). T·R·D
🚇 Aldgate East, Liverpool Street
Grade I listed English Baroque masterpiece by Nicholas Hawksmoor (1714-1729), restored by Whitfield Partners 1978-2002 and Purcell Miller Tritton. New crypt redevelopment by Dow Jones Architects (2015) opens the crypt as a public space. Nicholas Hawksmoor, 1714

## Club Row
🚶 Rochelle School & Club Row, Arnold Circus, E2 7ES
🕐 Sat/Sun 10am–5pm (general access to communal areas only) + architect-led tour of interior and exterior spaces including Main Hall and Former Marching Ground at 11am, 2pm (max 20) + Special exhibition of architectural and contextual materials about Club Row. T·R
❗ Pre-book only: london@quinnuk.com
🚇 Bethnal Green, Shoreditch High Street
A rare example of the schools of E R Robson. Following extended community consultations, the Grade II listed building was carefully refurbished and amended, providing 8,500 sq.ft of new office and gallery space. Edward Robson, 1878/ Quinn Architects (refurb), 2016
*quinnuk.com*

## Cranbrook Estate
🚶 Cranbrook Community Centre, Mace Street, E2 0RB
🕐 Sun 12pm–5pm (interior of one of the buildings will be accessible only via guided tour) + visit the interior of a flat decorated in mid-century style, hourly (12pm-4pm, max 12) + Cranbrook: Then and Now' exhibition. T·R·d
❗ Pre-book only: bit.ly/2uNo40q
🚇 Mile End, Liverpool Street
Iconic modernist estate designed by Lubetkin, replacing bomb-damaged Victorian terraces. Berthold Lubetkin & Francis Skinner, 1966

## Crossrail Place Roof Garden
🚶 One Canada Square, Canary Wharf, E14 5AB
🕐 Sat tours led by Gillespies Landscape Architects, hourly (10am-4pm). T·D
🚇 Poplar, Limehouse
The first new building to open for Crossrail. Located above the new station, the garden showcases unusual plants from across the globe, encased beneath an intricate lattice roof. Foster + Partners, 2016/ Gillespies (landscape), 2016

## Darbishire Place (Peabody Whitechapel Estate)
🚶 John Fisher Street, E1 8HA
🕐 Sat 10am–1pm, ½ hourly tour (no access to flats, max 10). d
🚇 Tower Hill
New block of 13 homes which completes an ensemble of six housing blocks surrounding an internal

courtyard. The façade complements the existing Victorian buildings by Henry Astley Darbishire. RIBA Award Winner & Stirling Prize shortlist 2015. Niall McLaughlin Architects, 2014

### Dennis Severs House
🕈 18 Folgate Street, E1 6BX
🕒 Sat 12pm–4pm (max 30)
ⓘ Pre-book only: info@dennissevershouse.co.uk
🚇 Liverpool Street, Shoreditch High Street
Originally part of the St John's and Tillards Estate, when Folgate street was known as White Lion Street. The house retains its panelled interior and staircase of 1724, and was altered in the early 19C.

### Four Corners
🕈 121 Roman Road, E2 0QN
🕒 Sat 10am–6pm + Tour of Darkroom's print space, hourly (10.30am-4.30pm, max 30). T·R·d
🚇 Bethnal Green
Refurbished extended building, a centre for film and photography. Central courtyard integrated 'hub' allows light and air to filter through. Loft conversion to create studio and work space. Sustainable features include sedum roof. JaK Studio, 2007

### Hermitage Community Moorings
🕈 16 Wapping High Street, E1W 1NG
🕒 Sat/Sun 11am–4pm (max 60, access to the moorings and visiting vessels but not to private residential vessels). T·R·d
🚇 Tower Hill, Wapping
A development of residential and recreational moorings for historic vessels on the Thames. The unique Pier House, built to a high specification, provides a floating community centre just downstream from Tower Bridge. Anna Versteeg & Ollie Price, 2010

### Hult International Business School
🕈 35 Commercial Road, E1 1LD
🕒 Sat/Sun 10am–5pm (max 100). T·D
🚇 Aldgate, Aldgate East
Transformation of a listed brewery and recent extension into a new undergraduate campus for the Hult International Business School. Sergison Bates Architects, 2014

### JJ House
🕈 35 Morgan Street, E3 5AA
🕒 Sat/Sun 11am–6pm (max 20, no access to the ground floor, 1st floor and rear garden) + architect-led tour, hourly (11am-5pm, max 10).
🚇 Mile End
Refurbishment and extension of a Grade II listed building in East London. The extensions consist of a frame-less glass box which is sunken below ground and a roof extension providing space for an additional master bedroom and a bathroom. Space Group Architects, 2014

### Kingsley Hall
🕈 Powis Road, off Bruce Road, E3 3HJ
🕒 Sat 11am–6pm (Gandhi's cell, Peace Garden, history and archives exhibition) + Hourly tours (12pm-5pm, max 18). T·R·P·d
🚇 Bromley By Bow, Bow Church
Pioneer community centre founded by peace campaigners Muriel & Doris Lester. Main hall, 6 rooftop cells for community volunteers. Links with Gandhi, George Lansbury, R D Laing's Philadelphia ↦

Crossrail Place Roof Garden ↘

Assoc. Set for Attenborough's Gandhi 1983.
Charles Cowles Voysey, 1928

## Limehouse Town Hall
- 🏃 646 Commercial Road, E14 7HA
- 🕐 Sat/Sun 12pm–5pm. T
- 🚇 Canary Wharf, Limehouse

Palazzo-style former town hall with stone dressings, vast arched windows to the upper Hall and grand Portland stone staircase. A & C Harston, 1881

## London Buddhist Centre
- 🏃 51 Roman Road , Bethnal Green, E2 0HU
- 🕐 Sun 10am–5pm (max 15) + tours at 11am, 4pm (max 20). T·R·B·D
- 🚇 Bethnal Green, Cambridge Heath

Ornate vernacular red brick Victorian former fire station. Grade II listed. Now a Buddhist Centre with 3 beautiful shrine rooms with Buddha figures and paintings. Robert Pearsall, 1888

## London Dock - Pennington Street Warehouse
- 🏃 Pennington Street, E1W 2AD
- 🕐 Sat/Sun 10am–5pm (max 60, access to basement only). T·P·D
- 🚇 Aldgate East, Wapping

The Grade II listed warehouse was built as part of the first enclosed commercial docks in London, and used for the storage of goods held in bond. The warehouse will be restored for commercial use as part of the London Dock development. Daniel Asher Alexander, 1805

## Metropolitan Wharf
- 🏃 Unit 305, Metropolitan Wharf, 70 Wapping Wall, E1W 3SS
- 🕐 Sat/Sun 10am–5pm (max 30, access to foyer of Metropolitan Wharf and Bell Phillips Office on 3rd floor only) + Next generation of designers (max 30). T·D
- 🚇 Shadwell, Wapping

Metropolitan Wharf is an iconic Grade II listed

JJ House © Luca Piffaretti ↘

Victorian tea warehouse, with views over the Thames. The building has been restored and Bell Phillips Architects occupy a third floor office with original features. HawkinsBrown (refurb), 2012
*www.bellphillips.com*

## Mint Street
- 🏃 Meeting point: outside The Pill Box Kitchen, 115 Coventry Road, E2 6GG
- 🕐 Sat 10am–1pm (max 15)
- ⓘ Pre-book: mintstreettours.eventbrite.co.uk (limited turn up on the day places also available)
- 🚇 Bethnal Green

A housing development of 67 flats for Peabody, close to the railway creating a new pedestrian public street. An example of how to combine affordable, shared ownership and market sale homes on a noisy urban site. RIBA Award Winner 2015. Pitman Tozer Architects, 2014

## Museum of London Docklands
- 🏃 No. 1 Warehouse, West India Quay (off Hertsmere Road), E14 4AL
- 🕐 Sat/Sun 10am–5.45pm + ½ hourly tour (11am–4.30pm, max 30). T·R·B·D
- 🚇 West India Quay, Canary Wharf

Grade 1 listed, late Georgian sugar warehouse now housing the Museum of London Docklands. Sensitively restored, the new multimedia displays coexist with the massive timber and brick structures of the original building. George Gwilt & Son, 1802

## One Bishops Square
- 🏃 1 Bishops Square, E1 6AD
- 🕐 Sun 10am–5pm (no access to working floors). T·R·D
- 🚇 Liverpool Street

'Intelligent' building with sustainable features, including London's largest office-based solar installation and inbuilt computer system aimed at efficiency and energy conservation. Lights and air conditioning operate only when area is populated. Foster + Partners, 2006

## One Canada Square, Canary Wharf Group Marketing Suite and Level 39
- 🏃 Meet: South Lobby, One Canada Square, E14 5AB
- 🕐 Sat tours to marketing suite and Level 39, hourly (10am-4pm, max 20). D
- ⓘ Pre-book only: openhouse@canarywharf.com (state names and preferred time)
- 🚇 Canary Wharf, Heron Quays

CWG has overseen the largest urban regeneration project ever undertaken in Europe. Canary Wharf has 115,000 visitors per day, houses Europe's most influential financial technology scaler, Level39 and will soon welcome its first residents. Cesar Pelli, 1991

## Oxford House in Bethnal Green
- 🏃 Derbyshire Street, E2 6HG
- 🕐 Sat 10am–5pm (max 15) + hourly tours of the secret Victorian Chapel and the small but clever Pocket Park (10am-4pm, max 15). T·d

The New Road Residence ↗

🏛 Shoreditch High Street, Bethnal Green
First *University Settlement" to open Sept 1884.
Now arts, community & heritage space. Grade II &
currently on Buildings at Risk Register. New Pocket
Park adjacent to building opened 2014. Heritage
project to start 2018. Sir Arthur Blomfield, 1892

## Poplar Pavilion
🚹 East India Square, Chrisp Street, London, E14 0EA
🕐 Sat/Sun 10am–5pm (max 50) + Collaborators
   Talks at 10.30am, 12.30pm, 2.30pm, 4.30pm). P·d
🏛 All Saints
The Poplar Pavilion explores ideas about wellbeing in
the city. Co-designed and built over 4 months with
the local population it is an experiment, learning
tool and a venue. Project lead: artist and Wellcome
Fellow Alex Julyan. collaborative architecture, 2017

## Queen Mary University of London: Mile End Campus
🚹 Graduate Centre, Queen Mary College, Mile End
   Road, E1 4NS
🕐 Sat 10am–5pm. T·D
🏛 Stepney Green, Mile End
The Graduate Centre creates a strong identity
through the juxtaposition of cantilevering brickwork
volumes, with a floating glass box at the top that
exploits the exceptional views from the campus over
the City of London and Canary Wharf. Wilkinson
Eyre Architects, 2012

## Sandys Row Synagogue
🚹 4a Sandys Row, E1 7HW
🕐 Sun 11am–4pm + History of the synagogue by
author Rachel Lichtenstein, hourly + Our Hidden
Histories (max 15, Film by Rachel Lichtenstein
featuring Sandys Row members recollections of
the synagogue and life in Jewish East End.). T·R·B
🏛 Liverpool Street, Shoreditch High Street
Hidden gem at the very heart of London. Built
originally as a Huguenot chapel in 1763, this
extraordinary building has been in continuous
use as a synagogue since 1860. Oldest Ashkenazi
synagogue in London.

## Society for the Protection of Ancient Buildings
🚹 37 Spital Square, E1 6DY
🕐 Sat 10am–5pm (No access to top floor) + Craft
   display. B
🏛 Moorgate, Shoreditch High Street
The only Georgian building left on Spital Square,
the headquarters of the Society for the Protection
of Ancient Buildings. It is likely that it was built in
1740 by Peter Ogier, a Huguenot silk merchant.

## St Anne's Church, Limehouse
🚹 Newell Street, E14 7HP
🕐 Sun 10am–5pm. T·R
🏛 Westferry, Limehouse
St Anne's Limehouse is an imposing Hawksmoor
Church in brick and portland stone. Nicholas
Hawksmoor, 1730

## St Boniface's RC German Church
🚹 47 Adler Street, E1 1EE
🕐 Sat 10am–5pm. d
🏛 Fenchurch Street, Aldgate East
Plain modern church serving the German-speaking ↦

Catholic community in London. Landmark tower featuring four bells, artwork and organ by artists and craftsmen from Germany. Donald Plaskett Marshall & Partners, 1960

### St Dunstan and All Saints Church
🏃 Stepney High Street, E1 0NR
🕐 Sat 10am–5pm/Sun 1pm–5pm + tour Sat 11am, Sun 2pm + 'Take A Line for a Walk' children's activity at 2pm (age 6+). T·R·D
🚇 Stepney Green, Limehouse
Grade I listed early medieval parish church (site in use from 952, pre-dating Tower of London). Fine interior: Anglo-Saxon Rood, Norman font, medieval 'squint', memorials, stained glass, brasses. Many founders of Trinity House buried here.

### St Matthias Old Church - Community Centre
🏃 113 Poplar High Street, E14 0AE
🕐 Sat/Sun 10am–5pm (one floor only). T·R·P·D
🚇 All Saints, Poplar
Oldest building in Docklands built in the Gothic and Classical styles, with original 17C stonework and fine mosaics. One of only three churches built during the Civil War, it was originally the East India Company Chapel. John Tanner, 1649

### St Paul's Bow Common
🏃 Cnr Burdett Road/St Paul's Way, E3 4AR
🕐 Sat 10am–5pm/Sun 1pm–5pm + ½ hourly tours (max 12). T·R·P·D
🚇 Mile End, Limehouse
Described as 'the most significant church built after the 2nd World War in Britain' – Brutalist, inclusive and influential signpost for future church design. Robert McGuire & Keith Murray, 1960

Queen Mary University © Jack Hobhouse ↘

### St Paul's Old Ford
🏃 St Stephen's Road, Nr Roman Road, E3 5JL
🕐 Sat 10am–4pm. T·R·D
🚇 Mile End, Bethnal Green
Victorian church rehabilitated to include a building within a building, a stunning Ark/Pod of tulipwood situated in the nave. *Stylish...thrilling" Jay Merrick in The Independent. Winner of RICS Community Benefit Award, London Region 2005. Matthew Lloyd Architects LLP, 2004

### Thames River Police
🏃 98 Wapping High Street, E1W 2NE
🕐 Sat/Sun 11am–5pm (museum only). d
🚇 Wapping
A unique ex-carpenters' workshop (1910), contained within a working police station. The workshop space now displays a history of Thames River Police.

### The Grim House
🏃 16 Underwood Road, E1 5AW
🕐 Sat 1pm-4.15pm/Sun 10.30am-1pm architect-led tours, every 45 mins (max 10).
⚠ Pre-book only: info@checaromero.com
🚇 Whitechapel, Bethnal Green
The Grim House has emerged from its 1980s cocoon, reimagining space and light to transform the footprint of this East London home into an innovative solution for a growing family. Checa Romero Architects, 2015

### The New Road Residence
🏃 33 New Road, E1 1HE
🕐 Sat/Sun 10am–5pm (max 15). T
🚇 Liverpool Street, Whitechapel
A 1797 wisteria-clad Georgian townhouse. Once a linen drapers' store, its immaculate character has been retained in the detailing. Through minimal structural intervention, an aesthetic overhaul has transformed it into a minimal haven.

### The Old Spratts Factory
🏃 Unit 4, Block B, 2 Fawe Street, E14 6PD
🕐 Sat 11am–6pm/Sun 11am-5pm (max 30) + hourly architect-led tours.
🚇 Bromley-by-Bow
A recently carefully restored and refurbished 3,000 sq ft residential unit within a converted dog biscuit factory, originally built in 1890. This particular building used to contain the grain & flour warehouse and two bakeries. Space Group Architects, 2016

### The Tree House
🏃 200 Jubilee Street, E1 3BP
🕐 Sun ½ hourly tours (10am-4.30pm, max 11). D
⚠ Pre-book only: bit.ly/2uNI6rw
🚇 Bethnal Green, Whitechapel
A timber framed and clad addition to two 1830s terraced cottages. Ramped interior reframes the activities of the house around the garden. The mother of a busy family remains central to activity whether in her wheelchair or resting. 6a Architects, 2013

### The Wash Houses (Formerly The Womens Library)
🚶 25 Old Castle Street, E1 7NT
🕐 Sat 10am–1pm (max 25, main exhibition spaces, reading room and small garden). T·d
🚇 Aldgate East, Whitechapel
RIBA award-winning building. Part listed frontage with purpose new build archive and exhibition building to the rear. The building houses the University's archives and the Frederick Parker Chair Collection which is on display. Wright and Wright Architects, 2002

### The Whitechapel Building
🚶 10 Whitechapel High Street, E1 8QS
🕐 Sat 10am–5pm/Sun 2pm–5pm (G/F lobby only) + architect present at 11am. d
🚇 Liverpool Street, Fenchurch Street
Major refurbishment of RBS's 1980s Aldgate Union into a 186,400 sq ft flexible office hub for creative occupiers. Newly positioned entrance, 7,000 sq ft lobby/atrium with break-out space, Grind café & outdoor terrace + bike store/showers. Fletcher Priest Architects, 2017

### Town Hall Hotel & Apartments
🚶 Patriot Square, E2 9NF
🕐 Sun 1pm–5pm (max 15, no access to the Bethnal Hall) + staff-led tours of the renovation, ½ hourly (1pm-3.30pm, max 15). T·R·D
🚇 Shoreditch High Street, Bethnal Green
Beautiful redevelopment of a Grade II listed town hall incorporating contemporary design complementing the original Edwardian/Art Deco features. Percy Robinson & W Alban Jones, 1909

### Trinity Buoy Wharf/Container City
🚶 64 Orchard Place, E14 0JW
🕐 Sat/Sun 10am–5pm + Tour at 12.30pm (max 40). T·d
🚇 Canning Town
Home to London's only lighthouse, fine stock buildings and examples of the innovative Container City buildings. This former buoy manufacturing site is now a centre for the creative industries with various sculptures and installations. James Douglass/Eric Reynolds/Buschow Henley/ABK Architects/Lacey and Partners, 1822-75/1950s-2014

### West India Dock Impounding Station
🚶 Western end of Marsh Wall, E14 8JT
🕐 Sat/Sun 10am–5pm.
🚇 Heron Quays
The recently automated impounding station controls the water level in the docks using the original Worthington Simpson pumps driven by Lancashire dynamo.

### Wilton's Music Hall
🚶 Graces Alley, E1 8JB
🕐 Sat 10am–1pm. T·R·d
🚇 Shadwell, London Bridge
The oldest grand music hall in the world, complete with papier-mâché balconies, barley sugar iron columns and unique atmosphere. Hall is fronted by five terrace houses; four Georgian and one 1990s. RIBA Award winner. Jacob Maggs, 1859

## Walks + Tours

### Tower Hamlets Cemetery Park
🚶 Meet: Tower Hamlets Cemetery Park, Southern Grove, Mile End, E3 4PX
🕐 Sat 2.30pm/Sun 11am–6pm + guided tours at 10.30am, 12.30pm, 2pm. T·R·P·D
🚇 Bow Road, Stratford
One of the magnificent 7 cemeteries. Burials ceased 1966, now 33 acres of woodland, meadows & ponds including the Soanes Centre (Robson Kelly 1993). Of outstanding importance for flora and fauna, set amongst funereal monuments, some listed. Thomas Wyatt & David Brandon, 1841

The Whitechapel Building © Hufton & Crow ↘

# Waltham Forest

| | |
|---|---|
| Borough area (km²) | **38.8** |
| Population | **276,200** |
| Average age | **35** |
| First Open House | **1994** |

Waltham Forest

### Black Ridge House
🏃 152 Winns Avenue, E17 5HA
🕐 Sat 10am–5pm (max 30) + architect-led tour of extension every 15 mins.
🚇 Blackhorse Road
Black timber-clad rear extension to a historic Warner house. Burnt cedar cladding juxtaposes against the Victorian brickwork, whilst skylights and sliding doors pierce the timber structure allowing access to the garden. Neil Dusheiko Architects, 2016
*www.neildusheiko.com*

### Blackhorse Sideshow
🏃 Forest Works, Forest Road, E17 6JF
🕐 Sat 10am–4pm. T·R·D
🚇 St.James' Street, Blackhorse Road
Sideshow will be a theatrical structure delivering a series of open events and a café hub, located where the first London bus was built in the 1920s. A giant marble run will also weave its way around the build through disused bus parts. Blackhorse Workshop, ehk! Architects, 2017

### Blackhorse Workshop
🏃 1-2 Sutherland Road Path, E17 6BX
🕐 Sat 10am–4pm + Tour at 2pm. T
❗ Pre-book only: www.blackhorseworkshop.co.uk
🚇 St.James' Street, Blackhorse Road
A makerspace offering open access to a fully equipped wood and metal workshop with bench

The Science Lab © MWV ↘

space, tools and machinery. Includes outdoor working area, education space, community café and 35 studios for creative businesses. Assemble, 2014

### Monoux Almshouses
🏃 Church End, E17 9RL
🕐 Sun 10am–1pm (Entry to Monoux Hall, former Monoux School only). T
🚇 Walthamstow Queens Road, Walthamstow Central
A row of 13 dwellings plus a hall used as a committee room and offices, constructed as one block on two floors. The building is divided by a jettied cross range. Grade II listed. Sir George Monoux, 1527

### Queen Elizabeth's Hunting Lodge and The View
🏃 6, Rangers Road, Chingford, E4 7QH
🕐 Sun 10am–5pm + Talk on the history of the building and Epping Forest in The View at 12pm. R
🚇 Chingford
Unique Grade II* listed timber-framed hunt-standing, commissioned by Henry VIII, with fine views of Epping Forest. Alongside is Epping Forest's main visitor centre, The View. with displays about the history and ecology of the area.

### St John the Baptist
🏃 High Road, Leytonstone, E11 1HH
🕐 Sat 10am-4pm + tours of the tower every 45 (11am-3pm, max 20).
🚇 Leytonstone
Built 1832-33, a listed building that sits at the heart of the Leytonstone community. It was the design of Edward Blore, an architect famous for completing John Nash's work at Buckingham Palace.

### The Science Lab
🏃 134, Trumpington Road, E7 9EQ
🕐 Sat/Sun 11am-6pm, tours of whole building (no tours between 1.30pm-3pm).
❗ Pre-book only: hello@madewithvolume.com
🚇 Wanstead Park, Leytonstone
A two-storey 1935 former school canteen, science lab and art department that was later used as recording studio. It has now been converted into a 200 sqm 4-bed residence with green roof/terrace including 21 large Crittall windows. Made with Volume, 2017

### The Walthamstow Pumphouse Museum

🏃 10 South Access Road, E17 8AX
🕐 Sat/Sun 10am–5pm + Stationary steam engines in operation at 11am. T·R·B·d
🚇 Blackhorse Road, St.James' Street

Grade II listed Victorian engine house remodelled to take a pair of Marshall steam engines, still in working order. George Jerram, 1885

### Turning Earth Ceramics E10

🏃 11 Argall Avenue, E10 7QE
🕐 Sat/Sun 10.30am–5pm (No access to the office, the glaze room or In Production room). T·P·D

New ceramics centre for the Lee Valley, covering the entire top floor of an old hardware factory. Three rooms, providing just over 8000 sq ft of floor space; the main room is capped by its original saw-tooth glass roof feature.

### Vestry House Museum

🏃 Vestry Road, E17 9NH
🕐 Sat/Sun 10am–5pm (public galleries and garden) + Historic Walthamstow Village tours Sat 11am, 3pm (max 20). T·B·d
🚇 Walthamstow Central, Walthamstow Queens Road

Built as a workhouse in 1730, the date plaque warns 'If any should not work neither should he eat'. It became a police station, then a private house, and from 1931 the Museum for Waltham Forest.

### Walthamstow Assembly Hall

🏃 Waltham Forest Town Hall Complex, Forest Road, E17 4JF
🕐 Sat/Sun 9am–11am. T·P·d
🚇 Walthamstow Queens Road, Walthamstow Central

A striking, grade II listed, Art Deco style building completed during World War II. Built in a restrained style in Portland stone. Renowned for its acoustics, the hall has been used for famous recordings and concerts. P D Hepworth, 1942

### Walthamstow Library

🏃 206 High Street, E17 7JN
🕐 Sat 9am–7pm/Sun 10am–4pm (max 50, no access to roof terrace) + tour at 11am (Sat) and 10am (Sun) (max 25). T·D
🚇 Walthamstow Central

The 1903 Reading Room and 1909 Wren-style red brick building with stone dressings were refurbished in 2006 creating a new 8m high glass foyer with terracotta cladding and a children's library. Faulkner Browns, 1909

### Walthamstow School for Girls

🏃 58-60 Church Hill, Walthamstow, E17 9RZ
🕐 Sat 10am–1pm + Tour at 10am. T·R·d
🚇 Walthamstow Central, Walthamstow Queens Road

Founded 1890, moving to present site in 1913, retaining St Mary's Vicarage (1902). Grade II listed frontage, in a red brick English Baroque style. Won a BCSE Design Award in 2011. Greek Theatre, 1935, within the grounds. C J Dawson, 1911

### William Morris Gallery

🏃 Lloyd Park, Forest Road, E17 4PP
🕐 Sat/Sun 10am–5pm (public galleries only) + tours of gallery, Lloyd Park and artists' Studios at 11am & 2pm (Sunday, max 25). T·R·P·B·D
🚇 Blackhorse Road, Walthamstow Queens Road

Starts with a tour of the William Morris Gallery, revealing the history of this Grade II* Georgian building and its last owners, the Lloyd family. The tour continues into Lloyd Park and ends with a visit to the Lloyd Park studios.

Turning Earth E10 © Artur Rummel ↘

# Wandsworth

| | |
|---|---|
| Borough area (km²) | **34.6** |
| Population | **321,000** |
| Average age | **35** |
| First Open House | **1994** |

### 4-8 Hafer Road
🏃 4A Hafer Road, SW11 1HF
🕐 Sun hourly tours (11am-3pm, max 15)
🚇 Clapham Common, Clapham Junction
A unique bunch of residents, working together in a quite extraordinary and very risky act of collective entrepreneurship, got together to build themselves better and bigger homes by knocking down an ex authority block. Peter Barber Architects, 2016

### Ark Putney Academy (formerly Elliott School)
🏃 Pullman Gardens, SW15 3DG
🕐 Sat 10am–2pm + architect-led tours of whole building, every 20 mins T·D
🚇 East Putney, Putney
A prime example of a post-war Modernist education building (Grade II listed), remodelled in order to meet the community's current and future learning needs. LCC Architects (G A Trevett), 1956

### Bakery Place
🏃 Altenburg Gardens, SW11 1AT
🕐 Sat/Sun 10am–5pm (max 10) + presentation by Jo Cowen Architects. R
🚇 Clapham South, Clapham Junction
A radical overhaul of a series of Victorian bakery buildings into 12 new homes in Battersea. The project combines contemporary design standards with a celebration of the development's particular historic legacy. Jo Cowen Architects, 2016

Burntwood School © Rob Parrish ↘

### Battersea Arts Centre
🏃 Lavender Hill, SW11 5TN
🕐 Sat 10am–5pm (access will be limited to parts of the building undergoing capital works) + 'If Walls Could Talk' tours at 12pm, 2pm, 4pm (max 10) + Grand Hall Exhibtion. T·d
🚇 Clapham Common, Clapham Junction
Designed and built as Battersea's Town Hall and home to Battersea Arts Centre for the last 30 years. Striking features include a glass bee mosaic floor, marble staircase and stained glass dome. E W Mountford, 1893

### Burntwood School
🏃 Burntwood Lane, SW17 0AQ
🕐 Sat 11am–5pm + architect led tours 11am, 1pm, 3pm. T·D
🚇 Tooting Broadway, Earlsfield
Striking new precast concrete-clad buildings and refurbishment of Leslie Martin-designed pool and assembly hall, with a new landscape plan for the school's original 1950s Modernist educational campus. Stirling Prize winner 2015. Allford Hall Monaghan Morris, 2014

### Double Concrete House
🏃 47 Nightingale Lane, SW12 8SU
🕐 Sat/Sun 10am–5pm (max 15, ground floor only). d
🚇 Clapham South, Clapham Junction
Semi-detached home with shortlisted exposed concrete extension. A folding plane of concrete wraps up, down, and over forming the kitchen/living area, drawing from the existing Arts & Crafts tradition to create a hand-crafted living space. Inter Urban Studios, 2016

### Emanuel School
🏃 Battersea Rise (entrance via bridge over the railway on Spencer Park), SW11 1HS
🕐 Sat 2pm-5.30pm + historical tour of the school site and grounds 2.30pm & 4pm (max 35) T·P·d
🚇 Clapham South, Clapham Junction
Former Royal Patriotic orphanage, converted to school 1883, with 1896 additions. High Victorian style with stained glass by Moira Forsyth. Set in 12 acres. Henry Saxon Snell, 1871

### Foster + Partners
🕴 Riverside, 22 Hester Road, SW11 4AN
🕐 Sat 1pm–5pm/Sun 10am–5pm (main studio and The Hub. Exhibition to celebrate 50th anniversary) T·d
🚇 Imperial Wharf, Fulham Broadway
Single-space, double-height purpose-built architects' studio 60 metres long – part of a larger riverside building that has 30 apartments. Foster + Partners, 1990

### Gala Bingo Hall (former Granada Cinema)
🕴 50 Mitcham Road, Tooting, SW17 9NA
🕐 Sun 9am–12pm + tours every 20 mins (max 40) + speech by guides at 11am (max 50) T·P·d
🚇 Earlsfield, Tooting Broadway
Exceptional example of the 'super cinema style' of the 1930s with outstanding Gothic interior by Theodore Komisarjevsky. The first Grade I listed cinema. Cecil Masey and Reginald Uren, 1931

### Graveney School Sixth Form Block
🕴 Welham Road, SW17 9BU
🕐 Sat 10.30am–5pm/Sun 11.30am–5pm. T·d
🚇 Tooting Broadway, Tooting
RIBA award-winning Sixth Form Block that sets a template for new school buildings. Innovative, sustainable and economical, the cross-laminated timber and polycarbonate building achieves maximum architectural output using minimal means. Urban Projects Bureau, 2015
*www.urbanprojectsbureau.com*

### Nightingale Lane
🕴 131 Nightingale Lane, SW12 8NE
🕐 Sat 10am–4.30pm ½ hourly architect-led tours, (max 8).
🚇 Clapham South, Wandsworth Common
A dramatic refurbishment of a 1930 semi. A carefully selected palette of materials is used throughout. The new sculptural staircase twists up through the centre of the house; its design pares back elements of the traditional domestic stair.

### Oily Cart
🕴 Smallwood School Annexe, Smallwood Road, SW17 0TW
🕐 Sat 11am–2pm (max 10). T·D
🚇 Tooting Broadway, Tooting
A children's theatre company based in Tooting has undergone a redevelopment which has seen increased access, efficiency and created an inspirational design, including a new mezzanine treehouse and a spectacular gold lift. Hawkins\Brown, 2013

### Pump House Gallery
🕴 Battersea Park, SW11 4NJ
🕐 Sat/Sun 11am–5pm + exhibition of new work by Canadian artist Zadie Xa. T·R·d
🚇 Sloane Square, Battersea Park
Beautiful Grade II listed Victorian ex-water tower overlooking Battersea Park lake. Now houses a contemporary art gallery. Visit website for more information on architectural tours and children's activities. James and William Simpson, 1861

Skinner-Trevino House ↘

Double Concrete House © Rosangela Photography ↗

### Quaker Meeting House, Wandsworth
🚶 59 Wandsworth High Street, SW18 2PT
🕐 Sat 1pm–5pm (max 20) + tour at 1pm (max 10, repeated as requested) · exhibition about building and Quaker history. B·T·R·d
🚇 East Putney, Wandsworth Town
Grade II listed, this is the oldest Quaker meeting house in Greater London, with original panelling and a ministers' gallery. Secluded burial ground and garden.

### RCA Battersea: Dyson and Woo Buildings
🚶 Dyson Building, 1 Hester Road, SW11 4AN
🕐 Sun 12pm–4pm + hourly tours of Dyson and Woo Buildings, (max 20, please arrive promptly). T·R·D
🚇 Imperial Wharf
The architect's concept is that of a large Art Factory, where three or four disciplines are visible on any one journey. As students learn by looking at each other's work, the interconnected spaces create a place brim full of ideas. Haworth Tompkins, 2012

### Skinner-Trevino House
🚶 67 Santos Road, SW18 1NT
🕐 Sat 10am–4.30pm, ½ hourly tours (max 12).
🚇 Wandsworth Town, East Putney
A late Victorian house which has been almost completely gutted; now flooded with light by a new glass extension opening onto the semi-open plan ground level and a glass box extension into the roof. Luis Trevino, 2007
*www.luistrevino.co.uk*

### St John's Hill
🚶 St John's Hill, SW11 1TY
🕐 Sat 10am–2pm (no access to flats) + hourly architect-led tours of development. D
🚇 Clapham Junction
Regeneration of a 1930s Peabody estate in three phases. The 351 existing homes are being replaced with 538 new ones. A new pedestrian avenue links Clapham Junction to Wandsworth Common. Scheme has new commercial space and a community hub. HawkinsBrown, 2014

### St Mary's Church, Battersea
🚶 Battersea Church Road, SW11 3NA
🕐 Sat/Sun 1pm–5pm. T·R·D
🚇 Sloane Square, Clapham Junction
Grade I listed Georgian church with outstanding interior and monuments. Joseph Dixon, 1775

### Tara Theatre
🚶 356 Garratt Lane, Earlsfield, SW18 4ES
🕐 Sat/Sun 10am–1pm (max 20) + hourly tours + presentation by architect and Artistic Director at 2pm (max 90) T·R·D
🚇 Earlsfield
An architectural fusion of East & West. 100-seat auditorium, a rehearsal Studio and an outdoor Patio Garden. Opened in September 2016 by Mayor of London Sadiq Khan, Tara Theatre is home to a world of stories. Aedas, 2016

Tara Theatre © Hélène Binet ↗

## Tooting Bec Lido
🚶 Tooting Bec Road, SW16 1RU
🕐 Sat/Sun 7am–5pm + architect talk and tour, every 240 mins (11am-3pm). T·R·D
🚇 Tooting Bec, Balham

Outdoor pool 100x33 yards. One million gallons of unheated water. Iconic outdoor cubicle doors, fountain and café added in the 1930s, with Art Deco style entrance. LCC Parks Dept, 1906

## Wistaston Cottage
🚶 65 Medfield Street, Roehampton, SW15 4JY
🕐 Sat 10am–5pm. T
🚇 East Putney

A new 2-storey timber rear extension to a Gothic revival semi-detached house. Shortlisted for the AJ Small Projects Award and RIBA London Award 2016. Simon Gill Architects, 2014

# Westminster

| | |
|---|---|
| Borough area (km²) | 21.5 |
| Population | 242,100 |
| Average age | 38 |
| First Open House | 1994 |

City of Westminster

## 4 Kingdom Street
🚶 4 Kingdom Street, W2 6BD
🕐 Sat/Sun 10am–5pm (reception & roof terrace only - if there is a floor plate available this will also be open) + tours at 11am, 2pm (1 hour). T·D
ℹ️ Pre-book only: www.paddingtoncentral.com/events (Will need to register for an account to book. email info@paddingtoncentral.com if having problems)
🚇 Royal Oak, Paddington
New office building at Paddington Central designed with the wellbeing of its occupants in mind, providing amenities including glass pod meeting rooms, private corner terraces, a large roof terrace and London's highest basketball court. Allies & Morrison, 2017

## 10 Downing Street
🚶 10 Downing Street, SW1A 2AA
🕐 Sat Tour at 11.30am, 1.30pm (max 24, by public ballot ONLY). T·D
ℹ️ Pre-book only: openhouselondon.open-city.org.uk/listings/2738 (Ballot will close 11.59pm 1 September.)
🚇 Embankment, Waterloo
10 Downing Street has been the residence of British Prime Ministers since 1735. Behind its famous black door the most important decisions affecting Britain for the last 277 years have been taken. William Kent, 1735

## 22 Whitehall - DFID (formerly 26 Whitehall)
🚶 22 Whitehall, SW1A 2EG
🕐 Sat/Sun 10am–4pm (old admiralty boardroom only). D
🚇 Westminster, Charing Cross
Grade I former Admiralty Building, behind Robert Adam's Admiralty Screen. Architect Thomas Ripley completed the build in 1725. Now owned by Department for International Development; works of art and antiques from MOD Art Collection. S P Cockerell, 1725

## 37a Leamington Road Villas
🚶 37a Leamington Road, W11 1HT
🕐 Sat/Sun 10am–5pm (max 12, tours from project architect, shoes off).
ℹ️ Pre-book only: daniel@studio1architects.co.uk
🚇 Westbourne Park
Exposed brickwork, concrete floors, skylights with floating oak steps in a unique 3 bed home converted from a 1 bed Victorian flat. 3x3m glass doors give a seamless transition into the rear multi-levelled landscaped garden. Studio 1 Architects, 2013
*www.studio1architects.co.uk*

## 55 Broadway (London Underground Head Office)
🚶 55 Broadway, SW1H 0BD
🕐 Sat/Sun 11.30am-3.30pm, hourly tours (max 20). T·d
ℹ️ Pre-book only: www.cvent.com/d/w5qvtv
🚇 St. James's Park, Victoria
HQ of London Underground described on opening as 'the cathedral of modernity'. Exterior features sculptures by eminent artists of the day, including Henry Moore, Jacob Epstein and Eric Gill. Charles Holden, 1927

## Admiralty House
🚶 Ripley Courtyard, Whitehall, SW1A 2DY
🕐 Sat/Sun 10am–5pm (max 20, ground floor function rooms only). d
🚇 Charing Cross, Westminster
Grade I listed former Admiralty Building, behind Robert Adam's Admiralty Screen on Whitehall. Owned by Cabinet Office; works of art and antiques from Ministry of Defence Art Collection. Samuel Pepys Cockerell, 1785

## Ampersand
🚶 178 Wardour Street, W1F 8FY
🕐 Sat architect-led tour at 10.30am/Sun architect-led tour at 12.30pm (max 20). T·D
ℹ️ Pre-book only: bit.ly/2vIPkKf
🚇 Piccadilly Circus, Charing Cross
Ampersand redefines the modern workplace. Conceived as a collaboration between architect, designer and graphic designer, it embodies Soho's unique character of commerce and creativity and is the London HQ for 'Candy Crush' creator, King. Darling Associates, 2015

**Argentine Ambassador's Residence**
🚶 49 Belgrave Square, SW1X 8QZ
🕐 Sat/Sun 1pm–6pm. D
🚇 Hyde Park Corner, Victoria
Known as the 'Independent North Mansion' and
christened by Sydney Herbert as 'Belgrave Villa' and
then simply 'The Villa' by his successor the 6th
Duke of Richmond. Owned by Argentina since 1936
and with sumptuous interiors still intact. Thomas
Cubitt, 1851

**Banqueting House**
🚶 Whitehall, SW1A 2ER
🕐 Sat/Sun 10am–5pm (max 450). T·B
🚇 Embankment, Charing Cross
Stunning regal building, the only surviving building
from Whitehall Palace, one of the first examples of
the principles of Palladianism being applied to an
English building. Site of a set of magnificent ceiling
paintings by Rubens. Inigo Jones, 1619

**Basement Flat, 23 Castellain Road**
🚶 23 Castellain Road, Maida Vale, W9 1EY
🕐 Sat/Sun 10am–5pm (max 12, shoes off).
❗ Pre-book only: daniel@studio1architects.co.uk
🚇 Maida Vale, Warwick Avenue
An elegant complete refurbishment, rear extension,
small vaulted basement and landscaped garden. This
shows the full potential of what a period basement
flat can be. Studio 1 Architects, 2017
www.studio1architects.co.uk

**Benjamin Franklin House**
🚶 36 Craven Street, WC2N 5NF
🕐 Sat/Sun 10.30am–4pm (max 15, public areas only)
  + ½ hourly tour. T
🚇 Charing Cross, Embankment
Grade I listed Georgian house, the only surviving
home of Benjamin Franklin, retaining many original
features including central staircase, lathing, 18C
panelling, stoves, windows, fittings and beams.
Patrick Dillon Architect, 1732

**Brown Hart Gardens**
🚶 Meet: in front of Garden Café, Brown Hart
  Gardens, W1K 6TD
🕐 Sat/Sun 10am–1pm (design team present to guide
  and answer questions).
🚇 Marble Arch, Oxford Circus
An elevated public square over a listed substation
immediately adjacent to Oxford Street. An accessible
stair and glazed platform lift draws shoppers
and tourists toward the new destination, and
offers a contemplative environment. Charles Stanley
Peach, 1905

**Burlington House**
🚶 Burlington House, Piccadilly, W1J 0BE
🚇 Green Park, Victoria, Piccadilly
1660s town-palace, remodelled in Palladian style by
Colen Campbell and William Kent for Lord Burlington.
The main building is at the northern end of the
courtyard and houses the Royal Academy, while five
learned societies occupy the two wings on the east
and west sides of the courtyard and the piccadilly
wing at the southern end.

**Linnean Society of London**
🕐 Sat 11am–6pm (Meeting Room and Library will
  be open to the public). d
The world's oldest active biological society. Founded
in 1788, the Society takes its name from the Swedish
naturalist Carl Linnaeus whose botanical,
zoological and library collections have been in
its keeping since 1829. Banks & Barry, 1873
www.linnean.org

**Royal Academy of Arts**
🕐 Sat/Sun 10am–6pm + family studio at 11am
  (Sunday). T·R·B·D
Main Galleries by Sidney Smirke RA, Sackler Wing of
Galleries by Foster + Partners. The RA is undergoing
a redevelopment, led by Sir David Chipperfield RA,
linking Burlington House and Burlington Gardens
for the RA's 250 anniversary in 2018. 1660
www.royalacademy.org.uk

**Society of Antiquaries of London**
🕐 Sat tours every 25 mins (10.30am-4.30pm, max 25,
  access to ground and first floor only). T·B·d
Part of New Burlington House, purpose built in
1875 for London's learned societies. Historic
apartments with highlights from the Library and
Museum collections on display. Imposing top-lit
library with double galleries and marbled columns.
Banks & Barry, 1875
www.sal.org.uk/open-house-london

**Royal Astronomical Society**
🕐 Sat 10am–5pm (max 25) + ½ hourly tours +
  children's science activities at 10.45am. T·D
❗ Pre-book only: www.ras.org.uk
The home of the Royal Astronomical Society
since 1874 with recent refurbishment. Part of
the extension to Burlington House to provide
accommodation for learned societies. Peregrine
Bryant Associates, 1874
www.ras.org.uk

**Royal Society of Chemistry**
🕐 Sat 10am–5pm.
Historical tour around the East Wing of Burlington
House, home to the Royal Society of Chemistry. Part
of the quadrangle building extension to Burlington
House, purpose built for the learned societies. Banks
& Barry, 1873
www.rsc.li/OHL2017

**The Geological Society of London**
🕐 Sat 10am–5pm + hourly tours (10am-4pm, max 20)
  + Geological workshops offered by the Geologists'
  Association. B·d
❗ Pre-book only: library@geolsoc.org.uk
Home to the oldest geological society in the world, ↪

founded in 1807. The Society has been based at Burlington House since 1874, and now has over 12,000 members worldwide. Banks & Barry, 1873
www.geolsoc.org.uk

## Canada House
🚶 Trafalgar Square, SW1Y 5BJ
🕐 Sat/Sun 10am–5pm (max 25). T·d
⚠ Pre-book only: www.unitedkingdom.gc.ca (Check website for EventBrite link closer to the time)
🚇 Charing Cross, Embankment
Canada's diplomatic home in the United Kingdom, the revitalised Canada House serves as a showcase for the very best of Canadian art and design in the 21st century. Sir Robert Smirke, 1823

## City of Westminster Archives Centre
🚶 10 St Ann's Street, SW1P 2DE
🕐 Sat 10am–5pm (max 20) + hourly tour of the archives Centre - search room, conservation, strong room (11am-4pm) + 'Swinging Sixties: Carnaby Street to King's Road' exhibition. T·R·B·D
🚇 St. James's Park, Victoria
Modern red brick building purpose-built to house City of Westminster's historic records. Opportunity to visit the conservation studio and strongrooms. Tim Drewitt, 1995

## Embassy of Hungary
🚶 35 Eaton Place, SW1X 8BY
🕐 Sat/Sun 10am–5pm (ground and 1st floors) + Greetings by the Ambassador at 10am Sat) T
🚇 Sloane Square, Victoria
The properties in Belgravia were developed as part of the Grosvenor Estate around 1820. The Embassy is located in a 4 storey white stucco house characteristic of the neighbourhood where main builder Thomas Cubitt carried out major projects. Thomas Cubitt, 1820

## Fitzrovia Chapel
🚶 2 Pearson Square, off Mortimer Street, W1T 3BF
🕐 Sun 10am–4pm. T·D
🚇 Goodge Street, Oxford Circus
Located within Pearson Square on the site of the former Middlesex Hospital. The chapel was designed as a secular chapel for the Middlesex Hospital staff and patients. John Loughborough Pearson, 1891

## Foreign & Commonwealth Office
🚶 King Charles Street, SW1A 2AH
🕐 Sat/Sun 11am–4pm. T·D
🚇 Victoria, Westminster
Grade I listed Victorian government office buildings. Route includes the magnificent and richly decorated Durbar Court, India Office council chamber, Locarno suite and Foreign Office grand staircase. Sir George Gilbert Scott & Matthew Digby Wyatt, 1861

## Former Conservative Club (HSBC offices)
🚶 78 St James's Street, SW1A 1JB

🕐 Sat 10am-12:30pm, ½ hourly tours (max 40). T·d
⚠ Pre-book only: 020 7024 1255
🚇 Victoria, Green Park
Grand and monumental building with rich carvings and spectacular decorated saloon at its heart. Conserved and refurbished to replace two wings and provide new glazing to atrium at junction of new and old sites. Sidney Smirke & George Basevi, 1844

## Gallery of Everything
🚶 4 Chiltern Street, W1U 7PS
🕐 Sat 10am–5pm/Sun 1pm–5pm + Curator's tour of current exhibition. T·R·B·d
🚇 Marylebone, Baker Street
London's only commercial space representing self-taught and private art makers. The Gallery is set in an old-barber shop on Chiltern Street renovated to its original period features.

## Gap House
🚶 28D Monmouth Road, W2 4UT
🕐 Sun 10am–12pm + ½ hourly architect-led tours (max 10).
⚠ Pre-book only: gaphousetours.eventbrite.co.uk
🚇 Queensway, Bayswater
Family home with a minimal carbon footprint on a very narrow site (8ft wide). Environmentally friendly house, utilising amongst many eco-friendly devices ground source heat pump heating & rainwater harvesting. RIBA Manser Medal Winner 2009. Pitman Tozer Architects, 2007

## HM Treasury
🚶 1 Horse Guards Road, SW1A 2HQ
🕐 Sat/Sun 11am–6pm + Exhibition space. T·R·D
🚇 Green Park, Victoria
Grade II* listed Government offices, Great George Street constructed 1900-17 in two phases. Refurbishment completed 2002, now occupied by HM Treasury. John Brydon & Sir Henry Tanner, 1917/Foster + Partners (refurb), 2002

## Hallfield Primary School
🚶 Hallfield Estate, W2 6HF
🕐 Sat 2pm-4.45pm + tours every 10 mins.
🚇 Royal Oak, Paddington
1950s masterpiece by Sir Denys Lasdun. The scale relates to a child's world with curved corridors, dappled by light and surrounded by beautiful trees. Two new buildings were added by Caruso St John in 2005. RIBA Award Winner 2006.

## Home House
🚶 20 Portman Square, W1H 6LW
🕐 Sun hourly tours (3pm-5pm, max 12) + History talk at 3pm. T·R·D
⚠ Pre-book only: openhouse@homehouse.co.uk
🚇 Baker Street, Paddington
The London base of the Countess of Home and probably the greatest surviving Georgian town house, with very fine interiors by Adam. James Wyatt & Robert Adam, 1776

Burlington House ↗

## House in Westminster
🚶 29 Tufton Street, SW1P 3QL
🕐 Sat/Sun 11am–4pm regular tours (max 6) . T
❗ Pre-book only: bwa@barbaraweissarchitects.com
🚇 Pimlico, Vauxhall
Located on a prominent corner in the heart of Westminster, this 1927 building, originally a pub and then used as a legal office, was carefully transformed into an unusual and extremely bespoke family home. Barbara Weiss Architects, 2012

## IET London: Savoy Place
🚶 2 Savoy Place, WC2R 0BL
🕐 Sat 10am–3pm. T·D
🚇 Waterloo (East), Temple
Originally built as a joint Examination Hall for the Royal College of Physicians and the Royal College of Surgeons, the building was renovated in 1909 for the Institution creating a spectacular 20C interior. Stephen Salter and H Percy Adams, 1886

## Italian Cultural Institute
🚶 39 Belgrave Square, SW1X 8NX
🕐 Sat 10am–5pm. d·T
🚇 Hyde Park Corner, Victoria
Grade I listed stucco-fronted Belgravia town house. Library extension built 1960s.

## King's College London, Strand Campus
🚶 Strand, WC2R 2LS
🕐 Sat/Sun 12pm–5pm. T·d
🚇 Waterloo, Temple
King's Grade I listed campus includes: the Chapel (George Gilbert Scott 1864) & the Archaeology Room, displaying foundations of the original Tudor Somerset House. See also nearby Maughan Library. Sir Robert Smirke, Harvey W. Corbett, 1829

## Lancaster House
🚶 Stable Yard, SW1A 1BB
🕐 Sat/Sun ½ hourly tour (9.30am-3.30pm, max 30, Duration 45-50 mins). T·D
❗ Pre-book only: bit.ly/2tBlzOY
🚇 Charing Cross, Green Park
Extravagant private palace originally built for the Duke of York, with magnificent central hall and staircase. Benjamin Wyatt, 1825

## ME London Hotel
🚶 336-337 Strand, WC2R 1HA
🕐 Sat/Sun 1pm-4pm tour of ½ hourly The Atrium (max 5) R·T·D
❗ Pre-book only: sales.melondon@melia.com
🚇 Temple, Covent Garden
The first hotel in which everything, from the shell of the building to the bathroom fittings, has been designed by Foster + Partners - with minimal detailing, simple, triangular oriel windows and Portland stone facade. Foster + Partners, 2013
@MELondonHotel

## Marlborough House
🚶 Pall Mall, SW1Y 5HX
🕐 Sat 11am–6pm (fine rooms, first floor). T·d
🚇 Piccadilly Circus, Charing Cross
Originally home of the Dukes of Marlborough, and later of Edward VII and Queen Mary. Now HQ of the Commonwealth Secretariat and Commonwealth Foundation. Sir Christopher Wren, Sir James Pennethorne, 1709

## Methodist Central Hall Westminster
🚶 Storey's Gate, SW1H 9NH
🕐 Sun 1.30pm–5pm + Organ recital given by Paul
Ayres at 3pm (Organ built by William Hill, 1912;
rebuilt Harrison & Harrison, 2011). T·R·B·d
🚇 Charing Cross, St. James's Park
A masterpiece of Edwardian neo-baroque
architecture. Great Hall was the venue for the
Inaugural General Assembly of the United Nations in
1946. Lanchester & Rickards, 1906

## National Audit Office
🚶 157-197 Buckingham Palace Road, SW1W 9SP
🕐 Sat/Sun 11am–6pm (public facing areas) + hourly
tours (max 10). T·R·D
🚇 Victoria
A prestigious Grade I listed building. Opened in 1939
by Imperial Airways and subsequently used by BOAC
and then British Airways. The building has been the
home of the National Audit Office since 1986 and was
refurbished in 2009. Albert Lakeman, 1938

## National Liberal Club
🚶 1 Whitehall Place, SW1A 2HE
🕐 Sat/Sun ½ hourly tour (11am-4.30pm, max 10). T
❗ Pre-book only: secretary@nlc.org.uk
🚇 Embankment, Charing Cross
An impressive Victorian neo-Classical building
overlooking the Embankment of the river Thames.
It is the second-largest clubhouse ever built,
the first London building to incorporate a lift
and to be entirely lit by electric lighting. Alfred
Waterhouse, 1886

## New Scotland Yard
🚶 Victoria Embankment, SW1A 2JL
🕐 Sat/Sun 11am-3.30pm, ½ hourly tours (max 8. No
children under 10. Must have photo ID). D
❗ Pre-book only: See website for details
🚇 Westminster, Charing Cross
Redevelopment and extension of the 1930s
Curtis Green building to create a new home for
the Metropolitan Police on the Embankment at
Whitehall, including a new curved glass pavilion
entrance and extensions to the rooftop and rear.
Allford Hall Monaghan Morris, 2016

## New West End Synagogue
🚶 St Petersburgh Place, W2 4JT
🕐 Sun 10am-2pm. T·d
🚇 Notting Hill Gate, Paddington
Magnificent Grade I listed Victorian synagogue,
Audsley's masterpiece. Includes metalwork, stained
glass and a mosaic by Audsley; stained glass by
NHJ Westlake. Further enrichment 1894/5 included
lighting designed by George Aitchison. George
Ashdown Audsley, 1877

## Nova Victoria
🚶 160 Victoria Street, Westminster, SW1E 5LB
🕐 Sat 10am-6.30pm + tours every 2 hours (duration
30 mins). T·D
🚇 Victoria
A game changing mixed use scheme in the heart
of London's West End. It comprises 2 world class
office buildings, 170 contemporary apartments and
17 new inventive restaurants and bars, set along a
pedestrianized, public space. Flanagan Lawrence,
PLP Architecture, Benson & Forsyth, 2017

## One Church Square
🚶 2-6 Moreton Street, SW1V 2PS
🕐 Sun 10am–1pm + ½ hourly architect-led tours,
(max 10). D
🚇 Battersea Park, Victoria
39 keyworkers apartments to rent in Westminster
in a unique listed setting. This highly sustainable
development creates a central London community
square, designed around a central, glass covered
circulation courtyard with landscaped roof. PDP
London, 2013
*pdplondon.com*

## Piccadilly Circus Station
🚶 Piccadilly Circus, W1J 9HP
🕐 Sat/Sun 11am-3pm, hourly tours ( max 15). T
❗ Pre-book only: www.cvent.com/d/65qvy7
🚇 Piccadilly Circus
Thought of as Holden's 'Civic Showpiece', an
elegant transport hub at the heart of London. The
tour will cover the original Leslie Green design,
Charles Holden refurbishment and the modern-day
renovation of platforms. Leslie Green, 1906

## Pimlico District Heating Undertaking (PDHU)
🚶 The Pumphouse, Churchill Gardens Road, SW1V
3JF
🕐 Sat/Sun 11am–6pm + tours every 45 mins (10am-
4pm, max 10). T·R
🚇 Pimlico, Victoria
The UK's first combined heat and power network,
providing heating and hot water services to over
3,000 properties. Built over 50 years ago to help
combat London's air pollution, the PDHU is a crucial
source of clean energy. Powell and Moya, 1950

## Portcullis House
🚶 Victoria Embankment, SW1A 2LW
🕐 Sat 11am–6pm (max 300). T·R·D
🚇 Westminster, Charing Cross
Portcullis House contrasts its imposing facade with a
generous light-filled courtyard covered by a glass roof
at second level and surrounded by a 2-storey cloister.
Extensive collection of Parliamentary portraiture
from Gilray to Scarfe. Hopkins Architects, 2001

## RIBA
🚶 66 Portland Place, W1B 1AD
🕐 Sat 10am–5pm + tours every 90 mins (max 20) +
Family Fun activities. d
🚇 Regent's Park, Oxford Circus
Fine example of Grade II* listed 1930s architecture
with many original features and fittings. Grey
Wornum, 1932

## ROOM by Antony Gormley

🏃 The Beaumont, Brown Hart Gardens, 8 Balderton Street, W1K 6TF
🕐 Sat/Sun hourly tours (2pm-6pm, max 6). T·R·d
❗ Pre-book only: bit.ly/2uN2rgN
🚇 Marble Arch, Bond Street

ROOM is a monumental, inhabitable sculpture by Antony Gormley placed on a wing of the listed façade of The Beaumont Hotel. The interior, a bedroom, is as important as its exterior: a giant crouching cuboid figure based on the artist's body. Antony Gormley, 2014

## Reform Club

🏃 104 Pall Mall, SW1Y 5EW
🕐 Sat 11am-6pm/Sun 11am-4pm (max 18).
❗ Pre-book only: paul.austin@reformclub.com
🚇 Piccadilly Circus, Charing Cross

Built as a Whig gentleman's club and inspired by Italian Renaissance palaces. Lobby leads to an enclosed colonnaded courtyard with complementary glazed roof and tessellated floor. Tunnelled staircase leads to upper floor. Sir Charles Barry, 1841

## Regent Street Cinema

🏃 309 Regent Street, W1B 2UW
🕐 Sat/Sun 10.15am-12.45pm ½ hourly tours (max 20). T·d
🚇 Oxford Circus

Built as a theatre for optical demonstrations as part of the Royal Polytechnic, the Lumiere Brothers showed the first film to a British Audience here. The space has been restored as repertory cinema, and acts as a heritage destination.

## 'Roman' Bath

🏃 5 Strand Lane (access via Surrey Street steps) WC2R 2NA
🕐 Sat 12pm-5pm/Sun 12pm-4pm. d
🚇 Temple, Blackfriars

A plunge bath, popularly known as the 'Roman' bath, originally a 17C feeder cistern for a grotto-fountain at the old Somerset House, located in a vault below a 19C building. Dickens' character David Copperfield took regular plunges there.

## Romanian Cultural Institute

🏃 1 Belgrave Square, SW1X 8PH
🕐 Sat/Sun 11am-6pm + photo exhibition. T·D
🚇 Hyde Park Corner, Victoria

Situated in one of the grandest and largest 19C squares in London, 1 Belgrave Square was acquired by Romania in 1936 and is now home to the Romanian Cultural Institute. Thomas Cubitt, 1828

## Royal Albert Hall

🏃 Kensington Gore . Entry via door 12, SW7 2AP
🕐 Sat 9.30am-3.30pm (access via a set route through most areas of the building) T·R·B·D
🚇 High Street Kensington, Victoria

One of Britain's most iconic buildings, designed by Royal Engineers. Now Grade I listed, it hosts over 370 main events every year including a full range of music, sport and films. Captain Fowke & General Scott, 1871

## Royal Automobile Club

🏃 89 Pall Mall, SW1Y 5HS
🕐 Sat/Sun tours at 10am, 11.30am, 3pm (max 20). T
❗ Pre-book only: bit.ly/2tBEtFt
🚇 St. James's Park, Charing Cross

Inspired by the French Beaux-Arts, the Royal Automobile's pioneering clubhouse was described as the 'Palace of Pall Mall' with thrilling interior spaces in a mix of styles. Mewes & Davis, 1911

## Royal College of Nursing

🏃 20 Cavendish Square, W1G 0RN
🕐 Sat 10am-5pm + guided tours every 20 mins (10am-4pm, max 15) + 'For Queen and Country: Nursing, Trauma and War' exhibition. T·R·B·D
🚇 Marylebone, Bond Street

A cleverly integrated mixture of architectural styles and periods, incorporating a late 1720s house with rare and Baroque painted staircase and the purpose-built College of Nursing (1926). Bisset Adams Architects, 2013

## Royal Courts of Justice

🏃 Strand, WC2A 2LL
🕐 Sat 10am-4pm (cells, prinson vans) + Q&A with court staff · Role of the High Court Tipstaff · Robing demonstrations · Courtroom workshops · Legal Costume Exhibition. T·R·d
🚇 Embankment, Blackfriars

Street's masterpiece and one of Victorian London's great public buildings. 13C Gothic given a Victorian interpretation. G E Street, 1874

## Royal Institution of Chartered Surveyors

🏃 12 Great George Street, Parliament Square SW1 3AD, SW1P 3AD
🕐 Sat 10am-5pm tours every 15 mins T·R·D
🚇 St. James's Park, Waterloo

Historic Grade II listed gabled Victorian building, purpose-built for the RICS in Franco-Flemish style. Only surviving Victorian building in the street. Alfred Waterhouse, 1899

## Royal Over-Seas League

🏃 Park Place, St James's Street, SW1A 1LR
🕐 Sat/Sun 10.30am-2.30pm tours every 90 mins (max 20). T
❗ Pre-book only: guestrelations@rosl.org.uk
🚇 Green Park, Victoria

Over-Seas House is an amalgamation of two Grade I listed houses - Rutland House (James Gibbs, 1736) and Vernon House (1835 rebuilt 1905). James Gibbs, William Kent, 1736
*www.rosl.org.uk*

## Royal Parks Foundation Education Centre

🏃 Hyde Park (north of the Serpentine, south-west of Speaker's Corner), W2 2UH

↦

Two Temple Place © Peter Dazeley ↗

○ Sat/Sun 11pm–4pm (max 60, no access to private office space) + Tour of building, hourly (11.30pm-3.30pm, max 30). T·D
⊞ Hyde Park Corner, Paddington
Old meets new at this eco-friendly building. Sitting proudly on top of a re-instated Victorian reservoir , this building emulates the canopy of a tree, blending into its listed surroundings of Hyde Park. Eco features include living roof. David Morley Architects, 2012

**Rudolf Steiner House**
⚲ 35 Park Road, NW1 6XT
○ Sun 1pm–5pm. T·R·B·D
⊞ Marylebone, Baker Street
Unique example of Expressionist architecture in London with sculptural staircase based on organic plant forms. Grade II listed. New cafe area and renovations in 2008. Montague Wheeler, 1926

**Soho Green - Art Loo**
⚲ St Anne's Churchyard, Wardour Street, W1D 6BA
○ Sat 10am–5pm (max 5). R·d
⊞ Piccadilly Circus, Charing Cross
A treasure trove of a toilet - " an egg shaped capsule in oak with etched glass hinting at the bodies buried below; an homage to the history of Soho within. Steven Johnson, 2007

**Somerset House**
⚲ Strand, WC2R 1LA
○ Sat/Sun 12pm–5pm (Selected areas). T·R·B·d
⊞ Temple, Waterloo
Grade I listed restored building of five wings, four of which surround large courtyard. Construction began in 1775. New Wing, overlooking Waterloo Bridge, dates from 1850 by Sir James Pennethorne. Sir William Chambers, 1775

**St Barnabas Church**
⚲ 5 St Barnabas Street, SW1W 8PF
○ Sat 10am–5pm/Sun 1pm–5pm + Live organ and harmonium performance at 2pm. T·R·d
⊞ Victoria, Sloane Square
Early English style, full of Pre-Raphaelite decoration. Important works by Bodley, Comper and Cundy and windows by Kempe and Tower. First Oxford Movement church. Recently restored 10 bell peal; bell ringing quarter peal during weekend. Thomas Cundy, 1850

**St John's Smith Square**
⚲ Smith Square, SW1P 3HA
○ Sat 10am–10pm + tours at 11am, 2.30pm, 6pm/ Sun 10am–2pm. T·R·D
⊞ Victoria, Vauxhall
A rare example of Thomas Archer's work and a ↱

masterpiece of English Baroque, this was originally dubbed Queen Anne's Footstool. A Grade I listed building, restored by Marshall Sisson after extensive bombing damage, now a busy concert hall. Thomas Archer, 1714

### St Martin-in-the-Fields
🏃 Trafalgar Square, WC2N 4JH
🕐 Sat 10am–5pm + tours of church and crypt interior 10am & 12pm (max 25). T·R·B·D
🚇 Charing Cross, Leicester Square
One of Britain's finest churches, built in the Italian Baroque tradition and beautifully restored in 2008. Sustainable features include new heating and management systems and lightwell. RIBA Award Winner 2009. Civic Trust Award Winner 2010. James Gibbs, 1726

### St Mary Magdalene-in-Paddington Parish Church
🏃 Rowington Close, W2 5TF
🕐 Sat 10am–3pm hourly tours (max 20).
ℹ️ Pre-book only: lucy@pdt.org.uk
🚇 Royal Oak, Paddington
Grade I listed Victorian Gothic church by G E Street, architect of the Royal Courts of Justice, including painted ceiling by Daniel Bell, and the magnificent Comper crypt chapel. Decorated in gilt, it is considered a Comper masterpiece. G E Street, 1867

### Studio McLeod
🏃 320 Kilburn Lane, W9 3EF
🕐 Sat 10am–5pm + architect-led tours, every 15 mins + exhibition of selected projects. T·d
🚇 Queen's Park
2017 RIBA London Award-winning architect's studio and home. Sculpted light, crafted materials and sliding staircase. Most Innovative Award Don't Move, Improve! 2017. BD Architect of the year finalist 2017. Exhibiting selected projects. Studio McLeod, 2015

### The British Academy
🏃 10-11 Carlton House Terrace, SW1Y 5AH
🕐 Sun 10am–4pm + Tour, ½ hourly (max 20). T·D
🚇 Piccadilly Circus, Charing Cross
Grade I listed Nash-designed terraced houses described as one of London's finest Georgian treasures. Former residence of William Gladstone and now home to the British Academy, the UK's national body for the humanities and social sciences. John Nash, 1833

### The Caledonian Club
🏃 9 Halkin Street, SW1X 7DR
🕐 Sun 12pm–5pm hourly tours (max 20). T·D
ℹ️ Pre-book only: ci@caledonianclub.com
🚇 Hyde Park Corner, Victoria
Built in Neoclassical style for Hugh Morrison (1868-1931), this was the last mansion house of its kind to be built in London. The club, founded in 1891, moved to the premises in 1946. Detmar Blow, 1908

### The College of Optometrists
🏃 42 Craven Street, WC2N 5NG
🕐 Sun 1pm–5pm (max 50, Lower three floors only) + Historical talks throughout the afternoon · Ask the experts. T·B·d
🚇 Charing Cross, Embankment
HQ of professional and examining body for UK optometrists occupying two terraced houses, No.41 (Flitcroft c1730 with later additions) and No. 42 (rebuilt by Tarmac plc, c1989) including Council chamber, print room, library and museum. Henry Flitcroft, 1730

### The Hellenic Centre
🏃 16-18, Paddington Street, W1U 5AS
🕐 Sat/Sun 11am–4pm (ground and lower ground floors only) + Mind caves exhibition of shadow sculptures by Greek artist Triantafyllos Vaitsis · Mediterranean encounters Andreas Georgiadis creates a visual art trail. T·d
🚇 Bond Street, Marylebone
Built in the early 1900s as the Swedish Academy of Gymnastics, it was used as a hospital during WWI for British wounded soldiers and later as a College of Education. A Greek cultural centre since 1994 with a rich programme of events.

### The House of St Barnabas
🏃 1 Greek Street, Soho Square, W1D 4NQ
🕐 Sun 10.15am–4pm tours every 15 mins (max 25). d·T·R
ℹ️ Pre-book only: hosb.org.uk/tickets
🚇 Leicester Square, Charing Cross
Soho's grandest Grade I listed Georgian townhouse. Fine Roccoco plasterwork commissioned 1754. Victorian Oxford Movement Chapel built 1862 by Joseph Clarke. Owned by charity supporting people affected by homelessness back into lasting work. Joseph Pearce, 1746

### The London Library
🏃 14 St James's Square, SW1Y 4LG
🕐 Sat hourly tours (10am-4pm, max 18). T·d
ℹ️ Pre-book only: bit.ly/2eFEUIs
🚇 Green Park, Charing Cross
The world's largest independent lending library with 175 years of history, 1m books & 17 miles of shelves. Atmospheric Victorian bookstacks, elegant Reading Rooms & contemporary RIBA award winning spaces provide a unique literary haven. James Osborne Smith, 1896

### The Photographers' Gallery
🏃 16-18 Ramillies Street, W1F 7LW
🕐 Sat 10am–12pm + 'Gregory Crewdson: Cathedral of the Pines' exhibition (free before 12noon). T·R·B·D
🚇 Oxford Circus, Euston
An elegantly redeveloped Edwardian red-brick warehouse, linked to a steel-framed extension through an external sleeve of black render, terrazzo and Angelim Pedra wood. O'Donnell + Tuomey, 2012

Westbourne Gardens © Megan Taylor ↗

### The Queen's Chapel (St James's Palace)
🏃 St James's Palace, Marlborough Road, SW1A 1BG
🕐 Sat 10am-2pm/Sun 10am-5pm. D
ⓘ Pre-book only: bit.ly/2vNG4Vj
🚇 Green Park, Victoria
The first Palladian style post-Reformation church in England and private chapel of Charles I's bride Henrietta Maria; later extensively refurbished by Sir Christopher Wren in 1682-3. Inigo Jones, 1623

### The Royal Society
🏃 6-9 Carlton House Terrace, SW1Y 5AG
🕐 Sat 10am-6pm/Sun 11am-4pm + ½ hourly tours (max 16). T·D
🚇 Piccadilly Circus, Charing Cross
Grade I listed Nash-designed town houses, refurbished in the 1890s before conversion into the German Embassy. 2004 refurbishment provided additional facilities for the home of the UK's national science academy. John Nash, 1831
*royalsociety.org*

### The UK Supreme Court (formerly the Middlesex Guildhall)
🏃 Parliament Square, SW1P 3BD
🕐 Sat/Sun 11am-6pm. T·R·D
🚇 St. James's Park, Charing Cross
Sensitive refurbishment of this neo-gothic Grade II* listed building to become home of UK's highest court. Admire original features including stained glass windows, wood panelling and ornate ceilings. Feilden + Mawson, 2009

### Two Temple Place
🏃 2 Temple Place, WC2R 3BD
🕐 Sun 10am-5pm. T·B·d
🚇 Waterloo, Temple
Finished in 1895 for William Waldorf Astor, to the elaborate architectural specifications of John Loughborough Pearson. The building overlooks the River Thames and embodies the outstanding workmanship of the late Victorian period. J L Pearson, 1895

### Westbourne Gardens
🏃 50c Westbourne Gardens, W2 5NS
🕐 Sat 10am-5pm (max 10) + hourly architect-led tours of project (11am-4pm). R
🚇 Queensway, Paddington
A first-floor apartment within a grand early-Victorian Terrace. Only 45m², yet a workable and liveable contemporary flat has been created that still retains the generosity of scale and detail of the original spaces. Nimtim Architects, 2016

### Westminster Hall
🏃 House of Commons (Cromwell Green entrance), SW1A 0AA

↱

○ Sun 11am–6pm (max 300, Public Areas Only. No access to either the Commons or Lords Chamber) + St Mary's Undercroft Chapel Tours, every 20 mins (11am-5.30pm, max 10) + Elizabeth Tower Talks (max 25, Regular talks from 12pm). T·R·d
ⓘ Pre-book only: visitparliament@parliament.uk (Booking only required for Chapel tours. )
🚇 Waterloo, Westminster

One of the finest and largest Medieval halls in Europe with a magnificent hammerbeam ceiling. Work began in 1097 and was completed in 1099 under William Rufus. Henry Yevele, 1380

## Wigmore Hall
🚶 36 Wigmore Street, W1U 2BP
○ Sat 10am-3pm + Open House Day (performances and workshops taking place and the chance to explore backstage. Family activities: a musical mystery trail around the building with Detective Insepctor Lucy Drever. Musicmaking workshops 11am, 12.15pm and 1.30pm). T·d
🚇 Oxford Circus, Bond Street

One of the world's great concert halls, Wigmore Hall specialises in chamber and instrumental music and song. Refurbished in 2004, it is renowned for its intimacy, crystalline acoustic and beautiful interior, with a capacity of 552 seats. Thomas E Collcutt, 1901

# Walks + Tours

## Engineering Walking Tour
🚶 Meet: in front of One Great George Street, SW1P 3AA
○ Sat 10am (max 20).
🚇 St. James's Park, Westminster

A walk through the engineering past, present & future of London, traveling from Westminster along the river to London Bridge with expert guides explaining how the city has been shaped by engineers like Brunel & Bazalgette.

## Leicester Square
🚶 Meet: Shakespeare Fountain at the centre of Leicester Square Gardens, WC2H 7NA
○ Sun 11am. T·R·D
🚇 Leicester Square, Charing Cross

The walk explains the creation of a coherent city block that underpins the 2012 redesign for Leicester Square, its history and the challenges this landmark public space experiences. Burns + Nice, 2012

## Secret Victoria
🚶 Meet: Portland House (opposite M&S), Cardinal Place, 76-98 Victoria Street, SW1E 5JD
○ Sat hourly tours (10am-3pm, max 25, duration 90 mins). D
🚇 Victoria

A walk with a Westminster Guide around Victoria's lesser known streets, looking Blewcoat School, 55 Broadway and Queen Anne's Gate.

## Secrets of the Devil's Acre
🚶 Meet: Portland House (opposite M&S), Cardinal Place, 76-98 Victoria Street, SW1E 5JD
○ Sat hourly tours (10.30am-3.30pm, max 25, duration 90 mins). D
🚇 Victoria

Tour of Victoria's unfamiliar streets with a Westminster Guide to discover social housing, social history, celebrated architects and Victorian philanthropists.

# Index

This index lists buildings organised by architectural type. An enhanced browsing experience is availble online and on our new, free app.

**Head to**
*openhouselondon.open-city.org.uk*

**Download the app**
for both iOS and Android on the App Store and Google Play

## Architectural practice

## Art Studio

## Bridge

## Cemetery

## Hostel

## Hotel

## Housing

## Industrial

# Support Open City for a free Open House

Open City is a charity that champions great design in London's building and places. We believe that well-designed cities can improve people's lives. London must strive to be a more equitable city – one in which all citizens can have a stake in the design, development and care of the built environment.

Open City

## Individual donations

If everyone who attended the Open House weekend donated just £1, the next event would be secured.

## Take a Tour

Open City runs a programme of year-round tours to help support Open House and our education initiatives. Led by expert guides, they take in the best of London's architecture on foot, on bikes and on boats.

## Benefactors

Open-City gives everyone the opportunity to discover and learn what makes great architecture. Those who share our passion can help us by joining our *Benefactor Scheme*.

## Memberships

Partner with us and position your company as making an important contribution to London's built environment. Your investment will go a long way.

Find out how to contribute to our programmes via our website open-city.org.uk

Open City would like to thank our members. Read about the organisations who have helped to make Open House possible.

Britsh Land is one of Europe's largest and most prestigious listed real estate investment companies. We own or manage a portfolio of high quality UK commercial property valued at £19.1 billion (British Land share: £13.9 billion) as at 31 March 2017. Our strategy is to provide environments which meet the needs of our customers and respond to changing lifestyles – Places People Prefer.

→ britishland.com

Founded in 1999, CMS is a full-service top 10 international law firm, based on the number of lawyers (Am Law 2016 Global 100). With 71 offices in 40 countries across the world, employing over 4,500 lawyers, CMS has longstanding expertise both at advising in its local jurisdictions and across borders.

→ cms.law

Peabody is one of the largest housing providers in London and the south-east. We provide services to 111,000 residents, 8,000 care and support customers, and the wider communities in which we work. Our ambitious housebuilding programme will deliver thousands of new homes by 2020, and we're driving forward the long-term regeneration of Thamesmead, London's new town.

→ peabody.org.uk

A central London law firm specialising in Real Estate, Private Wealth and Corporate. We provide our clients with 'big firm' expertise in our chosen areas of practice, but with an individual approach and personal service which only specialist firms can provide. Clients include private individuals, real estate and entrepreneurial businesses, family businesses and charitable foundations and trusts.

→ pglaw.co.uk

# DERWENT LONDON

# elliottwood

**D**erwent London owns a 6m sq ft portfolio of commercial real estate mainly in central London. Over the years we have commissioned a wide variety of contemporary architects resulting in a series of innovative and interesting schemes. Derwent London has become well known in the industry for its strong design-led philosophy and has won numerous awards.

→ derwentlondon.com

**E**lliott Wood uses design-led engineering to realise ambitious schemes, deliver outstanding projects and stay at the forefront of structural and civil engineering practices. With a history of award winning creative engineering, Elliott Wood deliver projects in every sector, from large scale commercial projects, through to specialist sculptures and other structurally demanding installations

→ elliottwood.co.uk

# ROCKET
## PROPERTIES

# make

**R**ocket Properties is a private property company creating design-led commercial, residential and mixed-use investment opportunities across London's premier locations. Rocket Properties pays close attention to inclusivity and sustainability in its design of developments.

→ rocket-investments.com

**M**ake is an award-winning international architectural practice with a reputation for challenging convention and pursuing design excellence. Since we opened our doors in 2004, we've worked on nearly 1,400 projects worldwide covering a wide range of sectors. We've delivered 67 built schemes from studios across 3 continents, including 42 buildings and over a dozen masterplans.

→ makearchitects.com

# Credits & acknowledgements

Open City is a charity promoting a people-centred approach to the design of our city.

**Director**
Rory Olcayto

**Trustees**
Alison Brooks RIBA
Richard Ehrman
Stephen Howlett
Crispin Kelly (Chair)
Helen Newman
Tony Pidgley CBE
Nick Raynsford
Alan Stanton OBE HonFRIBA

**Founder**
Victoria Thornton OBE HonFRIBA

**Open City Team**
Freya Healey
· Special projects and events
Adrianna Carroll-Battaglino
· Tours manager
Katerina Papavasileiou
· Sustainability manager
Jeni Hoskin
· Project manager
Antonio Bertossi
· Designer
Ed Davey
· Web developer
Sophie Martin
· Head of learning
Zoe Zotou
· Learning programmes manager
Suzie Zuber
· Associate
Natalya Wells
· Open House project manager
Rosalind Morris
· Open House marketing manager
Luke O'Donovan
· Open House assistant

**Volunteers**
Alasdair Bethley, Bob Dawes, Catherine Day, Bill Green, Rob Hurn, Alan Jacobs, Robin Key, Ulla Kite, Kit Lam, Ewa Lukaszczykiewicz, Elizabeth Nokes, Richard Purver, Rosemary Read, Leonora Robinson, Stuart Rock, Rick Smith, Miriam Sullivan, Alison Surtees, David Taylor, Sue Thorburn

**Individual Benefactors**
Alan Leibowitz & Barbara Weiss
Andrew McManus
David Neilson
John McElgunn
Julian Peddle
Julie Taylor
Tim Harris
Richard Hughes
Robin & Sue Hodges
Paul Carter
Tom Smith

**Chairman's Circle**
Richard Ehrman
Crispin Kelly
Bernard Kelly
Tony Pidgely
Peter Wylde

**Special thanks to**
BDP, Margaret Baddeley, Sonya Barber, Mike Clewley, James Closs, Anthony Coleman, Fenelle Collingridge, Coffey Architects, Toby Davey, Manpreet Dhesi, Maria Diaz-Palomares, Jake + Katherine Edgley, Robert Elms, Jamie Fobert , David Garrard, Maria Gillivan, Graphical House (Open City rebranding), Joe Kerr, Paul Lincoln, Tim & Jo Lucas, Andrea & Henry Luker, Penny Mason, John McElgunn, Sven Mündner, Benedict O'Looney, Alan Penn, Frosso Piminedes, Stephen Senior, Nick See, Wei Shin, Grant Smith, Louisa Stirling, Philippa Stockley, Henning Stummel, Richard Sykes, Ralph Ward, Erica Wolfe-Murray, Woollacott Gilmartin Architects

Thanks also to all the property owners, reps and managers; all the architects, landscape architects and engineers; the developers and builders and of course, our volunteers, for their incredible goodwill, free time and enthusiasm for Open House London over the past 25 years.

OPEN
CITY
OH

**Print**
Circulation
· 100.000
Typefaces
· Miller, Brown Standard, Officina Serif
Printed by Pureprint

**Contact**
openhouselondon.org.uk
open-city.org.uk
@openhouselondon
@opencityorg
18 Ensign Street London E1 8JD
hello@open-city.org.uk
020 3006 7008

Open City is a registered charity: 1072104

Part of the
Open House
Worldwide Family
openhouseworldwide.org